FONDAZIONE
MARIA
VALTORTA
CEV
onlus

www.mariavaltorta.com

VOLUME 3

THE GOSPEL AS REVEALED TO ME

7 parts

The birth and Hidden Life of Mary and Jesus
chapters 1–43

The first year of the Public Life of Jesus
chapters 44–140

The second year of the Public Life of Jesus
chapters 141–312

The third year of the Public Life of Jesus
chapters 313–540

Preparation for the Passion of Jesus
chapters 541–600

Passion and Death of Jesus
chapters 601–615

Glorification of Jesus and Mary
chapters 616–651

Farewell to the Work, chapter 652

10 volumes

Volume One, chapters 1-78
Volume Two, chapters 79-159
Volume Three, chapters 160-225
Volume Four, chapters 226-295
Volume Five, chapters 296-363
Volume Six, chapters 364-432
Volume Seven, chapters 433-500
Volume Eight, chapters 501-554
Volume Nine, chapters 555-600
Volume Ten, chapters 601-652

Maria Valtorta

THE GOSPEL AS REVEALED TO ME

VOLUME THREE
Chapters 160-225

CENTRO
EDITORIALE
VALTORTIANO

Original title:
Maria Valtorta,
L'Evangelo come mi è stato rivelato

Translated from Italian
by Nicandro Picozzi

Maria Valtorta,
The Gospel as revealed to me.
10 volumes.
Second edition

ISBN 978-88-7987-183-9
(Volume three)

ISBN 978-88-7987-180-8
(Complete work in 10 volumes)

Graphic and printing:
Centro Editoriale Valtortiano srl.,
Isola del Liri (FR) – Italy

Reprinted in Italy, 2019.

Previous edition:
Maria Valtorta, *The Poem of the Man-God*, 5 volumes,

INDEX

The Second Year of the Public Life of Jesus.

(continuation)

160. *Encounter with Rabbi Gamaliel on the Road from Naphtali to Giscala.* 13

161. *At Capernaum, the Grandson of the Pharisee Eli Is Cured and Saved from Certain Death.* 19

162. *The Conditional Conversions of the Pharisee Eli and Simon of Alphaeus.* 23

163. *Supper in the House of Eli the Pharisee of Capernaum.* 29

164. *Towards the Retreat on the Mountain Before the Apostolic Election.* **Mark 3:13-19; Luke 6:12-16** 34

165. *The Election of the Twelve Apostles.* **Mark 3:13-19; Luke 6:12-16** 37

166. *A Profusion of Miracles After the Apostolic Nomination. The First Sermon of Simon the Zealot and John.* **Matt 4:24-25; Mark 3:7-12; Luke 6:17-19** 44

167. *Meeting with the Roman Ladies in the Gardens of Johanna of Chuza.* 54

168. *Aglae in Mary's House in Nazareth.* 65

169. *The Sermon of the Mount. Part One: the Mission of the Apostles and the Disciples "You Are the Salt of the Earth".* **Matt 5:1-2.13-16; Mark 4:21-23; Luke 8:16-17; 14:34-35** 76

170. *The Sermon of the Mount. Part Two: the Sanctifying Grace and the Beatitudes.* **Matt 5:3-12; Luke 6:20-23** 85

171. *The Sermon of the Mount. Part Three: Jesus Has Come to Complete and Fulfill the Law.* **Matt 5:17-26.38-48; 7:12.15-20; Luke 6:27-36.38** 96

172. *The Sermon of the Mount. Part Four: the 'Swearing of Oaths', Secrecy in Praying or Fasting. Old Ismael and Sarah.* **Matt 5:33-37; 6:5-8.16-18; 7:7-11** 103

173. *The Sermon of the Mount. Part Five: the Right Use of Riches and Possessions, Secrecy on the Deeds of Charity.* **Matt 6:1-4.14-15.19-21.25-34** 114

174. *The Sermon of the Mount. Part Six: Adultery, Divorce and Temptations. Encounter with the Magdalene.* **Matt 5:27-32; 6:22-24; 7:1-6.24-29; Luke 6:24-26.37.41-42. 46-49** 123

175. *The Leper Cured at the Foot of the Mountain. The Generosity of the Scribe John.* **Matt 8:1-4** 144

176. *At the Foot of the Mountain, the Last Sermon During the Sabbath Rest. 'Those Who Do the Will of My Father Will Enter the Kingdom of Heaven'.* **Matt 7:21-23** 149

177. *At Capernaum, the Healing of the Centurion's Servant.* **Matt 8:5-13; Luke 7:1-10** 154

178. *Three Different Men Who Wish to Follow Jesus.* **Matt 8:18-22; Luke 9:57-62** 157

179. *The Parable of the Sower. In Korazim with the New Disciple Elias.* **Matt 13:1-9; Mark 4:1-9; Luke 8:4-8** 160

180. *At Bethsaida in Peter's Kitchen. Explanation of the Parable of the Sower. News of the Baptist's Second Capture.* **Matt 13:10-23; Mark 4:10-20.24-25; Luke 8:9-15.18** 169

181. *The Parable of the Wheat and the Darnel.* **Matt 13:24-30. 36-43** 179

182. *While Going to Magdala, Jesus Speaks to Some Shepherds. Little Orphan Zacharias.* 187

183. *Miracle on a Dying Man Stabbed in Mary's House in Magdala.* 191

184. *At Magdala, in the House of Little Benjamin's Mother. Two Parables on the Kingdom of Heaven.* **Matt 13:31-32; Mark 4:26-32; Luke 13: 18-19** 196

185. *The Calming of the Storm.* **Matt 8:23-27; Mark 4:35-41; Luke 8:22-25** 204

186. *The Two Demoniacs in the Country of the Gadarenes.* **Matt 8:28-34; Mark 5:1-20; Luke 8:26-39** 208

187. *From Tarichea Towards Jerusalem for the Second Passover. John Longs to Catch a Glimpse of the Great Sea from the Tabor.* 216

188. *Visit to the Cave of the Sorceress at Endor. The Encounter with the Miserable Felix Who Becomes the Disciple John.* 221

189. *The Son of the Widow of Nain.* **Luke 7:11-16** 233

190. *The Arrival in the Plain of Esdraelon at Sunset.* 237

191. *The Sabbath in Esdrelon. Little Jabez. The Parable of Rich Dives.* **Luke 16:19-31** 240

192. *A Prediction to James of Alphaeus. The Arrival at Engannim After a Stop in Mageddo.* 247

193. *From Engannim to Shechem in Two Days.* 253

194. *Revelations to Little Jabez While Going from Schechem to Beeroth.* 258

195. *John of Endor Endeavours to Teach the Iscariot. The Entrance in Jerusalem.* 264

196. *The Sabbath at Gethsemane. The Virgin Mary Archetype of Maternity. The Different Degrees of the Power of Love.* 269

197. *In the Temple with Joseph of Arimathea at the Hour of Incense.* 279

198. *Jesus Meets His Mother at Bethany. Little Jabez Becomes Marjiam.* 283

199. *A Visit to the Lepers of Siloam and Ben Hinnom. The Power of Mary's Intercession.* 292

200. *Aglae Meets the Master. Her Joy for Feeling Forgiven and Saved.* 304

201. *Marjiam's Examination for the Coming of Age.* 310

202. *At the Temple on the Eve of Passover. Judas of Iscariot Justly Reproached. The Arrival of Johanan's Peasants.* 316

203. *The Prayer of the "Our Father".* **Matt 6:9-13; Luke 11:1-13** 321

204. *Faith and Soul Explained to the Gentiles Through the Parable of the Temples.* 329

205. *First Assignment to John of Endor. The Parable of the Prodigal Son.* **Luke 15:11-32** 338

206. *Two Parables of the Kingdom of Heaven: the Ten Virgins and the Royal Wedding. The Stay in Bethany Ends.* **Matt 22:1-14; 25:1-13** 346

207. *In the Grotto of Bethlehem, the Holy Mother Recalls Jesus' Birth.* 360

208. *The Wrath of the Innocent Marjiam. Holy Mary with the Shepherd Elias. Going to Eliza's in Bethzur.* 371

209. *Jesus in Eliza's House Speaks of Sorrow that Bears Fruit.* 383

210. *Towards Hebron. The Ill-Disposed Judas Iscariot.* 390

211. *The Return to Hebron. Preaching and Miracles in the Garden of John the Baptist's House.* 395

212. *At Juttah. A Wave of Love for Jesus Who Speaks in the House of Isaac.* 405

213. *At Kerioth, Jesus Gives a Prophetic Speech in the Synagogue. The Beginning of the Apostolic Preaching.* 412

214. *The Blessed Virgin at Kerioth in Judas' House. Afflictions of a Mother Disclosed to Holy Mary.* 417

215. *Philip and Andrew Preach at Bethginna. Healing of the Lunatic Daughter of the Innkeeper.* 424

216. *In the Plain Towards Askelon. The Disciples' Wavering Allegiance Predicted with the Parable of the Dandelion.* 431

217. *The Ears of Corn Picked on the Sabbath. "The Son of Man is Lord of the Sabbath".* **Matt 12:1-8; Mark 2:23-28; Luke 6:1-5** 437

218. *Near Ashkelon, the Philistine Ananiah. Healing of Little Dinah's Mother.* 441

219. *At Ashkelon, the Apostles Learn that Preaching with Different Approaches Produces Different Effects.* 453

220. *The Heathens of Magdalgad. Jesus Incinerates a Pagan Idol and Saves a Woman in Childbirth.* 462

221. *Going to Jabneel. A Lesson on Prejudices Against Pagans: the Parable of the Deformed Son.* 469

222. *The Apostle John Has a Secret. To Judaea by the Unsafe Modin Road.* 477

223. *Jesus Speaks to the Highwaymen and Prevents an Attack on a Nuptial Caravan.* 481

224. *The Secret of the Apostle John Revealed. The Arrival at Bether, in the Rose Gardens of Johanna.* 488

225. *The Paralytic at the Pool of Bethzatha (Bethesda) Cured on Sabbath: "My Father Is at Work Until Now, so I Am at Work, Too".* **John 5:1-47** 495

(the "Second Year" continues in the fourth volume)

The Second Year of the Public Life of Jesus.

160. Encounter with Rabbi Gamaliel on the Road from Naphtali to Giscala.

10th May 1945.

[1] «Master! Master! Do You know who is ahead of us? There is 160.1
rabbi Gamaliel! He is sitting with his servants, in a caravan, in the shade in a wood, sheltered from the winds! They are roasting a lamb. What are we going to do now?»

«What we were going to do, My friends. We will proceed along our way...»

«But Gamaliel is of the Temple.»

«Gamaliel is not wicked. Do not be afraid. I will go ahead.»

«Oh! I am coming too» say His cousins at the same time, as well as all the Galileans and Simon. Only the Iscariot, and to a lesser degree, Thomas do not seem very anxious to proceed. But they follow the others.

They walk for a few yards along a mountainous road set deep between the wooded slopes of the mountain. The road then bends and opens onto a kind of tableland and crosses it, widening out, and soon after that it becomes once again narrow and winding under a roof of interwoven branches. In a sunny bare patch, which is however shaded by the first leaves of the wood, there are many people under a rich tent, while other people are busy in a corner turning the lamb on the fire.

There is no doubt about it! Gamaliel took very good care of himself. For one person traveling he set a crowd of servants in motion with I do not know how much luggage. He is now sitting in the centre of his tent: a cloth supported by four gilt poles, a kind of canopy under which there are low seats covered with cushions and a table, the top of which rests on carved wooden legs. A very fine tablecloth is spread on the table and the servants are laying precious dishes on it. Gamaliel looks like an idol. With his hands open on his knees, stiff and hieratic, he looks like a statue to me.

The servants move around him like large butterflies. But he pays no attention to them. He is pondering, his eyelashes rather lowered on his severe eyes, and when he raises them, his deep very dark pensive eyes are displayed in all their severe beauty at the sides of a long thin nose and under the high rather bald forehead of an elderly man. His forehead is marked by three parallel wrinkles and by a large bluish vein which forms a V shaped angle in the centre of his right temple.

160.2 [2]The noise of the oncoming people causes the servants to turn around. Gamaliel also looks around. He sees Jesus approaching ahead of everyone and he makes a gesture of surprise. He stands up and moves to the edge of the tent, but no farther. From there he bows low with his arms crossed on his chest. Jesus replies to him in the same way.

«You are here, Rabbi?» asks Gamaliel.

«I am here, rabbi» replies Jesus.

«May I ask You where You are going?»

«It is a pleasure for Me to tell you. I am coming from Naphtali and I am going to Giscala.»

«On foot? But it is a hard and long road along these mountains. You are tiring Yourself too much.»

«Believe Me. If I am welcomed and listened to, all fatigue disappears.»

«Well, then... allow me to be for once the one who will remove Your fatigue. The lamb is ready. We would have left the remains to the birds because I never take them with me. You can see that it is no trouble for me to offer food to You and to Your followers. I am friendly to You, Jesus. I do not consider You inferior to me, but greater than I am.»

«I believe you. And I accept your hospitality.»

Gamaliel speaks to a servant who appears to be the highest in authority and who passes on the order. The tent is extended and more seats and dishes for Jesus' disciples are taken off the many mules.

They bring bowls to purify their fingers. Jesus performs the rite with the greatest courtliness, whereas the apostles, on whom Gamaliel is casting sharp sidelong glances, do so as well as they can, with the exception of Simon, Judas of Kerioth, Bartholomew and Matthew, who are more accustomed to Jewish refinements.

Jesus is beside Gamaliel who is alone on one side of the table. The Zealot is in front of Jesus. After the prayer of thanksgiving, which Gamaliel says with calm solemnity, the servants carve the lamb and divide it among the guests and they fill the cups with wine or water sweetened with honey, for those who prefer it.

3 «We have met by chance, Rabbi. I was never expecting to see You and on the way to Giscala.» 160.3

«I am going towards the whole world.»

«Yes, You are the untiring Prophet. John is the stationary one, You are the roaming One.»

«It is easier, therefore, for souls to find Me.»

«I would not say so. Your continuous moving about disorientates them.»

«I disorient My enemies. But those who want Me, because they love the Word of God, find Me. Not *everybody* can come to the Master. And the Master, Who wants everybody, goes to everybody, helping thus the good and warding off the conspiracies of those who hate Me.»

«Are You referring to me? I do not hate You.»

«Not to you. But since you are just and frank, you can say that I am speaking the truth.»

«Yes, it is so. But… see… The fact is that we old people do not understand You well.»

«Yes, old Israel does not understand Me well. That is her misfortune… and because of her will.»

«No, no.»

«Yes, rabbi. They are not willing to understand the Master. And who confines himself to that, does evil, but a comparative evil. Many instead deliberately misunderstand and distort My word to harm God.»

«God? He is above human snares.»

«Yes. But every soul that goes astray or is led astray — and it is misleading to distort My word or My work, both with regards to oneself and to other people — harms God in the soul which is lost. Every soul that is lost is a wound to God.»

Gamaliel lowers his head, and closing his eyes, he meditates. He then presses his forehead between his long thin fingers, in an involuntary gesture of pain. Jesus watches him. Gamaliel raises his head, opens his eyes, looks at Jesus and says: «But You know that I am not one of those.»

«I know. But you are one of the former.»

«Oh! It is true. But it is not true that I am not willing to understand You. The truth is that Your word stops on my mind and does not penetrate further. My mind admires it as the word of a learned man and the spirit...»

«And the spirit cannot receive it, Gamaliel, because it is en-
160.4 cumbered with too many things. And ruined things. [4]A short while ago, coming here from Naphtali, I passed near a mountain, which juts out from the mountain chain. I was pleased to pass there to see the two beautiful lakes of Gennesaret and Merom, from high above, as eagles and the angels of the Lord see them, to say once again: "Thank You, Creator, for the beauty You grant us". Well, whilst the whole mountain is covered with flowers, green meadows, orchards, fields, woods, and the laurels smell sweet near the olive-trees, preparing the white host of thousands and thousands of flowers and also the strong oak-tree seems to become gentler as it dresses itself with wreaths of clematis and woodbine: over there, there is no flowering, no fertility, neither of man nor of nature. All the efforts of the winds, all the toil of men are frustrated because the Cyclopean ruins of ancient Hatzor encumber everything and between one large stone and another only nettles and bushes can grow and snakes can hide. Gamaliel...»

«I understand. We are ruins, too... I understand the parable, Jesus. But... I cannot... I cannot... do otherwise. The stones are too heavy.»

«One in Whom you believed said to you: "The stones shall vibrate hearing My last words". But why wait for the last words of the Messiah? Will you not regret that you did not follow Me before? The last!... Sad words, like those of a friend who is dying, and to whom we have to listen, but *too late*. But My words are more important than the words of a friend.»

«You are right... But I cannot. I am waiting for that sign, that I may believe.»

«When a piece of ground is barren, a thunderbolt is not sufficient to till it. The soil will not receive it. But the stones that cover the soil will receive it. Endeavour at least to remove them, Gamaliel. Otherwise, if they are left where they are, in the depth of your heart, the sign will not lead you to believe.»

[5] Gamaliel is silent, engrossed in thought. The meal is over. 160.5

Jesus stands up and says: «I thank You, My God, both for the meal and for the opportunity of speaking to a wise man. And thank you, Gamaliel.»

«Master, do not go away like that. I am afraid You are angry with me.»

«Oh! no! You must believe Me.»

«Then, do not go away. I am going to Hillel's tomb. Would You disdain coming with me? It will not take us long, because I have mules and donkeys for everybody. All we have to do is to take off their pack-saddles, which the servants will carry. And the hardest part of the road will be shortened for You.»

«I do not mind coming with you or going to Hillel's tomb. It is an honour. Let us go.»

Gamaliel gives the necessary instructions, and while they are all busy taking down the temporary dining-room, Jesus and Gamaliel mount two mules and they go ahead, one beside the other, along a quiet steep road, on which the iron shod hooves resound loudly.

Gamaliel is silent. Only twice he asks Jesus whether His saddle is comfortable. Jesus replies and then turns quiet, engrossed in thought. So much so that He does not notice that Gamaliel, holding his mule back a little, lets Him go forward by a full neck, so that he may study every gesture of His. The eyes of the old rabbi are so keen in penetration that they look like the eyes of a hawk gazing at its prey. But Jesus is not aware of it. He proceeds calmly, following the undulant pace of His mount, He is pensive and yet He observes all the features of what is around Him. He stretches out a hand to pick a hanging bunch of golden cytisus, He smiles at two little birds which are building their nest in a thick juniper, He stops the mule to listen to a black cap and, as a blessing, He nods assent to the anxious cry by which a wild dove urges her mate to work.

«You love herbs and animals very much, do You not?»

«Yes, very much. They are My living book. Man always has the foundations of faith in front of him. Genesis lives in nature. Now, one who knows how to see, knows also how to believe. This flower, so sweet in its scent and in the substance of its pendulous corollas, and in such a contrast with this thorny juniper and with that furze, how could it have made itself by itself? And look: that robin red-breast, could it have made itself with that dried bloodstain on its soft throat? And those two doves, where and how have they been able to paint those onyx collars on the veil of their grey feathers? And over there, those two butterflies: a black one with large gold and ruby rings, while the other, with blue stripes, where have they found the gems and ribbons for their wings? And this stream? It is water. Agreed. But where did it come from? Which is the first source of the water-element? Oh! To look means to believe, if one knows how to look.»

«To look means to believe. We look too little at the living Genesis that is in front of us.»

«Too much science, Gamaliel. And too little love, and too little humility.»

Gamaliel sighs and shakes his head.

160.6 [6]«Here. We have arrived, Jesus. Hillel is buried over there. Let us dismount and leave our mules here. A servant will take them.»

They dismount tying the two mules to a tree trunk and they turn their steps towards a burial ground which protrudes from the mountain near a large house completely closed up.

«I come here to meditate and prepare myself for the feasts of Israel» says Gamaliel pointing at the house.

«May Wisdom grant you all its light.»

«And here (and Gamaliel points at the sepulchre) to prepare myself to meet death. He was a just man.»

«He was a just man. I will be pleased to pray near his ashes. But, Gamaliel, Hillel must not teach you only to die. He must teach you to live.»

«How, Master?»

«"A man is great when he humbles himself" was his favourite saying...»

«How do You know if You have not met him?»

«I did meet him... in any case, even if I had never met Hillel, the rabbi, personally, I know his thought, because there is nothing I ignore of human thoughts.»

Gamaliel lowers his head and whispers: «God only can say that.»

«God and His Word. Because the Word knows the Thought and the Thought knows the Word, and loves Him, communicating with Him and granting Him all His treasures, to make Him participate in Himself. Love fastens the bonds and makes one Perfection of them. It is the Trinity that loves Itself, is divinely formed, generates, proceeds and is completed. Every holy thought was born in the Perfect Mind, and is reflected in the mind of the just man. Can the Word therefore ignore the thoughts of the just, since they are the thoughts of the Thought?»

They pray near the closed sepulchre. They pray for a long time. The disciples and then the servants reach them, the former on horseback, the latter carrying the luggage. But they stop at the edge of the meadow, beyond which is the sepulchre. The prayer is over.

«Goodbye, Gamaliel. Ascend as Hillel did.»

«What do You mean?»

«Ascend. He is ahead of you because he knew how to believe more humbly than you do. Peace be with you.»

161. At Capernaum, the Grandson of the Pharisee Eli Is Cured and Saved from Certain Death.

11th May 1945.

[1] Jesus is about to arrive in Capernaum by boat. The sun is al- 161.1
most setting and the lake is sparkling with red and yellow hues.

While the two boats are manoeuvring to draw near the coast, John says: «I will go to the fountain and bring You some water for Your thirst.»

«The water is good here» exclaims Andrew.

«Yes, it is good. And your love makes it even better for Me.»

«I will take the fish home. The women will prepare them for supper. Afterwards, will You speak to us and to them?»

«Yes, Peter, I will.»

«It is more pleasant now to come back home. Before we looked like a lot of nomads. But now, with the women, there is more order, more love. And then! When I see Your Mother, I no longer feel tired. I don't know...»

Jesus smiles and is quiet.

The boat grounds on the shingly shore. John and Andrew, who are wearing short undertunics, jump into the water and with the help of some young men they beach the boat and place a board as a wharf. Jesus is the first to come off, and He waits until the second boat is beached, in order to be together with all of His disciples. Then, walking with slow steps they go towards the fountain. A natural fountain of spring water, that wells up just outside the village, and plentiful, cold and silvery runs into a stone basin. The water is so limpid that it induces people to drink it. John, who has run ahead with an amphora, is already back and he hands the dripping pitcher to Jesus, Who has a long drink.

«How thirsty You were, my Master! And I, foolishly, did not get any water.»

«It does not matter, John. It is all over» and He caresses him.

161.2 [2] They are about to come back when they see Simon Peter arrive, running as fast as he can. He had gone home to take his fish.

«Master! Master!» he shouts panting. «The village is in turmoil, because the only grandchild of Eli, the Pharisee, is about to die from a snakebite. He had gone with the old man, and against his mother's wishes, to their olive-grove. Eli was overseeing some works, while the child was playing near the roots of an old olive-tree. He put his hand into a hole, hoping to find a lizard, and he found a snake. The old man seems to have become distraught. The child's mother, who incidentally hates her father-in-law, quite rightly as it happens, is accusing him of being a murderer. The boy is getting colder and colder every moment. Although relatives, they did not love one another! And they could not have been more closely related!»

«Family grudge is never a good thing!»

«Well , Master, I say that the snakes did not love the snake: Eli. And they have killed the little snake. I am sorry that he saw me and he shouted after me: "Is the Master there?". And I am sorry for the little one, He was a nice boy and it is not his fault that he was the grandson of a Pharisee.»

«Of course, it is not his fault.»

161.3 [3] They walk towards the village and they see a crowd of people, shouting and weeping, coming towards them, with the elderly Eli in front of them.

«He has found us! Let us go back!»

«Why? That old man is suffering.»

«That old man hates You, remember that. He is one of Your first and fiercest accusers at the Temple.»

«I remember that I am Mercy.»

Old Eli, unkempt and upset, with untidy garments, runs towards Jesus, his arms outstretched, and drops at His feet shouting: «Mercy! Mercy! Forgive me. Do not avenge Yourself on an innocent boy for my harshness. You are the only one who can save him! God, Your Father, has brought You here. I believe in You! I venerate You! I love You! Forgive me! I have been unfair! A liar! But I have been punished. These hours alone serve as a punishment. Help me! It's the boy! The only son of my dead son. And she is accusing me of killing him» and he weeps striking his head on the ground rhythmically.

«Come on! Do not cry like that. Do you want to die without having to look after your grandson any more?»

«He is dying! He is dying! Perhaps he is already dead. Let me die, too. Don't let me live in that empty house! Oh! My sad last days!»

«Eli, get up and let us go...»

«You... are You really coming? But do You know who I am?»

«An unhappy man. Let us go.»

The old man gets up and says: «I will go ahead, but run, run, be quick!» And he goes away, very quickly, because of the desperation piercing his heart.

«But, Lord, do You think that You will change him? Oh! what a wasted miracle! Let that little snake die! Also the old man will die broken-hearted... and there will be one less on Your way... God has seen to it...»

«Simon! To tell you the truth, you are now the snake.» Jesus severely repels Peter, who lowers his head, and He goes on.

[4]Near the largest square in Capernaum there is a beautiful 161.4
house before which the crowds are making a dreadful noise... Jesus moves towards it and is about to arrive when the old man comes out from the wide open door, followed by a ruffled woman, who is holding in her arms a little agonizing child. The poison has already paralyzed his organs and death is near. The little wounded hand is hanging down with the mark of the bite at the root of his thumb. Eli does nothing but shout: «Jesus! Jesus!»

And Jesus, squeezed and overwhelmed by the crowds who obstruct His movements, takes the little hand to His mouth, sucks the wound, then breathes on the waxen face and the glassy half closed eyes. He then straightens Himself up: «Here» He says, «the child will now wake up. Do not frighten him with your expressions which are so upset. He will already be afraid when he remembers the snake.»

In fact the boy, whose face colours up, opens his mouth in a big yawn, rubs his eyes, opens them and is surprised at being among so many people. He then remembers, and is about to run away, with such a sudden leap, that he would have fallen had Jesus not been ready to receive him in His arms.

«Good, good! What are you afraid of? Look how beautiful the sun is! Over there is the lake, your house, and your mother and grandfather are here.»

«And the snake?»

«It is no longer here. But I am.»

«You. Yes...» The child thinks... and then, in the innocent voice of truth, he says: «My grandfather used to tell me to say "cursed" to You. But I will not say it. I love You, I do.»

«I? I said that? The little one is raving. Do not believe him, Master. I have always respected You.» As fear passes away, the old nature comes to surface again.

«Words are and are not of value. I take them for what they are. Goodbye, little one, goodbye, woman, goodbye, Eli. Love one another and love Me, if you can.» Jesus turns around and goes towards the house where He lives.

161.5 [5] «Why, Master, did You not work a striking miracle? You should have ordered the poison to go out of the little one. You should have shown Yourself as being God. Instead You sucked the poison like any poor man.» Judas of Kerioth is not very happy. He wanted something sensational.

Also others are of the same opinion. «You should have crushed that enemy of Yours, with Your power. You heard him, eh! He became poisonous again at once...»

«His poison is of no importance. But you must consider that if I had done what you wanted Me to do, he would have said that I was helped by Beelzebub. His ruined soul can still acknowledge My power as a doctor. But no more. *A miracle leads to faith only those who are already on that way.* But in those without humility — faith always proves that there is humility in a soul — it leads to blasphemy. It is better therefore to avoid that danger by having recourse to forms of human appearance. The incurable misery is the misery of the incredulous. No means will eliminate it because no miracle induces them to believe or to be good. It does not matter. I fulfill My task. They follow their ill fate.»

«Why did You do it, then?»

«Because I am Goodness and because no one may say that I was vindictive with My enemies and provocative with provokers. I am heaping coal on their heads. And they are handing it to Me that I may heap it. Be good, Judas of Simon. Endeavour not to behave as they do! And that is all. Let us go to My Mother. She will be happy to hear that I cured a child.»

162. The Conditional Conversions of the Pharisee Eli and Simon of Alphaeus.

13th May 1945.

[1] From a vegetable garden, which is beginning to flourish in all its furrows, Jesus enters a very large kitchen where the two elder Maries (Mary of Clopas and Mary Salome) are cooking the supper. 162.1

«Peace to you!»

«Oh! Jesus! Master!» The two women turn around and greet Him, one holding in her hands a lovely fish, which she is gutting, the other still holding a pot full of vegetables, which are boiling, and which she has just removed from the fire to see whether they were cooked. Their kind withered faces, flushed by the fire and work, smile out of joy and seem to become younger and lovelier in their happiness.

«It will be ready in a moment, Jesus. Are You tired? You must be hungry» says aunt Mary, who has the familiarity of a relative and loves Jesus, I think, more than her own children.

«Not more than usual. But I will certainly eat with relish the good food that you and Mary have prepared for Me. And the others will do the same. Here they are coming.»

«Your Mother is upstairs. You know! Simon came... Oh! I am

as happy as a lark this evening! No. Not really because... You know when I would be as happy as a king.»

«Yes, I know.» Jesus draws His aunt close to Himself and kisses her forehead and then says: «I know your desire and your sinless envy of Salome. But the day will come when you will be
162.2 able to say like her: "All my sons belong to Jesus". [2]I am going to My Mother.»

He goes out, he climbs the little external staircase and goes onto the terrace, which covers a full half of the house, whereas the other half is taken up by a very large room, from which the strong voices of men can be heard, and at intervals, Mary's gentle voice, the limpid virginal voice of a girl, which years have not affected, the same voice that said: «I am the handmaid of the Lord» and which sang lullabies to Her Baby.

Jesus approaches silently, smiling because He hears His Mother say: «My home is My Son. I do not suffer being away from Nazareth, except when He is away. But if He is near Me... oh! I need nothing else. And I am not afraid for My house... You are here...»

«Oh! Look, there is Jesus!» shouts Alphaeus of Sarah, who facing the door, is the first to see Jesus.

«Yes, here I am. Peace to you all. Mother!» He kisses His Mother on Her forehead and is kissed by Her. He then turns to the unexpected guests, who are His cousin Simon, Alphaeus of Sarah, Isaac the shepherd and one Joseph who was received by Jesus at Emmaus after the verdict of the Sanhedrin.

«We went to Nazareth and Alphaeus told us that we had to come here. We came. And Alphaeus wanted to come with us, and also Simon» explains Isaac.

«I could not believe I was coming» says Alphaeus.

«I also wanted to see You, stay a little time with You and with Mary» concludes Simon.

«And I am very happy to be with you. I did the right thing in not staying any longer as the people of Kedesh desired, where I arrived coming from Gherghesa to Merom and going round the other side of the lake.»

«Is that where You came from?»

«Yes, I visited the places where I had already been and even further away. I went as far as Giscala.»

«What a long road!»

«But what a great harvest! Do you know, Isaac. We were the guests of rabbi Gamaliel. He was very kind to us. And then I met the synagogue leader of the Clear Water. He is coming, too. I entrust him to you. And then... and then I gained three disciples...» Jesus smiles frankly, blissfully.

«Who are they?»

«A little old man at Korazim. I helped him some time ago, and the poor man, who is a true Israelite without prejudice, to show Me his love, has worked his area as a perfect ploughman works the soil. The other is a boy, five years old, perhaps a little more. Intelligent and brave. I spoke also to him the first time I was at Bethsaida and he remembered better than adults. The third is an old leper. I cured him near Korazim one evening a long time ago and then I left him. I have now found him again, announcing Me on the mountains in Naphtali. And to confirm his words he shows what is left of his hands, cured but partly impaired, and his feet, which have also been cured but are deformed, and yet he walks a long way. People realise how ill he was when they see what is left of him and they believe his words which are dressed with tears of gratitude. It was easy for Me to speak there, because there was one who had already made Me known and had led other people to believe in Me. And I was able to work many miracles. So much can be done by one who really believes...»

Alphaeus nods assent without speaking, continuously absent-minded, while Simon lowers his head under the implicit reproach, and Isaac rejoices wholeheartedly because of the joy of his Master, Who is about to tell of the miracle worked shortly before on Eli's little grandchild.

[3] But supper is ready, and the women, with Mary, prepare the 162.3
table in the large room and take the dishes there and then withdraw downstairs. Only the men remain and Jesus offers, blesses and hands out the portions.

But only a few mouthfuls of food had been taken when Susanna goes upstairs saying: «Eli has come with servants and many gifts. But he would like to speak to You.»

«I will come at once, or better still, tell him to come up.»

Susanna goes out and comes back shortly afterwards with old Eli and two servants who are carrying a large basket. Behind them the women, with the exception of the Most Holy Mary, are casting curious glances.

«God be with You, my benefactor» greets the Pharisee.

«And with you, Eli. Come in. What do you want? Is your grandson not well again?»

«Oh! He is very well. He is jumping in the kitchen garden like a little kid. Before I was so dumbfounded and bewildered that I failed to fulfill my duty. I wish to show You my gratitude and I beg You not to refuse the little I am offering You. A little food for You and Your friends. It is the produce of my fields. And... I would like... I would like to have You at my table tomorrow. To thank You once again and honour You, with my friends. Do not refuse, Master. I would understand that You do not love me and that if You cured Elisha, it was only for his sake, not mine.»

«Thank you. But no gifts were needed.»

«Every great and learned man accepts them. It's the custom.»

162.4 «And I do. [4]But I accept very willingly one gift only, in fact I look for it.»

«Which is? If I can, I will give it to You.»

«Your hearts. Your thoughts. Give Me them. For your own good.»

«But I consecrate mine to You, blessed Jesus! Can You doubt it? Yes, I... I did You wrong. But now I have understood. I have also heard of the death of Doras, who offended You... Why are You smiling, Master?»

«I was remembering something.»

«I thought You did not believe what I was saying.»

«Oh! no. I know that you were moved by Doras' death. Even more than by this evening's miracle. But do not be afraid of God, if you have really understood, and if from now on you wish to be My friend.»

«I can see that You really are a prophet. It is true, I was more afraid... I was coming to You more out of fear of punishment like Doras', than because of the accident. And this evening I said: "There you are. The punishment has come. And it is even more severe because it did not strike the old oak in its own life, but in its love, in its joy for life, by striking the little oak, in which I rejoiced". I understood that it would have been just as it was for Doras...»

«You understood that it would have been just. But you did not believe yet in Him Who is good.»

«You are right. But it is no longer so. Now I have understood.
[5]So, are You coming to my house tomorrow?» 162.5

«Eli, I had decided to leave at dawn. But I will postpone My departure by one day, that you may not think that I despise you. I will be with you tomorrow.»

«Oh! You really are good. I will always remember it.»

«Goodbye, Eli. Thank you for everything. This fruit is beautiful, and the cheese must be as tasty as butter, and the wine certainly very good. But you could have given everything to the poor in My name.»

«There is something for them, if You wish so, at the bottom, under the rest. It was an offering for You.»

«Well, we will distribute it tomorrow together, before or after the meal, as you prefer. May the night be a peaceful one for you, Eli.»

«And for You. Goodbye» and he goes away with his servants.

Peter, who with all the mimicry of which he is capable, has pulled out the contents of the basket, to hand it back to the servants, puts the purse on the table in front of Jesus and says, as if he were concluding an internal speech: «And it will be the first time that the old owl gives alms.»

«It is true» confirms Matthew. «I was greedy, but he surpassed me. He doubled his capital by usury.»

«Well... if he mends his ways... It's a good thing, is it not?» says Isaac.

«It certainly is a good thing. And it appears to be so» state Philip and Bartholomew.

«Old Eli a convert! Ah! Ah!» Peter laughs heartily.

[6]Simon, the cousin, who has been pensive all the time, says: 162.6
«Jesus, I would like... I would like to follow You. Not like these. But at least as the women do. Let me join my mother and Yours. They are all coming... I, I, a relative... I do not expect to have a place amongst the disciples. But at least... at least as a good friend...»

«May God bless you, my son! How long have I been waiting to hear you say that!» shouts Mary of Alphaeus.

«Come. I reject no one, neither do I force anyone. I do not even exact *everything* from everybody. I take what you can give Me. It is a good thing that the women are not always alone, when we go to places unknown to them. Thank you, brother.»

«I am going to tell Mary» says Simon's mother and she adds: «She is down in Her little room, praying. She will be happy.»

162.7 [7]... It is rapidly growing dark. They light a lamp to go down the staircase which is already dark in twilight, and some go to the right, some to the left, to rest.

Jesus goes out, and walks to the shore of the lake. The village is quiet, the streets are deserted, there is no one on the shore or on the lake in the moonless night. There are only stars to be seen in the sky and the murmur of the surf to be heard on the shingly shore. Jesus goes on board the beached boat, sits down, lays one arm on the edge and rests His head on it. I do not know whether He is thinking or praying.

Matthew approaches Him very quietly: «Master, are You sleeping?» he asks in a low voice.

«No, I am thinking. Come here beside Me, since you are not sleeping.»

«I thought You were upset and I followed You. Are You not satisfied with Your day's work? You touched Eli's heart, You acquired Simon of Alphaeus as a disciple...»

«Matthew, you are not a simple man like Peter and John. You are astute and learned. Be also frank. Would you be happy because of those conquests?»

«But... Master... They are always better than I am and You told me, on that day, that You were very happy because of my conversion...»

«Yes. But you were *really* converted. And you were genuine in your evolution towards Good. You came to Me without any elaboration of thought, you came through the will of your spirit. But Eli is not like that... neither is Simon. Only the surface of the former has been touched: the man-Eli is shocked. Not the spirit-Eli. That is always the same. When the excitement caused by the miracles on Doras and his little grandchild is over, he will be the same Eli as yesterday and as always. Simon!... he, too, is nothing but a man. If he had seen Me insulted instead of honoured, he would have pitied Me, and as always, he would have left Me. This evening he heard that a little old man, a child, a leper can

do what he, although a relative, cannot do; he saw the pride of a Pharisee bend before Me and he decided: "I as well". But those conversions brought about by the spur of human evaluations, are not the ones that make Me happy. On the contrary, they dishearten Me. [8]Stay with Me, Matthew. It is not a moonlit night, but 162.8
at least the stars are twinkling. In My heart this evening there is nothing but tears. Let your company be the star of your distressed Master…»

«Master, if I can… You can imagine! The trouble is that I am always a poor miserable man, a good for-nothing. I have sinned too much to be able to please You. I am not good at speaking. I do not yet know how to say the new, pure, holy words, now that I have left my old language of fraud and lust. And I am afraid I will never be able to speak to You and about You.»

«No, Matthew. You are a man, with all the painful experience of a man. You are the one, who, having tasted mud and tasting now the celestial honey, can tell the two flavours, and give their true analysis, and understand and make your fellow creatures understand now and later. And they will believe you, because you are the man, the poor man, who by his own will, becomes the just man dreamt of by God. Let Me, the Man-God, lean on you, the mankind I have loved to the extent of leaving Heaven for you, and dying for you.»

«No, not to die. Don't tell me that You are dying for me!»

«Not for you, Matthew, but for all the Matthews of the world and centuries. Embrace Me, Matthew, kiss your Christ, for yourself and for everybody. Relieve My tiredness of an unappreciated Redeemer. I relieved you of your tiredness of a sinner. Wipe away My tears, because My bitterness, Matthew, is that I have been so little understood.»

«Oh! Lord, Lord! Yes. Of course!…» and Matthew, sitting near the Master and clasping Him with one arm, comforts Him with his love…

163. Supper in the House of Eli the Pharisee of Capernaum.

14th May 1945.

[1]Eli's house is very busy today. Servants and maidservants 163.1

come and go and amongst them there is little Elisha, a lively little child. Then there are two stately i\ndividuals and two more. I know the first two, as they are the ones who went with Eli to Matthew's house. I do not know the other two, but I hear them being called Samuel and Joachim. Jesus comes last with the Iscariot.

After solemn mutual greetings, there is the question: «Only with this one? And the others?»

«The others are around the country. They will come in the evening.»

«Oh! I am sorry. I thought it was... True, last night I invited only You, meaning all the rest with You. Now I was afraid they might be offended, or... they might disdain to come to my house, owing to past light disagreements... eh! eh!» The old man laughs...

«Oh! no! My disciples do not nourish proud touchiness or incurable grudge.»

163.2 «Of course! of course! Very well. [2]Let us go in then.»

The usual purification ceremony and then they go into the dining room, which opens onto a large yard, where the first roses bring a happy note.

Jesus caresses little Elisha, who is playing in the yard and who has only four little red marks on his hand from the past trouble. He does not even remember his past fear, but he remembers Jesus and he wants to kiss Him and be kissed by Him, with the spontaneity of children. With his little arms around Jesus' neck, he speaks to Him through His hair, confiding that when he is big he will go to Him and asks: «Do You want me?»

«I want everybody. Be good and you will come with Me.»

The little boy goes away bounding about.

They sit at the table and Eli wishes to be so perfect that he puts Jesus beside him and on the other side Judas, who is thus between Eli and Simon, as Jesus is between Eli and Uriah.

163.3 [3]The meal begins. Their conversation at first is inconsequential. It then becomes interesting. And since wounds are sore and chains are heavy, the talk turns to the eternal topic of the enslavement of Palestine by Rome. I do not know whether it was done deliberately or without any evil purpose. I know that the five Pharisees complain of the new Roman abuses, as of a sacrilege, and they want to get Jesus interested in the discussion.

«You know! They want to pry into our income, down to the last coin. And as they have realised that we meet in the synagogue to speak about that and about them, now they are threatening to come in, without any respect. I am afraid they will enter also the houses of priests, one of these days!» shouts Joachim.

«What do You say about that? Do You not feel disgusted?» asks Eli.

Jesus replies to the direct question: «As an Israelite yes, as a man no.»

«Why that distinction? I do not understand. Are You two in one?»

«No. But there is in Me flesh and blood: that is, the animal. And there is the spirit. The spirit of an Israelite, compliant with the Law, suffers because of such violations. The flesh and blood do not suffer, because I lack the goad that hurts you.»

«Which one?»

«Interest. You said that you meet in the synagogues to speak *also of business* without fear of intrusive ears. And you are afraid you will no longer be able to do so and consequently you are afraid you may not be able to conceal even a small coin from the tax-collectors and that you may be taxed exactly according to your assets. I possess nothing. I live on the charity of My neighbours and on My love for them. I have neither gold, nor fields, nor vineyards, nor houses, except My Mother's house in Nazareth, which is so small and poor as to be ignored by the tax-assessors. Consequently I am not afraid that they may find out that My statement of income is untrue and that I may be fined and punished. All I possess is the Word that God gave Me and that I give. But it is such a sublime thing that man has no means whatsoever to affect it.»

[4] «But if You were in our position what would You do?» 163.4

«Well, do not take it amiss if I tell you quite frankly My opinion, which is in contrast to yours. I solemnly tell you that I would behave differently.»

«How?»

«Not offending against the holy truth. It is always a sublime virtue, even when it is applied to such human things as taxes.»

«But... then... ! How they would fleece us! But You are not

considering that we own a lot and we would have to pay a lot!»

«You have said it. God has granted you a lot. In proportion you *must* give a lot. Why behave so badly, as unfortunately many do, so that poor people are taxed out of proportion? We are aware of the situation. How many taxes there are in Israel, our taxes, which are unjust! The great, who already have so much, benefit from them. Whereas they are the despair of poor people who have to pay them and have to starve to find the money. Love for our neighbour does not recommend that. We Israelites should be so thoughtful as to take upon us the burden of the poor.»

«You are saying that because You are poor, too.»

«No, Uriah. I am saying that because it is justice. Why has Rome been able to oppress us thus? Because we sinned and we are divided by hatred. The rich hate the poor, the poor hate the rich. Because there is no justice and the enemy takes advantage of the situation and has subdued us.»

«You have mentioned various reasons... Are there any more?»

«I would not like to go against the truth by twisting the nature of a place consecrated to religion and making it a sure shelter for human things.»

«Are You reproaching us?»

«No. I am replying to you. Listen to your own consciences. You are masters and therefore...»

163.5 [5] «I would say that it is time to rise, to rebel, to punish the invader and restore our kingdom.»

«True, true! You are right, Simon. But the Messiah is here. He must do it» replies Eli.

«But the Messiah, for the time being, forgive me, Jesus, is only Goodness. He advises everything, except to rebel. We will...»

«Listen, Simon. Remember the book of Kings. Saul was at *
Gilgal, the Philistines were at Michmash, the people were afraid and dispersed, the prophet Samuel was not coming. Saul decided to precede the servant of God and offer the sacrifice himself. Remember the answer that Samuel, on his arrival, gave to the imprudent Saul: "You have acted like a fool and you have not carried out the order that the Lord had commanded you. If you had not done that, now the Lord would have confirmed your sov-

* **the book of the Kings**: but the quote is taken from *1 Samuel 13,1-14.*

ereignty over Israel forever. But now your sovereignty will not last". An untimely and proud action served neither the king nor the people. God knows the hour. Man does not. God knows the means, man does not. Leave things to God and deserve His help by means of holy behaviour. My Kingdom is not a kingdom of rebellion and ferocity. But it will be established. It is not a preserve for a few people. It will be universal. Blessed are those who will come to it, who are not led into error by My poor appearance, according to the spirit of the world, and who will see the Saviour in Me. Be not afraid. I shall be King. The King who came from Israel. The King who will extend His Kingdom all over Mankind. But you, masters of Israel, must not misunderstand My words and those of the Prophets who announce Me. No human kingdom, no matter how powerful it may be, is universal and eternal. The Prophets say that Mine will be such. That should enlighten
you on the truth and spirituality of My Kingdom. [6]I leave you. 163.6
But I have a request to make to Eli. This is your purse. In a shelter of Simon of Jonas there are some poor people who have come from everywhere. Come with Me to give them the alms of love. Peace be with you all.»

«Stay a little longer» beg the Pharisees.

«I cannot. There are people, whose bodies and hearts are diseased, and they are waiting to be comforted. Tomorrow I will be going away. I want everyone to see Me leave without being disappointed.»

«Master, I... am old and tired. Please go in my name. You have Judas of Simon with You, *and we know him well*. Do it Yourself. God be with You.»

Jesus goes out with Judas who, as soon as they are in the square, says: «The old viper! What did he mean?»

«Forget about it! Or better still: just think that he wanted to praise you.»

«Impossible, Master! Those mouths never praise those who do good. I mean, never sincerely. And with regards to his coming!... It is because he loathes the poor and is afraid of their curses. He has tortured the poor people here so often. I can swear it without any fear. And therefore...»

«Be good, Judas. Be good. Let God judge.»

164. Towards the Retreat on the Mountain Before the Apostolic Election.

15th May 1945.

[...].

164.1 [1] The boats of Peter and John are sailing on the placid lake, followed by, I think, all the boats that exist on the shores of Tiberias, because they are so numerous, large and small, coming and going, endeavouring to reach and overtake the boat in which Jesus is and then forming a long line behind it. Prayers, entreaties, requests and outcries can be heard over the blue waves.

Jesus promises, replies and blesses. In His boat there is also Mary and the mother of James and Judas, whereas in the other boat there is Mary Salome with her son John and Susanna. «Yes, I will come back. I promise you. Be good. Remember My words, so that you may connect them with the ones I will tell you later. I will not be away long. Do not be selfish. I have come also for other people. Be good! You will hurt yourselves. Yes, I will pray for you. You will always have Me with you. The Lord be with you. Of course, I will remember your tears and you will be comforted. You must hope and have faith.»

And thus, blessing and promising while the boat is moving, they reach the shore. It is not Tiberias, but a tiny little village, a handful of poor, almost forlorn houses. Jesus and the disciples disembark and the boats handled by the servants and Zebedee go back. Also the other boats copy them, but many of the people in them disembark and want to follow Jesus at all costs. Among them I can see Isaac with his two protegés: Joseph and Timoneus. I do not recognise anybody else amongst the many people of all ages, from youngsters to old people.

164.2 [2] Jesus leaves the village, of which the few poorly dressed inhabitants remain quite indifferent. Jesus has given alms to them and then reaches the main road. He stops. «And now, let us part» He says. «Mother, You with Mary and Salome will go to Nazareth. Susanna can go to Cana. I will soon come back. You know what is to be done. God be with you!»

But for His Mother He has a special greeting, a salutation all smiles and also when Mary kneels down, setting an example to the others, in order to be blessed, Jesus smiles most kindly. The woman, with Alphaeus of Sarah and Simon, go towards their town.

Jesus addresses those who have stayed: «I leave you, but I am not sending you away. I leave you for a short time, as I am retiring with My disciples to those mountain gorges, which you can see over there. Those who wish to wait for Me, should do so here on this plain. Those who do not wish to wait, can go home. I am retiring to pray because I am on the eve of great events. Those who love the cause of the Father should pray, joining Me in spirit. Peace be with you, My children. Isaac, you know what you have to do. I bless you, My little shepherd.» Jesus smiles at emaciated Isaac, who is now the shepherd of men gathering around him.

[3] Jesus is now walking away from the lake, turning His steps 164.3
decidedly towards a gorge between the hills, which stretch in parallel lines, I would say, from the lake westward. A small but very noisy foamy stream runs down between one rocky rugged hill and the next one, which is so steep that it resembles a fjord. Above the stream there is the wild mountain with ugly looking plants, which have grown in all directions, wherever they could, in the crevices between stones. A very narrow steep path climbs up the more rugged hill. And Jesus takes it.

The disciples follow Him with difficulty, in single file, in dead silence. Only when Jesus stops to let them recover their breath, where the path, which looks like a scratch on the impervious mountain side, widens out, they look at one another without uttering a word. Their glances say: «But where is He taking us?», but they do not speak. They only look at one another more and more desolately as they see Jesus carry on walking up the wild gorge, with its many caves, crevices and rocks, where it is very difficult to walk, also because of the bramble and thorny bushes, which catch their clothes on all sides, and scratch them and cause them to stumble and hurt their faces. Also the younger ones, laden with heavy sacks, have lost their good humour.

[4] At last Jesus stops and says: «We shall stop here for a week in 164.4
prayer, to prepare you for a great event. That is why I wanted to be isolated in this desert place, away from all roads and villages. The grottoes here have already been useful to men in the past. They will be useful also to you. The water here is cool and plentiful, whereas the earth is dry. We have enough bread and food for

the time we shall be staying. Those who last year were with Me in the desert, know how I lived there. This is a royal palace compared with that place, and the season, which is now mild, is not affected by the icy bitterness of frost or the burning heat of the sun. You may, therefore, stay here cheerfully. Perhaps we shall never again be all together like this and all alone. This retreat must unite you, making not twelve men of you, *but one only institution.*

Are you not saying anything? Are you not asking any questions? Lay on that rock the loads that you are carrying and throw down the valley the other load that you have in your hearts: your humanity.

I have brought you here to speak to your spirits, to nourish your spirits, to make you spiritual. I shall not speak many words. I have told you so many in approximately one year that I have been with you! Enough of that. If I should have to change you by means of words, I would have to keep you ten years... one hundred years, and you would still be imperfect. It is now time that I make use of you. And to make use of you, I must form you. I will have recourse to the great medicine, to the great weapon: to prayer. I have always prayed for you. But now I want you to pray by yourselves. I will not yet teach you My prayer. But I will tell you how to pray and what prayer is. It is the conversation of sons with the Father, of spirits with the Spirit, an open, warm, trustful, quiet and frank conversation. Prayer is everything: it is confession, knowledge of ourselves, repentance, a promise to ourselves and to God, a request to God, all done at the feet of the Father. And it cannot be done in a turmoil, among distractions, unless one is a giant in prayer. And even giants suffer from the clash with the noise of the world in their time of prayer. You are not giants, but pygmies. You are but infants in your spirits. You are deficient in your spirits. You will reach here the age of spiritual reason. The rest will come later.

In the morning, at midday and in the evening, we shall gather together to pray with the old words of Israel and to break our bread, then each of you will go back to his grotto, in front of God and of his soul, in front of what I told you with regards to your mission and to your capabilities. Weigh yourselves, listen to yourselves, make up your minds. I am telling you for the last time. And after you will have to be perfect, as much as you can, without fatigue and without your humanity. Then you will no longer be Simon of Jonah and Judas of Simon. No longer Andrew or John, Matthew or Thomas. But you will be My ministers.

Go. Each by himself. I shall be in that cave. I shall always be present. But do not come without a good reason. You must learn to do things by yourselves and be all by yourselves. Because I solemnly tell you that a year ago we were about to become acquainted with one another, and in two years' time we shall be parting. Woe betide you and Me if you have not learned to act by yourselves. God be with you.

Judas, John, take the foodstuffs into My cave, that one. They must last and I will hand them out.»

«They are not enough!...» objects someone.

«They are sufficient not to die. A too full stomach makes the spirit dull. I want to elevate you and not make you dead weights.»

165. The Election of the Twelve Apostles.

16th May 1945.

[1] It is dawning and the soft light whitens the mountains and seems to soften the wild mountain side. Only the gurgling sound of the foamy stream at the bottom of the valley can be heard, a sound which becomes a strange noise, when echoed by the mountain and its many caves. Where the disciples have rested, there is some gentle rustling among the leaves and the herbs: the first birds to awake, or the last night-birds returning to their hiding places. A group of hares or wild rabbits, gnawing at a low bush of blackberries, run away frightened by a falling stone. Then they go back cautiously, moving their ears in all directions to pick up every sound and when they see that everything is peaceful, they return to the bush. All the leaves and stones are wet with dew and in the wood there is a strong smell of moss, mint and marjoram. 165.1

A redbreast flies down to the edge of a cave, the roof of which is formed by a huge protruding stone and standing up straight on its very thin legs, ready to fly away, it moves its little head round, looks into the cave and at the ground, chirping inquisitively and... gluttonously, because of some bread crumbs on the ground. But it does not make up its mind to fly down until it sees that it has been preceded by a big blackbird, which proceeds hopping sideways and is extremely comical in its urchin-like attitude with its profile of an old notary, who requires only a pair of spectacles to be the complete dignitary. The robin then flies down, hopping behind its daring fellow creature, which now and again thrusts its yellow beak into the moist ground, in archaeological research... for food and then proceeds further, after whistling, just like a real little rascal. The redbreast stuffs itself with the little bread crumbs and is amazed when it sees the blackbird, which had confidently gone into the silent cave, come out of it with a cheese-rind, which it knocks repeatedly against a stone to break it up and make a sumptous meal of it. It goes back in again, has a look around, and not finding anything else, it whistles scoffingly and flies away to complete its song on the top of an oak-tree, in the blue morning sky. Also the robin flies away, because of a noise from the interior of the cave... and it perches on a thin bough that dangles loosely.

165.2 [2] Jesus goes to the entrance of His cave and crumbles some bread, calling the little birds very gently, by means of a modulated whistle, which is a very good imitation of the twittering of many birds. He then moves away, climbing higher up and resting against a rock in order not to frighten His little friends, which soon fly down: the robin being the first and then many more of various kinds. Jesus' stillness and also His look are such that after a short time many birds are hopping only a few inches from Him. I like to believe, because of my own experience, that also the most distrustful animals go near people when their instinct tells them that they are not enemies but friends. The redbreast, which is now satisfied, flies to the top of the rock against which Jesus is leaning, it rests on a very thin branch of clematis, swings above Jesus' head and seems to be anxious to descend upon His fair hair or His shoulder. The meal is now over. The rising sun gilds the mountain tops and then the highest branches of the trees, whereas down below, the valley is still in the dim dawn light. The little birds, satisfied and full, fly towards the sun and sing at the top of their voices.

165.3 [3] «And now let us go and wake up these other children of Mine» says Jesus, and He walks down, as His cave is the highest one, and He enters the various caves calling the sleeping apostles by their names.

Simon, Bartholomew, Philip, James and Andrew reply at once. Matthew, Peter and Thomas take a little longer to reply. And while Judas Thaddeus goes to meet Jesus as soon as he sees Him appear at the entrance of his grotto, as he is already ready and wide awake, the other cousin, the Iscariot and John are fast asleep, so much so that Jesus has to shake them on their beds, made with tree branches and leaves, in order to wake them up.

John, the last one to be called, is so sound asleep, that he does not realise Who is calling him, and in the haze of his interrupted sleep, he whispers: «Yes, mother, I am coming at once...» But he turns round on his other side.

Jesus smiles, sits on the rustic mattress made of foliage picked in the wood, He bends and kisses the cheek of John, who opens his eyes and is dumbfounded at seeing Jesus. He sits up and says: «Do you need me? Here I am.»

«No. I woke you up as I did the others. But you thought it was your mother. So I kissed you, as mothers do.»

John, half naked in his under tunic, because he used his tunic and mantle as bed covers, clasps Jesus' neck and lays his head between Jesus' shoulder and cheek saying: «Oh! You are much more than a mother! I left her for You, but I would not leave You for her! She bore me to the earth. You are bearing me to Heaven. Oh! I know!»

4 «What do you know more than the others?» 165.4

«What the Lord told me in this cave. See, I never came to You and I think my companions said it was due to indifference and pride. But I am not concerned with what they think. I know that You know the truth. I was not coming to Jesus Christ, the Incarnate Son of God, but to what You are in the bosom of the Fire, that is the eternal Love of the Most Holy Trinity, its Nature, its Essence, its Real Essence — oh! I cannot tell, however, what I have understood in this dark gloomy cavern that has become so full of light for me, in this cold grotto where I have been burnt by a featureless fire that has descended into the depth of my being and has inflamed me with a sweet martyrdom, in this silent cave, which has, however, sung celestial truths to me — but to what You are, the Second Person of the ineffable Mystery, which is God and which I penetrated because God has drawn me to Himself and I have always had Him with me. And I have poured all my desires, all my tears, all my requests on Your divine bosom, Word of God. Amongst the many words I have heard from You, there never was one so comprehensive as the one You told me here, You, God the Son, You, God like the Father, You, God like the Holy Spirit, You, centre of the Trinity... oh! perhaps I am blaspheming, but that is what I think, because if You were not the love of the Father and the love for the Father, then the Love, the Divine Love would be missing, and Divinity would no longer be Triune and it would lack the most becoming attribute of God: His love! Oh! I have so much in here, but it is like water gurgling against a dam and cannot flow out... and I seem to be dying of it, so violent and sublime is the turmoil in my heart, since I have understood You... but I would not like to be freed of it for the whole world... Let me die of that love, my sweet God!» John smiles and weeps, panting, inflamed by his love, relaxing on Jesus' chest, as if he were exhausted by his ardour. And Jesus caresses him, burning with love Himself.

John composes himself and with deep humility he begs: «Do not tell the others what I told You. I am sure that they too have lived with God as I did during these past days. But leave the stone of silence on my secret.»

«Do not worry, John. No one will be aware of your wedding with the Love. Get dressed, come. We must leave.»

165.5 [5]Jesus goes out onto the path where the others are already gathered. Their faces look more venerable and serene. The old ones look like patriarchs, the younger ones have a maturity and dignity, which were previously concealed by their youth. The Iscariot looks at Jesus with a shy smile on his face marked by tears. Jesus caresses him passing by. Peter... is silent. And his silence is so strange that it is more striking than any other change. He looks at Jesus attentively, but with a new dignity that makes his bald forehead look more spacious and his eyes more severe, whereas before they were full of gentle intelligence only. Jesus calls him near Himself and keeps him there while waiting for John, who at last comes out. I could not say whether his face looks more pale or more flushed, it is certainly burning with a flame that does not change its colour, and yet is most obvious. They all look at him.

«Come here, John, near Me. And you, too, Andrew, and you, James of Zebedee. Then you, Simon, and you, Bartholomew, Philip, and you, My cousins, and Matthew. Judas of Simon here, in front of Me. Thomas, come here. Sit down. I must speak to you.»

They all sit down quietly, like good children, all engrossed in their internal world and yet paying attention to Jesus, as they never did before.

[6] «Do you know what I have done to you? You all know. Your 165.6
souls told your minds. But your souls, which were the queens these past days, have taught your minds two great virtues: humility and silence, the son of humility and prudence, which are the daughters of charity. Only eight days ago you would have come to proclaim your cleverness and your new knowledge, like clever children who are eager to astound people and overcome their rivals. Now you are silent. You have grown from children into adolescents and you are already aware that such a proclamation might humiliate a companion who was perhaps less helped by God, and therefore you do not speak.

You are also like pubescent girls. The holy reserve, concerning the change that revealed the nuptial mystery of souls with God, was born in you. These caves seemed cold, hostile and repulsive on the first day... now you are looking at them as if they were bright scented nuptial rooms. You have met God in them. Before you were aware of Him. But you did not know Him in the intimacy that blends two into one. Amongst you there are some who have been married for years, some who have had but a disappointing relationship with women, some who are chaste owing to various reasons. But the chaste ones now know what perfect love is, as the married ones know. Rather, I can say that nobody knows what perfect love is, as he who is unaware of carnal lusts. Because God reveals Himself in His fullness to the pure, both because He takes delight in giving Himself to those who are pure, as He, the Most Pure One, finds part of Himself in the creature free from lust, and because He wishes to compensate the creature for what it denies itself for His love.

[7] I solemnly tell you that because of the love I have for you and 165.7
of the wisdom I possess, if I did not have to accomplish the work

of the Father, I would keep you here and be with you, isolated, as I am sure that I would soon make *great* saints of you, and you would no longer be subject to confusion, defections, failures, slackening, recurrences. But I cannot. I must go. And you must go. The world is waiting for us. The desecrated and desecrating world, which needs teachers and redeemers, is waiting for us. I wanted you to know that you may love Him more than you love the world, which with all its affections is not worth one single smile of God. I wanted to make it possible for you to meditate on what the world is and what God is, so that you may yearn for what is better. At present you are yearning only for God. Oh! I wish I could secure you in your yearning of the present moment! But the world is waiting for us. And we shall go to the world, which is waiting for us, for the sake of the holy Charity that by My order is sending you to the world as it sent Me. But I implore you! Lock in your hearts, like a pearl in a coffer, the treasure of the past days in which you have examined, cured, elevated, renovated and united yourselves to God. And keep and preserve these precious memories in your hearts, like the witness stones erected by the Patriarchs in remembrance of the alliance with God.

165.8 [8] As from today you are no longer My favourite disciples, but the apostle, the chiefs of My Church. All the hierarchies of the Church, throughout centuries, shall descend from you, and will call you masters, having as their Master your God in His triple power, wisdom and charity. I have not chosen you because you are the most worthy, but for a number of reasons that you need not know now. I have chosen you instead of the shepherds who have been My disciples since I was born. Why did I do it? Because it was right to do so. Amongst you there are Galileans and Judaeans, learned and unlearned, rich and poor people. And that is because of the world, that it may not say that I have chosen one category only. But you will not be sufficient for everything there is to be done. Neither now, nor later.

Not all of you will remember a passage of the Book. I will remind you. Book 2 of Chronicles, Chapter 29, tells how Hezekiah, King of Judah, had the Temple purified, and after it was purified he had sacrifices offered in atonement, for his kingdom, for the Temple and for the whole of Judah, and then the offerings of the single individuals began. But as the priests were not sufficient for the sacrifices, the levites, who are consecrated with a shorter rite, were summoned.

That is what I will do. You are the priests, who have been prepared by Me, the Eternal Pontiff, diligently and for a long time. But you will not suffice for the work, which is much more extensive than the sacrifice of the offerings of individuals to the Lord their God. I will therefore associate with you the disciples who will remain such, those who are waiting for us at the foot of the mountain, those who are already higher up, those who are spread all over Israel and that later will be spread all over the world. They will be entrusted with equal tasks, because the mission is only one, but their position will be different in the eyes of the world. But not in the eyes of God, where there is justice, so that the obscure disciple, ignored by the apostles and by his brethren, who lives a holy life taking souls to God, will be greater than a known apostle, who has only the name of apostle and lowers his apostolic dignity for human purposes.

The task of the apostles and disciples will still be the same as the task of the priests and levites of Hezekiah: to perform the rites of the cult, to demolish idolatries, to purify hearts and places, to preach God and His Word. There is not a more holy task on the earth. Neither is there a dignity higher than yours. That is why I said to you: "Listen to yourselves and examine yourselves".

[9] Woe betide the apostle who falls! He drags many disciples 165.9
with him, and they drag a greater number of believers and the ruin grows larger and larger like a falling avalanche or a ring that expands on the lake when several stones are thrown in the same spot.

Will you all be perfect? No. Will the spirit of the present moment last? No. The world will throw its tentacles to choke your souls. That will be the victory of the world: to extinguish the light in the hearts of saints; the world, a son of Satan for five tenths, a servant of Satan for three more tenths, indifferent to God for the remaining two tenths. Defend yourselves from yourselves, against yourselves, against the world, flesh and the demon. Above all, defend yourselves from yourselves. Stand on your guard, My children, against pride, sensuality, duplicity, tepidity, spiritual drowsiness and against avarice! When your *in-*

ferior ego speaks and moans over alleged cruelty to it, hush it up by saying: "For a moment of hardship, which I give you now, I will procure for you, and forever, the banquet of ecstasy that you enjoyed in the mountain cave at the end of the month of Shebat".

165.10 [10] Let us go. Let us go and meet the others who in large numbers are awaiting My coming. And then I will go for a few hours to Tiberias and you, preaching Me, will go to wait for Me at the foot of the mountain that is on the road leading from Tiberias to the sea. I will come up there to preach. Take your bags and mantles. The retreat is over and the election has been made.»

17th May 1945.

165.11 [11] Jesus says:

«You are not feeling well and I will leave you in peace. I only wish to point out to you how a sentence omitted or a word wrongly copied can alter everything. And you, My writer, are alive and can make the correction at once. So consider and try to understand how twenty centuries have deprived the Gospel, the apostolic Gospel, of parts that did no harm to the doctrine, but prevented it from being easily understood. This — if we go back to the origin we find that it is still the work of Disorder — explains many things and lends itself to the children of Disorder for so many more things. And you can see how easy it is to make errors in copying... Little John, be good today. You are a broken flower. I will come later and mend your stalk. I need the tears of your wound today. God is with you.»

166. A Profusion of Miracles After the Apostolic Nomination. The First Sermon of Simon the Zealot and John.

18th May 1945.

166.1 [1] Jesus, half way down the mountain, finds many disciples and many more people, who by degrees have joined the disciples. They have come here urged by the need of a miracle, by the desire to hear Jesus' word, and have been guided here either by information of people or by the instinct of their souls. I think that the guardian angels of men have led them to the Son of God, as they were desirous of God. And I do not think I am telling an idle story. If we consider with what prompt and shrewd perseverance Satan led enemies to God and to His Word, every time his diabolical spirit could exhibit to men the semblance of a fault in Christ, it is admissible to think, rather than admissible it is indeed just to think also that the angels were no way inferior to demons and they led non-demoniacal spirits to Christ.

And Jesus does His utmost for all those who have been waiting for Him patiently and fearlessly and grants them miracles and the comfort of His word. How many miracles! As many as the flowers decorating the mountain crags. Some of the miracles are great, like the one for a boy who was rescued from a blazing straw-barn and was dreadfully burnt. The child was brought here on a stretcher, crying mournfully, a heap of scorched flesh under a linen cloth, with which he had been covered, so dreadful is the appearance of his burnt body. He is about to breathe his last breath. Jesus breathes over him and heals his burns that disappear completely, so much so that the boy gets up, absolutely naked, and runs happily towards his mother, who, weeping for joy, caresses his body now entirely cured, without any trace of burns. She kisses his eyes, which were expected to be burnt, and instead are bright and shining with joy. His hair is short, but not destroyed, as if the flames had acted as a razor and not as an instrument of destruction. Other miracles are minor, like the one in favour of a little elderly man suffering from asthmatic spasms, who says: «Not for my own sake, but because I have to act as a father to my little orphan grandchildren and I cannot work the land with this disease here, in my throat, choking me...»

There is also an invisible but real miracle brought about by Jesus' words: «Amongst you, there is one whose soul is weeping, but dare not say the words: "Have mercy on me!" My reply is: "Let it be done as you wish. You have all My pity, that you may know that I am Mercy". In my turn, however, I say to you: "Be generous". Be generous with God. Break all ties with the past. You perceive God, so come to Him Whom you perceive, with a free heart and complete love.» I do not know to whom, among the crowd, these words are addressed.

[2]Jesus also says: «These are My apostles. They are as many 166.2
Christs, because I have elected them as such. Apply to them

trustingly. They have learned from Me what is needed for your souls...» The apostles, thoroughly afraid, look at Jesus. But He smiles and goes on: «...and they will give your souls the light of stars and the refreshment of dew, to prevent you from languishing in darkness. And then I will come and give you perfect light and consolation and all wisdom to make you strong and happy by means of a supernatural strength and joy. Peace be with you, My children. I am expected by other people who are more unhappy and poorer than you are. But I will not leave you alone. I am leaving My apostles with you, which is the same as if I left the children of My love entrusted to the most amiable and reliable foster-mothers.»

Jesus waves His hand, blesses them and departs, pushing through the crowd, who do not want to let Him go, and just then He works the last miracle. An elderly partly-paralysed woman, brought here by her grandson, joyfully shakes her right arm, which before she could not move, and shouts: «He touched me lightly with His mantle, when passing by, and I am cured! I did not even ask for it, because I am old... But He felt pity also for my secret desire. And with His mantle, the hem of which hardly touched my useless arm, He cured me! Oh! What a great Son our holy David has! Glory be to his Messiah! But look! Look! Also my leg is moving like my arm... Oh! I feel as if I were only twenty years old!»

While many people rush towards the old woman, who is shouting her happiness at the top of her voice, Jesus can sneak away without being detained further. And the apostles follow Him.

166.3 [3] When they are in a lonely place, almost down on the plain, they stop for a moment in an area of heathland, which stretches towards the lake. Jesus says: «I bless you! Go back to your work and continue it until I come back, as I told you.»

Peter, who has been quiet so far, bursts out: «But, my Lord, what have You done? Why did You say that we have everything that souls need? It is true that You have told us many things. But we are blockheads, at least I am, and... and of all You gave me, little is left, very little indeed. I am like one, who after a meal, still has in his stomach the heavy part of the food. The rest is no longer there.»

Jesus smiles frankly: «Where is the rest of the food, then?»

«Well... I don't know. I know that when I eat delicate food, after an hour my stomach feels empty. But if I eat horse-radish, or lentils dressed with oil, eh! it takes a long time to get rid of them!»

«It does. But you can be sure that horse-radish and lentils, which seem to fill you more, are the less nourishing: it is meal that goes through with little benefit. Whereas the delicate dishes that you feel no longer, within an hour, are no longer in your stomach, but in your blood. When food has been digested it is no longer in one's stomach, but its juice is in the blood and is more useful. Now you and your companions think that nothing, or only a little, is left in you of what I told you. Perhaps you remember whatever is more pertinent to one's own nature: the violent the violent parts, the contemplative the contemplative parts, the affectionate the loving parts... But believe Me: *everything is within you*. Even if it seems to have gone. You have absorbed it. Your thoughts will wind off like a multicoloured thread showing you light or strong hues according to what you require. Be not afraid. Consider that I know and I would *never* send you if I knew that you were unable to do it. Goodbye, Peter. Cheer up! Smile! Have faith! A good act of faith in the Omnipresent Wisdom. Goodbye, everybody. The Lord is with you.» And He leaves them quickly, while they are still amazed and worried about what they have heard they must do.

[4] «And yet we must obey» says Thomas. 166.4

«Yes... of course... Oh! poor me! I feel like running after Him...» grumbles Peter.

«No. Don't. To obey is to love Him» says James of Alphaeus.

«It is only reasonable and also according to holy prudence that we should start while He is still near us and can advise us if we make mistakes. We must help Him» suggests the Zealot.

«That's true. Jesus is rather tired. We must relieve Him a little, as best we can. It is not enough to carry the bags, make the beds and prepare the food. Anyone can do that. But we must help Him in His mission, as He wants us to» confirms Bartholomew.

«It's all right for you, because you are a learned man. But I... I am almost completely ignorant...» moans James of Zebedee.

«O Lord! There are those who were up there. They are coming here! What shall we do?» exclaims Andrew.

And Matthew says: «Excuse me, if I, the most miserable one, give you my advice. Would it not be better to pray the Lord, instead of standing here complaining about things complaints cannot mend? Come on, Judas, you know the Scriptures so well, say for us all the prayer of Solomon to obtain Wisdom. Quick! * Before they arrive here.»

And Thaddeus in his beautiful baritone voice begins: «God of my ancestors, Lord of mercy, Who by Your word have made all things... etc... etc.» down to: «... all those were saved by Wisdom, who pleased You, o Lord, from the beginning.» He finishes in time, just before the people arrive, and gather around them asking thousands of questions as to where the Master has gone, when He will come back, and a more difficult one to be answered, requesting: «How can they follow the Master, not with their legs, but with their souls, along the Way pointed out by Him?»

The apostles are embarrassed by the question. They look at one another and the Iscariot replies: «By following perfection» as if his reply explained everything!...

James of Alphaeus, who is more humble and quiet, becomes pensive, then says: «The perfection to which my companion refers is achieved by obeying the Law. Because the Law is justice and justice is perfection.»

166.5 [5]But the crowd are not yet satisfied and one, who appears to be a leader, asks: «But we are like little children with regard to doing good. Children do not yet know the meaning of Good and Evil, they cannot tell one from the other. And on this way, which He points out to us, we are so inexperienced that we are unable to distinguish between them. There was a way known to us, the old one, which we were taught at school. It is so difficult, long and frightening! Now, listening to His words, we feel that it is like that aqueduct we can see from here. Below, there is the road for animals and men, above, on the light arches, high up in the sun and in the blue sky, near the tallest branches rustling in the wind and resounding with the singing of birds, there is another road, as smooth, clean and clear, as the inferior one is rough, dirty and dark, there is a way for the gurgling limpid water, which is a blessing, because of the water that comes from

* **prayer**, in: *Wisdom, 9.*

God and is caressed by what is of God: rays of the sun and of the stars, new leaves, flowers and wings of swallows. We would like to climb up to that higher way, which is His way, but we do not know how to do so, because we are bound down here, under the weight of the old construction. What shall we do?»

The person who has spoken is a young man about twenty-five years old, dark, strong, with an intelligent mien. He does not seem to be a man of the people like the majority of the crowd present. He is leaning on an older man.

The Iscariot, tall as he is, sees him and whispers to his companions: «Quick, explain things properly. There is Hermas with Stephen, who is loved by Gamaliel!» And that is enough to embarrass the apostles completely.

[6] At last the Zealot replies: «There would be no arch, if there 166.6
was no foundation in the dark road. The latter is the matrix of the former, which rises from it and climbs towards the blue sky, of which you are desirous. The stones fixed in the ground and holding the weight without enjoying rays or flights are aware that they are set there, because now and again a swallow, squeaking, flies down as far as the mud, and caresses the base of the arch, and a ray of the sun or of a star filters through to say how beautiful is the vault of heaven. Thus, in past centuries, a divine word of promise, a celestial ray of wisdom, descended now and again to caress the stone oppressed by divine wrath. Because the stones were necessary. They are not, were not and never will be useless. Time and the perfection of human knowledge have risen slowly on them and have reached the freedom of present days and the wisdom of supernatural knowledge.

I already see your objection, it is written on your face. It is the one we have all had, before we were able to understand that this is the New Doctrine, the Gospel preached to those who, because of a retarding process, have not become adults through the elevation of the stones of knowledge, but have grown darker and darker like a wall that sinks into a dark abyss.

In order to get out of this affliction of a supernatural darkness, we must bravely free the foundation stone from all the others laid on top of it. Do not be afraid to knock down the high wall that does not carry the pure lymph of the eternal spring. Go back to the foundation, which is not to be changed. It comes from God.

It is immovable. But before rejecting the stones, because they are not all bad and useless, examine them one by one, at the sound of the word of God. If you hear that they are sound, keep them and use them again to rebuild. But if you hear in them the dissonant sound of human voice or the rending sound of a satanic voice — and you cannot be mistaken because if it is God's voice it is a sound of love, if it is a human voice it is a sensual sound, if it is a satanic voice it is a sound of hatred — then break the wicked stones into shivers. I say: *break them into shivers,* because it is charity not to leave behind germs or evil things, as they may seduce the wayfarer and induce him to use them to his own disadvantage. You should literally crush all your deeds to smithereens, writings, teachings and acts that were not good. It is better to be left with little, to rise by hardly one cubit with good stones, rather than by yards with wicked stones. Sunbeams and swallows descend also to low walls, which hardly rise above the ground and the humble little flowers at the edge of the road easily reach the low stones to caress them. On the contrary, the proud useless rough stones that want to rise higher receive nothing but thorny caresses and poisonous embraces. Demolish in order to rebuild and to ascend, testing the goodness of your old stones to the sound of the voice of God.»

166.7 [7] «You are a good speaker, man. We must ascend! But how? We have told you that we are less than babies. Who will enable us to climb the steep column? We will test the stones to the sound of the voice of God. We will break up the ones that are not good. But how can we ascend? We feel giddy only at the thought of it!» says Stephen.

166.8 [8] John, who has been listening with his head lowered, smiling to himself, raises his head. His face is bright and he begins to speak:

«Brothers! The thought of ascending makes you feel giddy. It is true. But who told you that it is necessary to attack the ascent direct? Not only babies, but even adults cannot do it. Only angels can glide in the blue skies, because they are free from all material weight. And only heroes in holiness can do it amongst men.

We have a living being, who in this dejected world, is still a holy hero, like the ancient people who adorned Israel, when the Patriarchs were friends of God and the word of the eternal Code was the only one and was obeyed by every righteous creature. John, the Precursor teaches us how to attack the ascent direct. John is a man. But the Grace, which the Fire of God communicated to him, purifying him in his mother's womb, as the lips of the Prophet were cleansed by the Seraph, so that he might precede the Messiah without leaving the stench of original sin along the royal way of Christ, that Grace has given John the wings of an angel and Penance has made them grow, suppressing at the same time the human weight which his nature of a man born of a woman had retained. John, therefore, from the cavern where he preached penance, with his spirit married to Grace burning in his body, can ascend to the top of the arch beyond which is God, the Most High Lord our God, and dominating the past centuries, the present day and the future, with the voice of a prophet and the eye of an eagle that can stare at the eternal sun and recognise it, he can announce: "There is the Lamb of God that takes away the sin of the world". And he can die after this sublime song, which will be sung not only in our limited time, but also in the endless Time in the eternal blessed Jerusalem, to applaud the Second Person, to invoke Him on human miseries, to sing hosannas in the eternal brightness.

[9]But the Lamb of God, the Most Sweet Lamb Who left His 166.9
bright abode in Heaven, where He is the Fire of God in an embrace of fire — oh! the eternal generation, of the Father Who conceives His Word through His unlimited and most holy thought, and absorbs Him producing an effusion of love, from which the Spirit of Love proceeds, the centre of Power and Wisdom — but the Lamb of God, Who left His most pure incorporeal form, to enclose His infinite purity, holiness and divine nature in mortal flesh, knows that we have not been cleansed by Grace, not yet, and knows that we could not ascend to the high summit, where God, One and Triune is, like the eagle, which is John. We are little sparrows living on roofs and on roads, we are swallows that fly in the sky but feed on insects, we are woodlarks who want to sing imitating the angels, but our singing, when compared to theirs, is a dissonant high-pitched drone of cicadas in summer. The Sweet Lamb of God, Who came to take away the sin of the world, knows that. Because if He is no longer the Infinite Spirit of Heaven, having taken human flesh, His infinity is not dimin-

ished thereby and He knows everything because His wisdom is always infinite.

And so He teaches us His way. The way of love. He is the Love, which out of mercy for us, became flesh. And that Merciful Love created for us a way, which also little ones can ascend. And He is the first to ascend it, not because of His own need, but to teach us. Neither would He need to spread His wings to return to the Father. His spirit, I swear it to you, is closed down here, on the miserable earth, but it is always with the Father, because God can do everything, and He is God. But He goes ahead, leaving behind Him the perfume of His holiness, the gold and fire of His love. Look at His way. Oh! It does reach the summit of the arch! But how peaceful and safe it is! It is not straight: it is spiral. It is longer and the sacrifice of His merciful love is revealed by such length where He delays for the sake of us, the weak ones. It is longer, but better suited to our misery. The ascent to love, to God, is as simple as Love. But it is vast, because God is an abyss, which I would say is immeasurable if He did not bend across to be reached, to be kissed by the souls in love with Him (John speaks and weeps, smiling with his lips, in the ecstasy of revealing God). The simple way of love is long, because the Abyss, which is God, is limitless, and one could climb as much as one would like. But the Admirable Abyss calls our miserable abyss. It calls it by means of its light and says: "Come to Me!" Oh! The invitation of God! The invitation of the Father!

166.10 [10] Listen! Listen! The kindest words are coming towards us from the Heavens left open, because Christ opened the gates wide and left the angels of Mercy and Forgiveness to keep them open, so that while men are waiting for the Grace, at least light, scents, songs and peace should flow down to attract the hearts of men in a holy manner. It is the voice of God Who is speaking. And the Voice says: "Your childhood? But it is your most valuable money! I would like you to become really little, so that you would have the humility, the sincerity and the love of children, the confident love of children for their fathers. Your inability? But that is My glory! Oh! Come. I do not even ask you to test the sound of the good and bad stones by yourselves. Give them to Me! I will pick them and you will do the rebuilding. The ascent to perfection? Oh! no, My little children. Join hands with My Son, your

Brother now, and thus ascend beside Him...".

To ascend! To come to You, Eternal Love! To achieve Your likeness, that is Love! To love! That is the secret!... To love! To give oneself... To love! To suppress oneself... To love! To melt... The flesh? It is nothing. Sorrow? It is nothing. Time? It is nothing. Sin itself becomes nothing if I dissolve it in Your fire, o God! Only Love exists. Love. The Love that gave us the Incarnate God, will give us all forgiveness. And no one knows how to love better than children. And no one is loved more than a child.

[11] O you, whom I do not know, who want to know what Good is, 166.11
to distinguish it from Evil, to possess the blue sky, the celestial Sun, and everything that is supernatural joy, love and you will achieve it. Love Christ. You will die to the life of this world, but you will rise again in your spirit. With your new spirit, without any further need for stones, you will be forever an inextinguishable fire. A flame rises. It needs neither steps nor wings to rise. Free your *ego* from every construction, put love into yourself. You will blaze up. Let that happen without any restriction. On the contrary, kindle the fire, throwing into it your past passions and knowledge. What is not goodwill be destroyed by the flames, what is already a noble metal will become pure. Cast yourself, brother, into the active joyful love of the Trinity. You will understand what now seems incomprehensible to you, because you will understand God, Who can be understood only by those who give themselves, without any limitation, to His sacrificing fire. You will be fixed, in the end, in God in a loving embrace, praying for me, the child of Christ, who dared to speak to you of Love.»

[12] They are all dumbfounded: the apostles, the disciples, the be- 166.12
lievers... The man to whom the words were addressed is pale, while John's face is flushed, not so much because of the effort as because of his love.

Stephen at last shouts: «May you be blessed! But tell me, who are you?»

And John — his attitude reminds me so much of the Virgin at the Annunciation — replies in a low voice, bending as if he were adoring Him Whom he mentions: «I am John. You see in me the least of the servants of the Lord.»

«But who was your master before?»

«No one but God. Because I received my spiritual milk from

John, the presanctified of God, now I eat the bread of Christ, the Word of God, and I drink God's fire that comes to me from Heaven, Glory be to the Lord!»

«Ah! I am not going to leave you! Neither you nor him, I will part from none of you. Take me with you!»

«When... Oh! But Peter is here, he is our chief» and John takes Peter, who is dumbfounded, and proclaims him «the first».

And Peter collects himself and says: «Son, a considered reflection is required for a great mission. This man is our angel and he inflames us. But it is necessary to know whether the flame will last in us. Measure yourself and then come to the Lord. We will open our hearts to you as to a most dear brother. In the meantime, if you wish to become better acquainted with our life, you may stay. The flocks of Christ may grow exceedingly so that the true lambs may be separated from the false rams, choosing among the perfect and imperfect ones.»

And the first apostolic revelation ends in this way.

167. Meeting with the Roman Ladies in the Gardens of Johanna of Chuza.

19th May 1945.

167.1 [1] Jesus comes off a boat at the wharf at Chuza's garden, helped by a boatman who had taken Him there. A gardener who has seen Him runs to open the gate which closes the entrance to the property on the lake side. It is a strong tall gate, which, however, is concealed by a very thick high hedge of laurel and box on the outer side, towards the lake, and by roses of all colours on the inner side, towards the house. The magnificent rose-bushes decorate the bronze laurel and box leaves, they creep through the branches and peep out on the other side, or they pass over the green barrier and let their flowery heads fall on the other side. Only the central part of the gate, across the avenue, is barren and is opened there to let through people going to or coming from the lake.

«Peace to this house and to you, Joanna. Where is your mistress?»

«Over there, with her friends. I will call her at once. They have been waiting for You three days, because they were afraid of being late.»

Jesus smiles. The servant runs away to call Johanna. In the meantime Jesus walks slowly towards the place mentioned by the servant, admiring the wonderful garden, one could say the wonderful rosery, which Chuza had built for his wife. Magnificent early roses of all types, sizes and shapes are a blaze of colours in this sheltered inlet of the lake. There are other flower plants. But they are not yet in bloom and they are very few compared to the quantity of rose-bushes.

[2]Johanna arrives. She has not even laid down the basket half 167.2
full of roses, nor the scissors she was using to cut them, and she runs in this way, her arms stretched out, agile and beautiful in her wide dress of very thin woolen material, of a very light pink hue, the folds of which are held in place by silver filigree studs and buckles, decorated with sparkling pale garnets.

On her dark wavy hair a mitre-shaped diadem, also in silver and garnets, holds a very light pink byssus veil, which hangs over her back, leaving uncovered her ears, adorned with earrings matching the diadem, her smiling face and thin neck, around which she wears a shining necklace which is made like the rest of her precious ornaments.

She drops her basket at Jesus' feet and kneels down to kiss His tunic, among the roses spread on the ground.

«Peace to you, Johanna. I have come.»

«And I am happy. They have come, too. Oh! Now I seem to have done the wrong thing by organising this meeting! How will you manage to understand one another? They are heathens!» Johanna is somewhat worried.

Jesus smiles, and laying His hand on her head He says: «Be not afraid. We will understand one another very well. You have done the right thing "by organising this meeting". Our meeting will be full of blessings as your garden is full of roses. Now, pick up those poor roses which you dropped and let us go to your friends.»

«Oh! There are plenty of roses. I was picking them to pass the time and then my friends are so... so voluptuous. They love flowers as if they were... I do not know...»

«I love them, too! See, we have already found a subject on

which we can understand one another. Come on! Let us pick up these wonderful roses...» and Jesus bends to set the example.

«Not You! Not You, my Lord! If You really want to... well... it's done.»

167.3 [3] They walk as far as a bower made by multicoloured interlaced rose-bushes. Three Roman ladies are casting glances at them from the threshold: Plautina, Valeria and Lydia. The first and last ones are hesitant, but Valeria runs out and makes a curtsy saying: «Hail, Saviour of my little Fausta!»

«Peace and light to you and to your friends.»

The friends curtsy without speaking.

We already know Plautina. Tall, stately, with beautiful dark, rather authoritative eyes, under a smooth very white forehead, a perfect straight nose, a well shaped rather tumid mouth, a roundish well defined chin, she reminds me of some beautiful statues of Roman empresses. Heavy rings shine on her beautiful hands and large golden bracelets round her statuesque arms, on her wrists and above her elbows which appear pinkish white, smooth and perfect under her short draped sleeves.

Lydia, on the other hand, is fair-haired, thinner and younger. Her beauty is not the stately beauty of Plautina, but she possesses all the grace of feminine youth which is still a little unripe. And since we are on a pagan subject, I could say that if Plautina looks like the statue of an empress, Lydia could well be Diana or a gentle modest looking nymph.

Valeria, who is not in the desperate situation in which we saw her at Caesarea, appears in the beauty of a young mother, rather plumply shaped but still very young, with the quiet look of a mother who is happy to breastfeed her own child and see it grow healthy. Rosy and brown, her smile is a quiet but very kind one.

I am under the impression that the two ladies are of a lower rank than Plautina, whom they respect as a queen, as is obvious also from their attitude.

167.4 [4] «Were you attending to flowers? Go on, go on. We can talk also while you pick this beautiful work of the Creator, which flowers are, and while you arrange them in these precious vases with the ability of which Rome is mistress, to lengthen their lives, which unfortunately are too short... If we admire this bud, which is just opening its yellow pink petal in a lovely smile, how can we not be sorry to see it dying? Oh! How amazed the Jews would be if they heard Me speak thus! But also in a flower we feel there is something which is alive. And we regret to see its end. But plants are wiser than we are. They know that on every wound caused by cutting a stem a new shoot will grow and it will become a new rose. And so we must learn the lesson and make of our somewhat sensual love for flowers a spur to a higher thought.»

«Which one, Master?» asks Plautina, who is listening diligently and is intrigued by the refined thought of the Jewish Master.

«This one. That as a plant does not die as long as its roots are nourished by the soil, it does not die because its stems die, mankind does not die because one being ends his earthly life. But new flowers are always born. And — a thought which is even higher and will make us bless the Creator — while a flower, once it is dead, will not come to life again, which is sad, man, when he is asleep in his last sleep, is not dead, but he lives a brighter life, drawing, through his better part, eternal life and splendour from the Creator Who formed him. [5]Therefore, Valeria, if 167.5
your little girl had died, you would not have lost her caresses. The kisses of your creature would have always come to your soul, because, although separated from you, she would not have forgotten your love. See how pleasant it is to have faith in eternal life? Where is your little one now?»

«In that covered cradle. I never parted from her before, because the love for my husband and for my daughter were the only interests of my life. But now that I know what it is to see her dying, I do not leave her even for a moment.»

Jesus goes towards a seat on which there is a kind of wooden cradle, covered by an expensive cover. He uncovers it and looks at the sleeping child, whom the fresher air awakes tenderly. Her little eyes seem surprised when they open and her lips part in an angel's smile, while her tiny hands, which before were closed, are now open and anxious to get hold of Jesus' wavy hair. The twittering of a sparrow marks the progress of speech in her little mind. At last the great universal word trills: «Mummy!»

«Pick her up, pick her up» says Jesus Who moves to one side to let Valeria bend over the cradle.

«She will cause You trouble! I will call a slave and have her taken into the garden.»

«Trouble? Oh! No! Children are never any trouble. They are always My friends.»

«Have You any children or grandchildren, Master?» asks Plautina, who watches how Jesus, smiling, teases the baby to make her laugh.

«No, I have neither children nor grandchildren. But I love children as I love flowers. Because they are pure and without malice. In fact, give Me your little one, woman. It is such a great joy for Me to press a little angel to My heart.» And He sits down holding the little baby, who watches Him and ruffles His beard and then finds something more interesting to do playing with the fringes of His mantle and with the cord of His tunic, to which she devotes a long mysterious speech.

167.6 [6]Plautina says: «Our good and wise friend, one of the few who does not disdain us and does not become corrupt associating with us, will have told You that we were anxious to see You and hear You, to judge You for what You are, because Rome does not believe in idle stories;.. Why are You smiling, Master?»

«I will tell you later. Go on.»

«Because Rome does not believe in idle stories and wants to judge with true knowledge and conscience before condemning and extolling. Your people exalt You and calumniate You to the same degree. Your deeds would convince one to exalt You. The words of many Jews would induce people to consider You little less than a criminal. Your words are solemn and wise like a philosopher's. Rome is very fond of philosophic doctrines and... I must admit it, our present philosophers do not have a satisfactory doctrine, also because their ways of living do not correspond to their doctrines.»

«They cannot have a way of living corresponding to their doctrine.»

«Because they are pagans, is that right?»

«No, because they are atheists.»

«Atheists? But they have their gods.»

«They do not even have those any more, woman. I remind you of the ancient philosophers, the greatest ones. They were heathens, too. However, consider how high was the moral tone of their lives! It was mingled with errors, because man is inclined to err. But when they were confronted with the greatest mysteries: life and death, when they had to face the dilemma of Honesty or Dishonesty, of Virtue or Vice, of Heroism or Cowardice and they considered that if they turned to evil, a great misfortune would befall their fatherland and their fellow citizens, then with a super effort of will they rejected the tentacles of evil polyps and, holy and free, they chose Good, at all costs. That Good which is no one else but God.»

7 «You are God, so they say. Is that true?» 167.7

«I am the Son of the True God, I became flesh, but I still remain God.»

«But what is God? The greatest Master, if we look at You.»

«God is much more than a Master. Do not minimise the sublime idea of Divinity to a limitation of wisdom.»

«Wisdom is a deity. We have Minerva. She is the goddess of knowledge.»

«You have also Venus, the goddess of pleasure. Can you admit that a god, that is a being superior to men, possesses, raised to the highest degree, all the horrible vices of mortals? Can you conceive that an eternal being has for eternity the petty, mean, humiliating delights of those who have only one hour? And that the superior being makes them the objective of his life? Do you not consider what a desecrated heaven is the one you call Olympus, where the most acrid juices of mankind ferment? If you look at your heaven, what can you see? Lust, crime, hatred, war, thefts, crapulence, snares, revenge. If you wish to celebrate the feast of your gods, what do you do? You indulge in orgies. What cult do you give them? Where is the true chastity of the virgins consecrated to Vesta? On what divine code of law do your pontifices base their judgement? What words can your augurs read in the flight of birds or in the peal of thunder? And what answers can the bleeding entrails of sacrificed animals give to your haruspices? You said: "Rome does not believe in idle stories". Why does she believe, then, that twelve poor men, by sending a pig, a sheep and a bull round the fields and sacrificing them, can gain Ceres' favour, when you have an endless number of deities, one hating the other, and you believe in their revenges? No. God is something quite different. He is Eternal, One and Spiritual.»

«But You say that You are God and yet You are flesh.»

«There is an altar with no god in the fatherland of gods. Man's wisdom has devoted it to the unknown God. Because wise men, the true philosophers, have realised that there is something beyond the illustrated scenario created for the eternal children, that is for men whose souls are enveloped in the swaddling clothes of error. If those wise men — who realised that there is something beyond the false scenario, something really sublime and divine, which created everything that exists and from which comes all the good there is in the world — if those men wanted an altar to the unknown God, Whom they perceived to be the True God, how can you call god what is not god and how can you say that you know what you do not know? Learn, therefore, what
167.8 God is, that you may know and honour Him. [8]God is the Being Who by His thought made everything from nothing. Does the tale of stones transformed into men convince you and satisfy you? I solemnly tell you that there are men more hard and wicked than stones, and stones more useful than men. But is it not more pleasant for you, Valeria, to say, looking at your little baby: "She is the living will of God, created and formed by Him, gifted by Him with a second life which does not end, so that I will have my little Fausta forever and ever, if I believe in the True God", rather than say: "This rosy flesh, this hair thinner than a spider's web, these clear eyes originate from a stone"? Or to say: "I am entirely like a she-wolf or a mare, and like an animal I mate, like an animal I procreate, like an animal I rear, and my daughter is the fruit of my beastly instinct and she is an animal like me, and tomorrow, when she is dead and I am dead, we shall be two carrions which will dissolve with a foul odour and will never see each other again"? Tell Me! Which of the two choices would your maternal heart prefer?»

«Certainly not the latter, my Lord! If I had known that Fausta was not a thing that could be dissolved forever, my grief, when she was in agony, would not have been so violent. Because I would have said: "I have lost a pearl. But it still exists. And I will find it".»

167.9 «You are right. [9]When I was coming towards you, your friend told me that she was amazed at your passion for flowers. And she was afraid that it might upset Me. But I reassured her saying to her: "I love flowers, too, so we will understand each other quite well". But I wish to bring you to love flowers, as I have brought Valeria to love her baby, of whom she will now take greater care, as she knows that Fausta has a soul, which is a particle of God enclosed in the body which her mother made for her; a particle which will not die and which her mother will find again in Heaven, if she believes in the True God.

The same applies to you. Look at this beautiful rose. The purple which adorns the imperial robe is not so magnificent as this petal, which is not only a pleasure to the eye because of its hue, but is also a joy to touch because of its smoothness and to smell because of its scent. And look at this one, and this one, and this one. The first one is like blood gushing from a heart, the second is like fresh fallen snow, the third one is pale gold, the last one is like the sweet face of this child smiling in My lap. And further: the first one is stiff on an almost thornless stem, the leaves of which are reddish as if they had been sprayed with blood, the second has only a few thorns, and its leaves are pale and dull on the stem, the third one is as flexible as a reed and its small leaves are as shiny as green wax, the stem of the last one is so thick with thorns that it seems anxious to prevent all possible access to its rosy corolla. It looks like a file with very sharp teeth.

Now consider this. Who made all that? How? When? Where? What was this place in the night of time? It was nothing. It was an amorphous stirring of elements. One: God, said: "I want" and the elements separated and formed family groups. And another "I want" thundered and the elements arranged themselves, one with the other: the water between the lands; or one on the other: air and light on the formed planet. One more "I want" and plants were made. And then the stars, then animals and at last man. And God, to make man, His favourite creature, happy, granted him, as magnificent toys, flowers, stars and finally the joy of procreating not what dies, but what survives death, by the gift of God, and which is the soul. These roses are as many "wills" of the Father. His infinite power makes it clear in an infinite number of beautiful things.

[10]My explanation is a rather difficult one because it clashes 167.10
with the brazen resistance of your beliefs. But I hope, as it is our first meeting, that we have understood one another a little. Let your souls ponder on what I have told you. Have you any ques-

tions to ask? Ask them. I am here to clarify things. Ignorance is not a disgrace. It is disgraceful to persist in ignorance where there is someone willing to clarify doubts.»

And Jesus, as if He were the most experienced father, goes out holding the little child, who is taking her first steps and wants to go towards a jet of water swaying in the sunshine.

167.11 [11] The ladies remain where they were, speaking to one another. And Johanna, hesitating between two desires, is standing on the threshold of the bower.

At last Lydia makes up her mind and followed by the others goes towards Jesus, Who is laughing because the little one is trying to catch the rays of sun from the water with her hand and grasps nothing but light, and she insists over and over again, babbling with her rosy lips.

«Master... I have not understood why You said that our masters cannot lead a good life because they are atheists. They believe in Olympus. But they believe...»

«They have but the exterior appearance of belief. As long as they really believed, as the truly wise men believed in the Unknown God I mentioned to you, in that God Who satisfied their souls, even if He was nameless, even if inadvertently they did not want to, as long as they turned their thoughts to that Being, by far superior to the poor gods full of the faults of mankind, of the low faults of mankind, the gods that paganism created for itself, they somehow reflected God, by necessity. A soul is a mirror that reflects and an echo that repeats...»

«What, Master?»

«God.»

«It's a great word!»

«It is a great truth.»

167.12 [12] Valeria, who is fascinated by the thought of immortality, asks: «Master, tell me where the soul of my child is. I will kiss that spot like a shrine and I will worship it, because it is part of God.»

«The soul! It is like this light that little Fausta wishes to grasp and cannot, because it is incorporeal. But it is there. You, I, your friends can see it. Likewise a soul can be seen in everything that differentiates man from animals. When your little one will tell you her first thoughts, you can say that such understanding is her soul which is revealing itself. When she will love you not by instinct, but with her reason, consider that that love is her soul. When she will grow beautiful beside you, not so much in her body as in virtue, consider that that beauty is her soul. And do not worship her soul, but God Who created it, God Who wishes every soul to be a throne for Him.»

«But where is this incorporeal and sublime thing: in one's heart? in one's brains?»

«It is in the whole of man. It contains you and is contained within you. When it leaves you, you become a corpse. When it is killed by a crime that man commits against himself, you are damned, separated from God forever.»

«You therefore agree that the philosopher who said that we are "immortal" was right, although he was a heathen?» asks Plautina.

«I do not only agree. I will go further. I say that it is an article of faith. The immortality of the soul, that is the immortality of the superior part of man is the most certain and most comforting mystery to believe. It is the one that assures us of where we come from, where we go, who we are, and it removes all the bitterness of every separation.»

[13] Plautina is deeply absorbed in thought. Jesus watches her and 167.13
is silent. At last she asks: «And have You a soul?»

Jesus replies: «Certainly.»

«But are You or are You not God?»

«I am God. I told you. But now I have taken the nature of Man. And do you know why? Because only by this sacrifice of Mine I was able to resolve the points which were insuperable for your reason, and after demolishing errors and freeing minds, I was also able to free souls from a slavery which I cannot explain to you just now. I therefore enclosed Wisdom and Holiness in a body. I spread Wisdom like seeds on the ground and pollen to the winds. Holiness will flow, as from a precious broken amphora, onto the world in the hour of Grace and will sanctify men. Then the Unknown God will become known.»

«But You are already known. He who doubts Your power and Your wisdom, is either wicked or a liar.»

«I am known. But this is only daybreak. Midday will be full of the knowledge of Me.»

«What will Your midday be like? A triumph? Shall I see it?»

«Truly, it will be a triumph. And you will be present. Because you loathe what you know and you crave for what you ignore. Your soul hungers.»

«That is true. I hunger for truth.»

«I am the Truth.»

«Then, give Yourself to me who am hungry.»

«All you have to do is to come to My table. My word is the bread of truth.»

167.14 [14] «But what will our gods say if we abandon them? Will they not avenge themselves on us?» asks fearful Lydia.

«Woman: have you ever seen a foggy morning? The meadows are lost in the vapour that conceals them. Then the sun shines and the vapour is dissolved and the glistening meadows are more beautiful. The same applies to your gods, the fog of a poor human thought, which, ignoring God and needing to believe, because faith is a permanent necessity for man, created Olympus, a real non-existent idle story. And thus your gods, when the sun, that is, the True God rises, will dissolve in your hearts without being able to do any harm. Because they do not exist.»

«We shall have to listen to You again... quite a lot... We are most definitely before the unknown. Everything You say is new to us.»

«But does it disgust you? Can you accept it?»

«Plautina replies sure of herself: «No. It does not. I feel more proud of the little I know now, and which Caesar does not know, than I do of my name.»

167.15 «Well, then, persevere. [15]I leave you with My peace.»

«What? Are You not staying, my Lord?» Johanna is desolate.

«No, I am not staying. I have a lot to do...»

«Oh! I wanted to speak to You about my trouble!»

Jesus, Who had begun to walk, after saying goodbye to the Roman ladies, turns around and says: «Come as far as the boat and you will tell Me what your pain is.»

And Johanna goes. And she says: «Chuza wants to send me to Jerusalem for some time and I am not happy about it. He is doing it because he does not want me to be confined any longer now that I am healthy...»

«You, too, are creating useless fogs for yourself!» says Jesus

Who is stepping onto the boat. «If you considered that you can thus give Me hospitality or follow Me more easily, you would be happy and would say: "Bounty has seen to it".»

«Oh!... that is true, my Lord. I had not thought about that.»

«So, you can see! Be a good wife and obey. Obedience will give you the reward of having Me as your guest at next Passover and the honour of helping Me to evangelize your friends. My peace be always with you.»

The boat sets out and it all ends.

168. Aglae in Mary's House in Nazareth.

20th May 1945. Pentecost.

[1] Mary is working quietly at a piece of cloth. It is evening, all 168.1
the doors are closed, a three flame lamp lights up the little room in Nazareth, particularly the table at which the Virgin is sitting. The cloth, perhaps a bed sheet, hangs from the chest and from Her knees onto the floor, so that Mary, Who is wearing a dark blue dress, seems to emerge from a pile of snow. She is alone. She is sowing fast, Her head bent over Her work, and the light of the lamp causes the top part of Her hair to shine with pale gold shades. The rest of Her face is in half-light.

There is dead silence in the tidy room. No noise can be heard either from the road, deserted at night, or from the kitchen garden. The heavy door of the room where Mary works, where She takes Her meals and receives Her friends, and which opens onto the kitchen garden, is closed, so that not even the noise of the fountain water running into the basin can be heard. It is really the deepest silence. I wonder what Mary is thinking of while Her hands are working swiftly...

There is a light tapping at the main door. Mary looks up and listens... The tapping has been so light that Mary must be thinking that it was caused by some night animal or by the wind and She bends Her head once again to Her work. But the knocking is repeated and more loudly. Mary stands up and goes to the door. Before opening She asks: «Who is knocking?»

A thin voice replies: «A woman. In the name of Jesus, have mercy on me.»

Mary opens the door at once holding the lamp up to see the pilgrim. She sees a heap of clothes, through which no one appears. A poor heap of clothes, stooping very low and saying: «Hail! My Lady!» and then once again: «In the name of Jesus, have mercy on me.»

«Come in and tell Me what you want. I do not know you.»

«Nobody and many know me. Vice knows me. And Holiness knows me. But now I need compassion to open Her arms to me. And You are compassion...» and she weeps.

«Come in, then... And tell me... You have said enough to make Me understand that you are unhappy... But I do not yet know who you are. Your name, sister...»

«Oh! no! Not sister! I cannot be Your sister... You are the Mother of Good... I... I am Evil...» and she cries louder and louder under her mantle, which covers her completely.

Mary lays the lamp on a chair; she takes the hand of the unknown woman kneeling on the threshold and compels her to stand up.

168.2 [2] Mary does not know her... but I do. She is the Veiled woman of the Clear Water.

She stands up, dejected, trembling, shaken by her sobs, and is still reluctant to go in. She says: «I am a heathen, my Lady. I am filth, for you Jews, even if I were holy. I am twice filth because I am a prostitute.»

«If you come to Me, if you look for My Son through Me, you can only be a repentant heart. This house welcomes those whose name is Sorrow» and She leads her in, closing the door, lays the lamp on table, and asks her to sit down and says: «Speak.»

But the Veiled woman does not want to sit down; still stooping, she continues to weep. Mary is in front of her, kind and queenly. She waits, praying, for her to calm down. Her whole attitude tells me that She is praying, although nothing about Her takes the form of prayer: neither Her hands which are holding all the time the little hand of the Veiled woman, nor Her lips which are closed.

At last her weeping calms down. The Veiled woman dries her face with her veil and then says: «And yet I have not come from so far as to be unknown. It is the hour of my redemption and I must reveal myself... to show with how many wounds my heart is covered. And You are a mother... and His Mother... You will, therefore, have mercy on me.»

«Yes, My daughter.»

«Oh! yes! Call me daughter! I had a mother... and I left her... I was later told that she died of a broken heart... I had a father... he cursed me... and he says to those in town: "I no longer have a daughter"»... (she carries on crying more bitterly. Mary turns pale with anguish, but lays Her hand on her head to comfort her). The Veiled woman goes on: «No one will call me daughter any more!... Yes, caress me thus, as my mother used to do when I was pure and good... Let me kiss Your hand and wipe my tears with it. My tears alone will not cleanse me. How much have I wept when I realised! Also before I used to weep, because it is horrible to be nothing but flesh, abused and insulted by man. But they were the tears of an ill-treated animal that hates and rebels against him who tortures and fouls it more and more... because I changed master, but I did not change bestiality... I have been weeping for eight months... because I have understood... I understood my misery and my depravity, I am covered and saturated with it and I feel disgusted... But my tears, although more and more conscious, do not yet cleanse me. They mix with my depravity and do not wash it away. Oh! Mother! Wipe my tears and I shall be so cleansed as to be able to go near my Saviour!»

«Yes, My daughter, yes, I will. Sit down. Here, near Me. And speak calmly. Leave your burden here, on My knees of a Mother» and Mary sits down.

[3] But the Veiled woman sinks to the ground at Her feet, as she 168.3
wishes to speak to Her in this way. She begins slowly: «I come from Syracuse... I am twenty-six years old... I was the daughter of a steward, as you would call him, we say a procurator, of a wealthy Roman gentleman. I was an only child. My life was a happy one. We lived near the seaside, in a beautiful villa, where my father was the steward. Now and again the owner of the villa, or his wife or children would come. They treated us very well and were very good to me. The girls used to play with me... My mother was happy and... proud of me. I was beautiful... intelligent and I succeeded in everything... But I loved frivolous things more than good things. There is a great theatre at Syracuse. A great theatre... Beautiful... huge... It is used for games and

plays... Mimers are widely employed in the comedies and tragedies which are performed there. They emphasize the meaning of the chorus by their silent dances. You do not know... but also by means of our hands or through the movements of our bodies we can express the feelings of a man agitated by passion. Young boys and girls are trained as mimers in a special school. They must be as beautiful as gods and as agile as butterflies... I loved to go to a kind of high spot overlooking that place and see the mimers dance. I then imitated them on the flowery meadows, on the golden sands of my land, in the garden of the villa. I looked like an artistic statue, or a light blowing breeze, so clever I was in taking on statuesque postures or flying about almost without touching the ground. My wealthy friends admired me... my mother was proud of me...»

The Veiled woman speaks, remembers, sees and dreams of her past and weeps. Her sobs are like commas in her speech.

«One day... it was May... The whole of Syracuse was blooming with flowers. The celebrations were just over and I had gone into raptures over a dance performed in the theatre... The owners had taken me there with their daughters. I was fourteen years old... In that dance the mimers, who were to represent the springtime nymphs running to worship Ceres, danced crowned with roses and clad with roses... Only with roses because their dresses were very light veils, a cobweb spread with roses... While dancing they looked like winged Hebes, so light they glided about, while their magnificent bodies appeared through the ruffled strips of their flowery veils, flowing like wings behind them. I studied the dance... and one day... one day»...

168.4 [4] The Veiled woman cries louder... She then composes herself.

«I was beautiful. I still am. Look.» She stands up throwing her veil behind her and letting her large mantle drop. And I am dumbfounded, because I see Aglae emerge from the discarded clothes. She is beautiful, even in her modest dress, in her simple plaited hair-style, without any jewels, without pompous garments. Her body is like a real flower, slender and perfect, with a beautiful light brown face and velvet eyes full of ardour.

She kneels down again in front of Mary. «I was beautiful, unfortunately. And I was crazy. On that day I put on veils, the daughters of our landlord helped me as they loved to see me dance… I got dressed on a strip of the golden beach, facing the blue sea. On the deserted beach there were white and yellow wild flowers, with the sharp scent of almonds, of vanilla, of clean human bodies. Waves of strong perfumes came also from the citrus gardens and the rose gardens in Syracuse gave off a scent, as well as the sea and the sand on the beach; the sun drew a smell from all things… something panicky that went to my head. I felt as if I were a nymph, too, and I was worshiping… whom? The fertile Earth? The fecundating Sun? I do not know. A heathen amongst heathens, I think I was worshiping Sense, my despotic king, whom I did not know I had, but who was more powerful than a god… I put on a wreath of roses picked in the garden… and I danced. I was enraptured by the light, the scents, by the pleasure of being young, agile and beautiful. I danced… and I was noticed. I saw I was being looked at. But I was not ashamed of appearing nude in the presence of two greedy eyes of a man. On the contrary, I took pleasure in dancing more lively. The satisfaction of being admired gave wings to my feet. And it was my ruin. Three days later I was left all by myself because the landlords left to go back to their patrician dwelling in Rome. But I did not stay at home… The two adimiring eyes had revealed something else to me, beyond dancing… They had revealed sensuality and sex.»

Mary makes an involuntary gesture of disgust, which is noted by Aglae. «Oh! but You are pure! Perhaps I disgust You…»

«Speak, My daughter. It is better if you speak to Mary than to Him. Mary is a sea that washes…»

«Yes, it is better if I tell You. I thought that myself when I heard that He had a mother… Because before, seeing Him so different from every other man, the only thoroughly spiritual man — now I know there is the spirit and what it is — before I could not have said what Your Son was made of, as He was without sensuality although a man, and within myself I thought He had no mother, but He had descended upon the earth to save the horrible wretches of whom I am the worst.

[5]Everyday I went back to that place hoping to see the young handsome swarthy man… And after some time I saw him 168.5
again… He spoke to me. He said to me: "Come to Rome with me. I will take you to the imperial court, you will be the pearl of Rome". I replied: "Yes. I will be your faithful wife. Come and

see my father". He laughed mockingly and kissed me. He said: "Not my wife. But you shall be the goddess and I your priest and I will reveal the secrets of life and pleasure to you". I was thoroughly infatuated, I was a young girl. But although a young girl, I knew what life is… I was shrewd, I was infatuated, but not yet depraved… and I was disgusted by his proposal. I tore myself away from his embrace and I ran home… But I did not speak to my mother about it… and I did not resist the desire to see him again… His kisses had made me more enthralled than ever… And I went back… I had hardly reached the deserted beach when he embraced me kissing me with frenzy, with a storm of kisses, with loving words, with questions: "Is there not everything in this love? Is this not sweeter than a bond? What else do you want? Can you live without this?"

Oh! Mother… I eloped the same evening with the filthy patrician… and I became a rag trampled on by his beastliness… I was not a goddess: but mud. Not a pearl: but trash. Life was not revealed to me, but the filth of life, the infamy, the disgust, the pain, the shame, the infinite misery of not even belonging to myself… And then… utter ruin. After six months of orgies, he became tired of me and passed onto fresh love affairs and I lived on the streets. I made the most of my dancing talent… I already knew that my mother had died of a broken heart and that I no longer had a home or a father… A dancing master accepted me in his academy. He perfected me… he enjoyed me… and he launched me into the corrupt Roman patriciate as a flower fully skilled in every sensual art. The already dirty flower fell into a cloaca. For ten years I fell lower and lower into the abyss. I was then brought here to delight Herod's leisure time and I was engaged here by a new master. Oh! No chained dog is more chained than one of us! And there is no dog trainer more brutal than the man who possesses a woman! Mother… You are trembling! I am filling You with horror!»

Mary has taken Her hand to Her heart, as if it had been wounded. But She replies: «No, not you. The Evil, which is such a powerful master on the earth, is horrifying Me. Go on, My poor creature.»

«He took me to Hebron… Was I free? Was I rich? Yes, I was, because I was not in jail and I was covered with jewels. No, I was not, because I could see only those whom he wanted and I had no right to myself.

[6] One day a man, the "Man", Your Son, came to Hebron. The 168.6
house was dear to Him. I realised it and I invited Him to enter. Shammai was not there... and from the window I had already heard words and seen a sight which had upset my heart. But I swear to You, Mother, that it was not the flesh that drove me towards Your Jesus. It was something that He revealed to me that He at the door, defying the quips of the populace, to say to me "Come in". It was the soul that I then learned I had. He said to me: "My Name means: Saviour. I save those who are anxious to be saved. I save by teaching to be pure, to desire and accept sorrow with honour, to desire Good at all costs. I am the One Who seeks those who are lost and gives Life. I am Purity and Truth!". He told me that I also had a soul and that I had killed it by my way of living. But He did not curse me, neither did He mock me. And He never looked at me! The first man who did not strip me with his greedy eyes, because I lie under the terrible curse of attracting men... He told me that he who looks for Him will find Him because He is where a doctor and a medicine are needed. And He went away. But His words were in here. And they have never come out. I used to say to myself: "His Name means Saviour", as if I were beginning to wish to be cured. I was left with His words and with His friends, the shepherds. And I took the first step by giving them alms and asking for their prayers... And then... I ran away...

Oh! It was a holy flight! I ran away from sin seeking the Saviour. I went about looking for Him. I was sure I would find Him because He had promised me. They sent me to a man whose name is John, thinking it was He. But it was not. A Jew sent me to the Clear Water. I lived selling the large quantity of gold I had. During the months when I wandered about I had to keep my face covered to avoid being captured and also because, really, Aglae was buried under that veil. The old Aglae was dead. Under the veil there was her wounded bloodless soul seeking its doctor. Many a time I was compelled to flee the sensuality of men who persecuted me, although I was so disguised in my attire. Also one of the friends of Your Son...

[7] At the Clear Water I lived like an animal: poor but happy. And 168.7

the dew and the river did not clean me as much as His words. Oh! Not one was lost! Once He forgave a murderer. I heard... and I was about to say: "Forgive me, too". Another time He spoke of lost inocence... Oh! How many tears of regret! Another time He cured a leper... and I was about to shout: "Cleanse me too, of my sin..." Another time He cured a madman, a Roman... and I wept... and He got someone to tell me that fatherlands pass away, but Heaven remains. One stormy night He sheltered me in His house... and later He asked the steward to give me hospitality and He told a child to say to me: "Do not weep"... Oh! His kindness! My misery! Both so great that I did not dare to take my misery to His feet... notwithstanding that one of His disciples during the night instructed me in the infinite mercy of Your Son. And then, when those who considered sinful the desire of a soul to be reborn laid snares for Him, my Saviour went away... and I waited for Him... But He was also awaited by the vengeance of those who are by far less worthy of looking at Him than I am. Because I, as a heathen, sinned against myself, whereas they, who already know God, sin against the Son of God... and they hit me and they have hurt me more with their accusations than with stones and they have wounded my soul more than my body, as they led me to despair.

Oh! What a dreadful struggle against myself! Worn out, bleeding, wounded, feverish, without my Doctor, homeless, without food, I looked behind me and in front of me... My past would say to me: "Come back", my present said: "Kill yourself", my future used to say: "Hope". I did hope... I did not commit suicide. I would, if He rejected me, because I do not want to be what I was!... I dragged myself to a village asking for shelter... But they recognised me. Like an animal I had to run away, here, there, always chased, always scorned at, always cursed, because I wanted to be honest and because I had disappointed those who, through me, wanted to strike Your Son. Following the river I came up to Galilee and I came here... You were not here... I went to Capernaum. You had just left. But an old man saw me. One of His enemies, who wanted me to bear witness against Your Son, and as I was weeping without reacting, he said to me: "Everything could change in your favour if you would become my lover and my accomplice in accusing the Rabbi of Nazareth. It is enough for you to say, in the presence of my friends, that He was your lover..." I ran away like a person who sees a snake creep out of a flowery bush.

8 I thus understood that I can no longer go to Him... and I came 168.8
to You. Here I am: tread on me, for I am mud. Here I am: reject me, for I am a sinner. Here I am: call me by my name: prostitute. I will accept anything from You. But, Mother, have mercy on me. Take my poor soiled soul and take it to Him. It is a crime to put my lust into Your hands. But only there it will be protected from the world that wants it and it will become penance. Tell me how I must behave. Tell me what I have to do. Tell me which means I must use to be no longer Aglae. What must I mutilate in myself? What must I tear away from myself that I may no longer be sin, or an allurement, that I may no longer have to be afraid of myself and of men? Shall I put out my eyes? Or burn my lips? Or cut my tongue? My eyes, lips and tongue have served me in evil deeds. I no longer want evil and I am willing to punish myself and them by sacrificing them. Or shall I tear off these greedy loins which have driven me to perverted love? Or these unappeasable viscera which I am afraid may be aroused afresh? Tell me, please tell me how can a woman forget she is a female and how can she make other people forget!»

Mary is upset. She weeps and suffers, but the only sign of Her grief are the tears that fall on the repentant woman.

«I want to die only after I have been forgiven. I want to die remembering nothing but my Saviour. I want to die knowing that His wisdom is friendly to me... and I cannot go near Him because the world looks at Him and at me suspiciously to accuse us...» Aglae cries, prostrate with grief.

9 Mary stands up whispering: «How difficult it is to be re- 168.9
deemers!» She is almost breathless.

Aglae, who hears the whisper and understands Her gesture, moans: «See? You can see that You are disgusted, too. I will now go away. I am done for!»

«No, My daughter. You are not done for. No, you are beginning now. Listen, poor soul. I am not moaning because of you, but because of the cruel world. I will not let you go, but I will pick you up, a poor swallow tossed by the storm against the walls of My house. I will take you to Jesus and He will show you your way to redemption...»

«I no longer hope... The world is right. I cannot be forgiven.»

«Not by the world but by God. Let me speak to you in the name of the Supreme Love, Who gave Me a Son that I may give Him to the world. He took Me out of the blessed simplicity of my consecrated virginity so that the world might receive Forgiveness. He drew My blood not from My childbirth but from My heart by revealing to Me that My Creature is the Great Victim. Look at Me, daughter. There is a large wound in this heart. It has been groaning for over thirty years and it is becoming deeper and deeper and it consumes Me. Do you know its name?»

«Sorrow.»

«No. Love. It is love that bleeds Me so that My Son may not be the only one to save. It is love that sets Me on fire that I may purify those who dare not go to My Son. It is love that causes Me to weep that I may wash sinners. You wanted My caresses. I am giving you My tears that will already cleanse you and enable you to look at My Lord. Do not weep in this way! You are not the only sinner who has come to the Lord and has left redeemed. Other women came, many more will come.

You are not sure that He can forgive you? But can you not see in everything that happened to you the mysterious will of Divine Goodness? Who brought you to Judaea? Who took you to John's house? Who placed you at the window that morning? Who lit a light to illuminate His words for you? Who made you understand that charity, when joined to the prayers of those who have been helped, obtains help from God? Who gave you the strength to run away from Shammai's house and to persevere during the first days until His arrival? Who led you to His way? Who enabled you to live as a repentant sinner to cleanse your soul more and more? Who gave you a martyr's soul, a believer's soul, a persevering and pure soul?

Do not shake your head. Do you think that only he is pure who has never known sensuality? Do you think that a soul can never again become virgin and beautiful? Oh! My daughter! Between the purity which is entirely a grace of the Lord and your heroic ascent to climb back to the summit of your lost purity, you must believe that yours is the greater. You are building it against sensuality, against need and habit. For Me it is a natural endowment, like breathing. You have to break off your thoughts, your feelings, your flesh, in order not to remember, not to desire, not to yield... I... Oh! Can a little child, a few hours old, have carnal desires? And does he have any merit thereby? The same applies to Me. I do not know what that tragic hunger is that made mankind a victim. I know but the most holy hunger for God. But you did not know it and you learned it by yourself. But you subdued the other hunger, the tragic and horrible one, for the sake of God, your only love at present. Smile, daughter of divine mercy! My Son is working on you what He told you at Hebron. He has already done that. You are already saved, because of your goodwill to be saved, because you have come to know of purity, of sorrow, of Good. Your soul has revived. Yes, you need His word saying to you in the name of God: "You are forgiven". I cannot say that. But I give you My kiss as a promise, as a beginning of forgiveness...

O Eternal Spirit, a little of You is always in Your Mary! Allow Her to pour forth Your Sanctifying Spirit on this creature who is weeping and hoping. For the sake of Our Son, o God of Love, save this woman who is expecting salvation from God. May the Grace, with which the Angel said that God has filled Me, may that Grace by a miracle rest upon her and support her until Jesus, the Blessed Saviour, the Supreme Priest, absolves her in the name of the Father, and of the Son and of the Spirit...

[10] It is late, My daughter. You are tired and worn out. Come, rest. 168.10
You will go away tomorrow... I will send you to an honest family, because too many people come here now. And I will give you a dress like Mine and you will look like a Jewess. And as I will see My Son only in Judaea, because Passover is near and at the new moon of April we shall be in Bethany, I will speak to Him of you. Come to the house of Simon the Zealot. You will find Me there and I will take you to Him.»

Aglae is weeping again. But now she is at peace.

She is sitting on the floor. Also Mary has sat down again. And Aglae rests her head on Her knees and kisses Her hand... She then moans: «They will recognise me...»

«Oh! They will not. Do not be afraid. Your dress was too well known. But I will prepare you for your journey towards Forgiveness and you will be like a virgin going to her wedding: you will be different and unknown to the people unaware of the rite. Come. There is a little room near Mine. Saints and pilgrims wishing to go to God have rested in it. It will shelter you, too.»

Aglae is about to pick up her large mantle and her veil.

«Leave them. They are the clothes of poor lost Aglae. But she no longer exists... and not even her dress is to remain. It experienced too much hatred... and hatred hurts as much as sin.»

They go out into the dark kitchen garden and then into Joseph's little room. Mary lights the little lamp on the shelf, caresses the repentant woman once again, closes the door and with her triple light she looks to see where She can take Aglae's torn mantle so that nobody may see it the following day.

169. The Sermon of the Mount. Part One: the Mission of the Apostles and the Disciples "You Are the Salt of the Earth".

22nd May 1945.

169.1 [1] Jesus is walking fast along a main road. He is alone. He is going towards a mountain, which is best to describe what it is like, as it is not possible through a drawing. This is the drawing: *

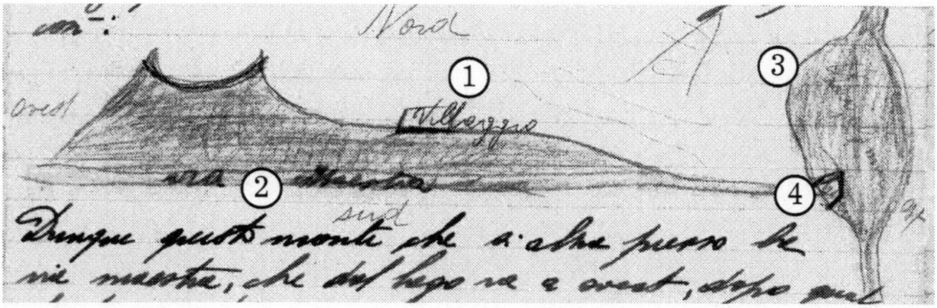

Therefore this mount, which rises near a main road running eastwards from the lake, and it begins to rise with a low mild elevation, which extends for a good distance, forming a tableland from which one can see all the lake and the town of Tiberias towards the south, as well as other towns, not quite so beautiful, stretching towards the north. There is then a crag and the mountain rises rather steeply up to a peak, and then slopes down and rises once again up to another peak, similar to the previous one,

* **1.** Village; **2.** Main road; **3.** Lake of Genazareth; **4.** Tiberias.

thus forming a kind of strange saddle.

Jesus begins climbing towards the tableland along a mule-track, which is still quite comfortable and reaches a small village, the inhabitants of which work the tableland, where the corn is beginning to come to ear. He goes through the village and proceeds through the fields and meadows all strewn with flowers and rustling with crops. The clear day displays all the beauty of the surrounding nature.

Besides the lonely little mountain, towards which Jesus is going, to the north lies the imposing peak of Mount Hermon, the top of which looks like a huge pearl laid on a base of emeralds, so white is the peak covered with snow, whereas the woody slope is green. Beyond the lake, which is between the lake and Mount Hermon, the plain is green. Lake Merom is there, but cannot be seen from here. There are more mountains towards the lake of Tiberias on the north-west side and beyond the lake there is a lovely flat country and other mountains, the contours of which are softened by the distance. To the south, on the other side of the main road, I can see the hills, which I think conceal Nazareth. The more one climbs, the wider the view. I cannot see what lies to the west, because the mountain acts as a wall.

[2]Jesus first meets the apostle Philip, who seems to have been 169.2
posted there as sentinel. «What, Master? You are here? We were expecting to meet You on the main road. I am waiting here for my companions who have gone to get some milk from the shepherds who pasture their flocks on these mountains. Down, on the road, there is Simon with Judas of Simon and Isaac, and... Oh! here... Come! Come! The Master is here!»

The apostles, who are coming down with flasks and containers, begin to run and the younger ones, of course, arrive first. The welcome they give the Master is really touching. At last they are all together and while Jesus smiles, they all want to speak and tell Him...

«But we were waiting for You on the road!»

«We were just thinking that You were not coming even today.»

«You know, there are many people.»

«Oh! We were embarrassed, there are some scribes and even some of Gamaliel's disciples...»

«That's right, my Lord! You left us just at the right moment! I have never been so afraid as I was just then. Don't play such a trick on me again!»

Peter complains and Jesus smiles and asks: «Did anything wrong happen to you?»

«Oh! no! On the contrary... Oh! Master! Don't You know that John gave a sermon?.. It sounded as if You were speaking through him. I... we were all dumbfounded... That boy who only a year ago was able only to cast a net... oh!» Peter is still amazed and he shakes John who smiles but is silent. «Do you believe that it is possible that this boy spoke those words with these smiling lips? He sounded like Solomon.»

«Also Simon spoke very well, my Lord. He was really "the chief"» says John.

«No wonder! He took me and pushed me there! Who knows!... They say that I gave a good sermon. Perhaps I did. I don't know... because what with the surprise at John's words, what with the fear of speaking to so many people and causing You to cut a poor figure, I was bewildered...»

«Causing Me to cut a poor figure? But you were speaking and you would have cut a poor figure, Simon» teases Jesus.

«Oh! As far as I am concerned... I was not worried about myself. I did not want them to sneer at You and consider You a fool for choosing a blockhead as your apostle.»

Jesus sparkles with joy because of Peter's humility and love. But He only asks: «And what about the others?»

«Also the Zealot spoke very well. But he... we all know. But this boy was the great surprise! Of course, since we retired to pray, the boy's soul seems to be in Heaven all the time.»

«That is true, very true.» They all confirm Peter's words. And they continue telling Jesus...

«You know? Among the disciples now there are two who, according to Judas of Simon, are very important. Judas is very active. Of course! He knows many of those... high up and knows how to deal with them. And he likes to speak... He speaks very well. But the people prefer to hear Simon, Your cousins and above all this boy Yesterday a man said to me: "That young man speaks very well — he was referring to Judas — but I prefer you". Oh! poor fellow! He prefers me and I can hardly put a few words together!... But why did You come here? The meeting place was the road, and we have been there.»

«Because I knew I was going to find you here. [3]Now listen. Go down and tell the others to come up, also the known disciples. The people are not to come today. I want to speak to you alone.» 169.3

«In that case it is better to wait until evening. When the sun is about to set, the people spread among the nearby villages and they come back the following morning waiting for You. Otherwise... who will hold them back?»

«Alright. Do that. I will wait for you up there, at the top. The nights are mild now and we can sleep in the open.»

«Wherever You wish, Master. Providing You are with us.»

The disciples go away and Jesus resumes climbing up to the top, which is the same one as I already saw last year in the vi-
* sion for the end of the sermon of the Mount and the first meeting with Mary Magdalene. The view is now wider and is becoming brighter in the sunset.

Jesus sits on a rock and is recollected in meditation. And He remains in this way until the shuffling of feet on the path warns Him that the apostles are back. It is getting dark, but the sun still shines on the mountain top, drawing scents from every herb and flower... There is a strong smell of wild lilies of the valley while the tall stems of narcissi shake their stars and buds as if they were asking for dew.

Jesus gets up and greets them: «Peace be with you.»

There are many disciples who come up with the apostles. Isaac leads them smiling. His smiling face is the thin face of an ascetic. They all gather around Jesus Who is greeting Judas Iscariot and Simon Zealot particularly.

«I wanted you all here with Me, to be for a few hours with you alone and speak only to you. I have something to tell you to prepare you for your mission. Let us take our food and then we shall speak, and while you are sleeping your souls will continue to relish the doctrine.»

They have their frugal meal and then form a circle around Jesus Who is sitting on a large stone. They are about one hundred, perhaps more, between disciples and apostles: a circle of

---

* **the vision** to be found in 174.11/14.

attentive faces, which the flames of two fires light up oddly.
169.4 [4]Jesus speaks slowly, gesticulating quietly. His face looks paler, as it emerges from His dark blue tunic and also because it is lit up by the rays of the new moon, which illuminates the spot where He is, a small spot of a moon in the sky, a ray of light that caresses the Master of Heaven and earth.

«I wanted you here, aside, because you are My friends. I called you together after the first test of the Twelve, to widen the circle of My active disciples, and to hear from you your first reactions to being guided by those whom I am giving to you to continue My work. I know that everything went well. I supported with My prayer the souls of the apostles, who had come out of a praying retreat with a new strength in their minds and in their hearts. A strength that does not come from human effort, but from complete reliance in God.

169.5 [5] *The ones that have given the most are the ones that have forgotten the most about themselves.*

To forget onself is a difficult task. Man is made of recollections and the ones that raise their voice most are the memories of one's *ego*. You must distinguish between *ego* and *ego*. There is the spiritual *ego* of the soul that remembers God and its origin from God, and there is the inferior *ego* of the flesh that remembers its passions and the numerous demands concerning its whole being. They are so many voices as to form a choir, and unless the spirit is quite strong, they overcome the solitary voice of the spirit that remembers its nobility as a child of God. It is therefore necessary — with the exception of this holy memory that should always be stimulated and kept green and bright — it is necessary to learn how to forget yourselves, in all the memories, the needs, the timid reflections of the human *ego,* in order to be perfect disciples.

In this first test of My Twelve, those who have given most are the ones who forgot themselves most. They forgot not only their past, but also their limited personality. They are the ones who no longer remembered what they were, and were so united to God as to be afraid of nothing. Why were some standoffish? Because they remembered their habitual scruples, their usual considerations and prejudice. Why were others laconic? Because they remembered their doctrinal inability and they were afraid of cutting a bad figure or causing Me to cut one. Why the showy ostentation of others? Because they remembered their usual pride, their desire to show off, to be applauded, to rise above the others, to be "someone". Finally, why the sudden revelation of a triumphal, rabbinic, persuasive, firm eloquence in others? Because they, and they alone did remember God. Like those who so far have been humble and have endeavoured to pass unnoticed and at the right moment were able, all of a sudden, to assume the preeminent lest conferred to them, and which they never wanted to exert lest they should presume too much. The first three groups rememered their inferior *ego*. The other group, the fourth, remembered their superior *ego* and were not afraid. They felt God with themselves and in themselves and were not afraid. Oh! holy boldness which comes from being with God!

[6] Therefore now listen, both you apostles and you disciples. You 169.6
apostles have already heard these concepts. But now you will understand them in greater depth. You disciples have never heard of them or you have only heard fragments of them. And you must engrave them on your hearts. Because I will make greater and greater use of you, as Christ's flock is becoming more and more numerous. Because the world will attack you more and more violently, and its wolves will increase in number against Me, the Shepherd and against the flock and I want to put in your hands the weapons to defend both the Doctrine and My flock. What is sufficient for the herd is not sufficient for you, little shepherds. If the sheep are allowed to make mistakes, browsing in herbs which make blood bitter or desires crazy, you are not allowed to make the same mistakes, leading a large herd to ruin. Because you must realise that where there is an idolatrous shepherd the sheep either die of poison or are devoured by wolves.

[7] You are the salt of the earth and the light of the world. But 169.7
should you fail in your mission you would become a tasteless and useless salt. Nothing could give you flavour again, since God could not give it to you, considering that it was given to you as a gift, and you have desalted it, by washing it in the insipid dirty water of mankind, by sweetening it by means of the corrupt sweetness of sensuality, thus mixing the corruption of pride, avarice, gluttony, lust, wrath, sloth with the pure salt of God so that there is a grain of salt to seven times seven grains

of each vice. Your salt, therefore, is but a mixture of stones in which the poor grain of lost salt cannot be found, a mixture of stones screeching under your teeth and leaving in your mouths the flavour of earth, that makes food horrible and disgusting. It is not even useful for inferior use, as the flavour of the seven vices would harm every human employment as well. The salt then can only be spread and trodden on by the careless feet of the people. How many people will therefore be able to tread heavily on the men of God! Because those chosen men will allow the careless people to trample on them, as they no longer are a substance employed to give the flavour of noble heavenly things, as they are nothing but *corruption*.

You are the light of the world. You are like this mountain top which was the last to be kissed by the sun and the first to be silvered by the moon. He who is in a high place shines and can be seen because even the most dreamy eye looks now and again at high spots. I would say that the physical eye, which is said to be the mirror of the soul, reflects the yearning of the soul, a yearning often unnoticed but always alive as long as a man is not a demon, a yearning after heights where by instinct reason places the Most High. And searching for Heaven, at least some times in life the eye looks at heights.

I beg you to remember what we all have done, since our childhood, entering Jerusalem. Where do our eyes turn? To Mount Moriah, triumphantly crowned with the marbles and gold of the Temple. And where do we turn our eyes when we are in the enclosure of the Temple? We look at the precious domes shining in the sun. How much beauty there is in the sacred enclosure, spread in its halls, porches and yards! But what is up there strikes our eyes. I also beg you to remember what happens when we are on the way to some place. Where do we turn our eyes, almost to forget the length of the journey, the boredom, the tiredness, the heat, the dust of the road? They turn to the mountain tops, even if they are not very high, even if they are far away. And what a relief it is to see them appear if we are walking in a flat unvarying plain! Is there mud on the road? There is neatness up there. Is it sultry on the plain? It is cool up there. Is the view limited down here? It is wide up there. And only by looking at the mountain tops we feel less the heat of the day, the mud is not so slippery, and walking is not so painful. If there is a town shining on the mountain top, no eye will refrain from admiring it. We could say that even a modest place becomes beautiful if placed, almost like an airy place, on a mountain top. That is why in the true and false religions, the temples were placed, whenever possible, on high spots, and if there was no hill or mountain, they built a stone pedestal, thus building with human labour the elevation on which to lay the temple. Why is that done? Because men want the temple to be seen so that its sight will remind mankind of God.

Likewise I said that you are lights. When in the evening you light a lamp in the house, where do you put it? In a hole under the oven? In the cave used as a cellar? Or do you close it in a chest? Or do you hide it under a bushel? No, you do not. Otherwise it would be useless lighting it. The light instead is placed on top of a shelf, or it is put on a lamp-stand, so that being high up, it may brighten up the whole room and illuminate the people living in it. And precisely because what is placed on a high place is to remind men of God and illuminate, it must be able to fulfill its task.

[8] You must remember the True God. Thus you must ensure that 169.8
you do not have within yourselves the sevenfold paganism. Otherwise you would become profane high places with thickets sacred to this or to that god, and you would drag into your paganism those who look at you as the temples of God. You must bear the light of God. A dirty wick, a wick not nourished with oil, smokes and gives no light, it has a horrible smell and does not illuminate. A lamp hidden behind a dirty quartz-crystal does not create the splendid gracefulness or the dazzling effects of light on the bright mineral. But it fades behind the veil of black smoke that makes the crystal cover dull.

The light of God shines where wills are zealous in removing every day the scum produced by work itself, with its contacts, reactions and disappointments. The light of God shines where the wick is immersed into plenty of liquid full of prayer and charity. The light of God multiplies into infinite splendid reflections, as many as the perfections of God, each of which excites in the saint a virtue practised heroically, if the servant of God keeps the unattackable quartz of his soul clear from the smoke of every soiling passion. The unattackable quartz. Unattackable! (Jesus thunders out in this conclusion and His voice resounds in the natural amphitheatre).

Only God has the right and the power to scratch that crystal, to write His Most Holy Name on it with the diamond of His will. That Name then becomes the ornament that emphasizes the brighter facets of supernatural beauty on the most pure quartz. But if the foolish servant of the Lord, losing control of himself and the sight of his mission, *a completely and solely supernatural one,* allows false ornaments and scratches, instead of engravings to be cut on his quartz, that is, mysterious and satanic figures made by the hot claw of Satan, then the wonderful lamp no longer retains its intact beauty, but it cracks and breaks and the fragments of the splintered crystal suffocate the flame, and even if it does not break, a tangle of marks of unmistakable nature forms on its surface and soot penetrates into them spoiling it.

169.9 [9] Woe, three times woe, to the shepherds who lose charity, who refuse to climb day by day to take upwards their flocks that expect their ascent in order to ascend themselves. I will strike them down and remove them from their positions and I will put out their smoke altogether.

Woe, three times woe, to the masters who reject Wisdom to become saturated with a science, which is often opposed and always proud, sometimes satanic, because it makes them men, whereas — listen and remember — if every man is destined to become like God, through the sanctification that makes man a son of God, a master, a priest should already have in this world the aspect of a son of God, and only such aspect. He should have the aspect of a creature entirely devoted to souls and to perfection. *He should have* such aspect to lead his disciples to God. Anathema to the masters of a supernatural doctrine, who become human knowledge.

Woe, seven times woe, to those among My priests who are dead to the spirit, who with their lack of savour and ill-living flesh live as miserable sluggish human beings. Their sleep is full of hallucinated apparitions of everything, except God One and Triune and is also full of all sorts of calculations, except the superhuman desire to increase the wealth of hearts and of God. They live a material, miserable dull life, dragging into their dead water those who follow them, believing that they are "Life". The curse of God on those who corrupt My little beloved flock. I will not punish those who perish through your laziness, o negligent servants of the Lord, but I will ask you to account for every hour and all the time lost and all evil consequences and I will punish you.

Remember those words. And now go. I am climbing to the top You may sleep. Tomorrow the Shepherd will open the pastures of Truth to His flock.»

170. The Sermon of the Mount.
Part Two: the Sanctifying Grace and the Beatitudes.

24th May 1945.

170.1 [1] Jesus speaks to the apostles assigning a place to each one, so that they may direct and watch over the crowd who are climbing up the mountain since the early hours of the morning, with sick people whom they carry in their arms or in stretchers or who have dragged themselves along on crutches. Among the people there are Stephen and Hermas.

The air is clear and rather chilly, but the sun soon softens the fresh mountain air, which in turn moderates the heat of the sun, drawing benefit from it, as it becomes pure and cool but not sharp.

The people sit on the stones scattered in the little valley between the two crests, but some wait for the sun to dry the grass, wet with dew, so that they may sit down on the ground. There is a huge crowd from all the districts in Palestine and the people are from all conditions. The apostles disappear in the multitude, but like bees that come and go from the meadows to the beehives, now and again they go back to the Master to inform Him, to ask for advice, and for the pleasure of being seen near Him.

Jesus climbs a little higher up than the meadow, which is at the bottom of the little valley, He leans against the rock and begins speaking.

170.2 [2] «Many have asked Me, during a year of preaching: "You say that You are the Son of God, tell us what is Heaven, what is the Kingdom, what is God. Because our notions are hazy. We know that there is Heaven with God and the angels. But no one has ever come to tell us what it is like, because it is closed to righteous people". They have also asked Me what the Kingdom is and what God is. And I have endeavoured to explain to you what the Kingdom is and what God is. I have striven not because it was difficult for Me to give an explanation, but because it is difficult for many reasons to get you to accept the truth that clashes, as far as the Kingdom is concerned, with a multitude of ideas, which have risen over the centuries and, as far as God is concerned, with the sublimity of His Nature.

Others have also asked Me: "All right. That is the Kingdom and that is God. But how do we achieve them?" Here again I have tried to explain to you patiently the true spirit of the Law of Sinai. He who abides by that spirit conquers Heaven. But to explain the Law of Sinai to you it is necessary to make you hear the loud thunder of the Lawgiver and of His Prophet, who, while promising blessings to obedient believers, threaten terrible punishments and curses to those who disobey. The Epiphany of Sinai was frightful and its dreadfulness is reflected in the entire Law, and has been reflected throughout centuries and in all souls.

But God is not only a Legislator... God is a Father. And a Father of immense goodness.

Probably, or rather, certainly, your souls are not in a position to rise and contemplate the infinite perfections of God, and His goodness least of all, because goodness and love are the rarest virtues amongst men. The reason is that your souls are weakened by original sin, by passions, by your own sins, by your own selfishness and the selfishness of other people: the former closes your souls, the latter irritates them. Goodness! How sweet it is to be good, with no hatred, no envy, no pride! How sweet it is to have eyes that look only for love and hands that stretch out only in gestures of love, and lips that utter only words of love and a heart, above all a heart, that full only of love, urges eyes, hands and lips to acts of love!

170.3 [3] The most learned amongst you know with which gifts God had enriched Adam, both for himself and for his descendants. Also the most ignorant amongst the children of Israel know that there is a soul in us. Only the poor heathens are unaware of this royal guest, of this vital breath and celestial light that sanctifies and gives life to our bodies. But the most learned know which gifts were given to man and to the soul of man.

God was not less munificent to the soul than to the flesh and of the creature made by Him with a little mud and His breath. As He gave the natural gifts of beauty and integrity, of intelligence and willpower, and the capability of loving oneself and other people, He also gave moral gifts and the subjection of senses to reason. Therefore the wicked captivity of senses and passions did not permeate the freedom and control of Adam and of his will, with which God had gifted him, thus he was free to love, free to wish, free to enjoy in justice, without what makes you slaves, causing you to feel the bite of the poison that Satan spread and which now overflows, carrying you out of the limpid river-bed onto the slimy fields and putrescent ponds, where the fever of carnal and moral senses fermentates. Because you must realise that also the concupiscence of thought is sensual. And they received supernatural gifts, that is, sanctifying Grace, a heavenly destiny, the vision of God.

[4]Sanctifying Grace: the life of the soul. The most spiritual 170.4
thing deposited in our spiritual soul. The Grace that makes us children of God, because it preserves us from the death of sin, and he who is not dead *"lives"* in the house of the Father: Paradise; in My Kingdom: Heaven. What is this Grace that sanctifies and gives Life and Kingdom? Oh! Not many words are required! Grace is love. Grace is therefore God. It is God Who admiring Himself in the creature whom He created perfect, loves Himself, contemplates Himself, desires Himself, gives Himself what is His own to multiply it, to delight in the multiplication, to love Himself in the many others who are others Himself.

Oh! My children! Do not defraud God of this right of His! Do not deprive God of what belongs to Him! Do not disappoint God in His desire! Consider that He acts out of love. Even if you did not exist, He would still be Infinite, and His power would not diminish. But He, although He is complete in His infinite immeasurable measure, does not want anything for Himself and in Himself — which He could not, because He is already Infinite — but for Creation, His creature. He wants to increase His love for all rational creatures contained in Creation, and therefore gives you His Grace: Love, that you may carry it within yourselves to the perfection of saints, and you may pour this treasure, taken from the treasure that God has given you with His Grace and increased by all the holy deeds in all your heroic lives of saints, into the infinite Ocean where God is: in Heaven.

You are divine reservoirs of Love! That is what you are, and no death is given to your being, because you are eternal, as God is, being like God. You shall be, and there will be no end to your being, because you are immortal like the holy spirits that super-nourished you, returning to you enriched by their own merits. You live and nourish, you live and enrich, you live and form the most holy thing which is the Communion of the spirits, from God, the Most Perfect Spirit, down to the last born baby, who sucks his mother's breast for the first time.

Do not criticise Me in your hearts, o learned men! Do not say: "He is crazy, He is a liar! Because He speaks foolishly saying that there is Grace in us, when Sin has deprived us of it. He lies stating that we are already one thing with God". Yes, there is sin and there is separation. But before the power of the Redeemer, Sin, the cruel separation between the Father and the children, will collapse like a wall shaken by a new Samson. I have already got hold of it and I am shaking it and it is about to fall and Satan is trembling with wrath and impotence, as he can avail nothing against My power and he realises that so much prey is being snatched from him and that it is becoming more difficult to drag man to sin. Because when I take you to My Father, through Me, and you have been cleansed and strengthened by My Blood and sorrow, Grace will come back to you, lively and powerful and you will be triumphant, if you so wish. God does not violate your thoughts or your sanctification. You are free. But He gives you back your strength. He gives you back your freedom from Satan's empire. It is up to you to take upon yourselves the infernal yoke or to put angelical wings on your souls. It depends on you, with Me as your brother to guide you and nourish you with immortal food.

170.5 [5] You may ask: "How can one conquer God and His Kingdom through a milder road than the harsh Sinai one?" There is no other road but that one. But let us look at it not from the point of view of a threat, but from the point of view of love. Let us not say: "Woe to me, if I do not do that!" trembling with fear of sinning, of not being able not to sin. But let us say: "Blessed I shall be if I do that!" and with the impulse of a supernatural joy, full of happiness, let us rush towards these beatitudes, brought about by compliance with the Law, as roses sprout from a thorny bush.

"Blessed I shall be if I am poor in spirit, because mine shall be the Kingdom of Heaven!

Blessed I shall be if I am meek because I shall inherit the earth!

Blessed I shall be if I mourn without rebelling, because I will be comforted!

Blessed I shall be if I hunger and thirst for justice more than I do for bread and wine to satisfy the flesh, because Justice will satisfy me!

Blessed I shall be if I am merciful, because I will have divine mercy shown to me!

Blessed I shall be if I am pure in heart, because God will bend over my pure heart and I will see Him!

Blessed I shall be if I am peaceful in spirit, because there is love in peace and God is Love and loves those who are like Him!

Blessed I shall be if I am persecuted in the cause of right, because God, my Father, to reward me for my earthly persecutions, will give me the Kingdom of Heaven!

Blessed I shall be if I am abused and accused falsely for being Your worthy son, o God! It must not cause me desolation but joy, as it will make me equal to Your best servants, to the Prophets, who were persecuted for the same reason and with whom I firmly believe shall share the same great eternal reward in Heaven, which is mine!".

Let us look at the road to salvation in this way: through the joy of saints.

6 *"Blessed I shall be if I am poor in spirit".* 170.6

Oh! Satanic thirst for wealth, to what frenzy you lead both rich and poor! The rich who live for their gold: the ill-famed idol of their ruined spirits. The poor who live hating the rich because of their gold, and even if they do not murder them physically, they curse the rich wishing them all sorts of evil. It is not enough not to do evil, one must not even wish to do it. He who curses wishing calamities and death is very like him who kills physically, because he wishes the death of the person he hates. I solemnly tell you that such a wish is like an action held back, it is like a foetus conceived in a womb and formed, but not yet ejected. A wicked desire corrupts and ruins man, because it lasts longer than a violent action and is deeper than the action itself.

If a rich man is poor in spirit he does not sin for the sake of his gold but he turns his gold into sanctification, because he turns it into love. Loved and blessed, he is like spring water that saves travelers in a desert, as he gives generously, without avarice, happy to be able to relieve desperate situations. If he is poor, he is happy in his poverty and eats his bread which is sweetened by the joy of being free from the thirst of gold, he sleeps free from nightmares and gets up well rested for his tranquil work, which is always light when done without greed or envy.

What makes man materially rich is gold, what makes him morally rich are his affections. Gold includes not only money but also houses, fields, jewels, furniture, herds, everything, in other words, what life wealthy materially. Affections include: blood or marriage ties, friendship, intellectual soundness, public offices. As you can see, if for the first group a poor man can say: "Oh! as far as I am concerned, providing I do not envy those who are rich, I am all right because I am poor, and thus I am settled by force of circumstances", with regard to the second group also a poor man must be careful, because even the poorest man can become sinfully rich in spirit. He who is immoderately attached to a thing, commits a sin.

You may say: "Are we then to hate the wealth that God granted us? Why then does He command us to love our fathers, mothers wives, children and say: 'You shall love your neighbour as yourself?'". You must distinguish. We must love our fathers, mothers, wives and our neighbour, but in the degree indicated by God: "As ourselves". Whereas God is to be loved above everything and with our wholeselves. We must not love God as we love the dearest people among our neighbours: because a woman suckled us or because she sleeps on our chest and procreates children for us, but we must love Him with our *wholeselves, that is, with all the ability to love* that is in man: the love of a son, of a husband, of a friend and — do not be scandalised — the love of a father. Yes, we must have for the interests of God the same care that a father has for his children, for whom he lovingly protects his wealth and increase it, and he takes care of and is anxious for their physical growth and intellectual education and for their success in the world.

Love is not an evil and must not become an evil. The graces, which God grants us, are not evil and must not become so. They are love, granted out of love. We must make a loving use of such wealth granted to us by God in personal affections and in worldly goods. And only he who does not make an idol of such wealth but uses it to serve God in holiness, shows that he has no sinful attachment. One then practises that holy poverty in spirit that itself of everything in order to be more free to conquer God, the Holy Supreme Wealth. To conquer God: that is to have the Kingdom of Heaven.

[7] *"Blessed I shall be if I am meek".* 170.7

This may seem to be in contrast with the facts of daily life. Those who are not meek seem to be prominent and successful in their families, towns and countries. But is theirs a real triumph? No, it is fear that apparently keeps subdued those who are overwhelmed by the despot, but in actual fact it is nothing but a veil drawn over the rebellion seething against the tyrant. Irascible and overbearing people do not win the love of their relatives, of their own citizens or of their subjects. Neither are intellects or souls convinced in following the doctrines of masters who impose themselves by stating: "I said so, thus it is". Such masters only create self-taught men seeking the key that can open the closed doors of wisdom or of science which they feel to be, and actually is the opposite of what is imposed on them.

Those priests who do not endeavour to conquer souls by means of a patient, humble and loving kindness, do not win any souls to God, but they look like armed warriors who start a fierce attack, such is their intolerant rashness in dealing with souls... Oh! poor souls! If they were holy they would not need you, o priests, to reach the Light. They would already have it within themselves. If they were just, they would not need you, o judges, to be put under the restraint of justice, as they would already have justice within themselves. If they were healthy, they would not need a doctor. Therefore be gentle. Do not put souls to flight. Attract them through love. Because lowliness is love, as poverty in spirit is love.

If you are such you will have the Earth for your heritage and you will take this place to God, whereas before it belonged to Satan, because your lowliness, which besides love is also humility, will have overcome Hatred and Pride, expelling the vile king of hatred and pride from souls, and the world will belong to you, that is, to God, because you will be the just souls that will acknowledge God as the Absolute Master of creation, to Whom praise and blessing are due and everything else which belongs to Him.

170.8 [8] *"Blessed I shall be if I mourn without rebelling".*

Sorrow is on the earth and sorrow wrings tears from men. Sorrow did not exist but man brought it on to the earth and because of his corrupt intellect he continuously strives to increase it in every possible way. Besides diseases and calamities created by thunderbolts, storms, avalanches, earthquakes, man, in order to suffer and above all to make other people suffer — because we would like only other people, and not ourselves, to suffer the effects of means studied to make people suffer — man invents deadly weapons, which are more and more dreadful, and moral hardships, which are more and more cunning. How many tears man wrings from his fellow man through the instigation of his secret king: Satan! And I solemnly tell you that those tears are not an impairment but a perfection of man.

Man is an absent-minded child, a thoughtless superficial child, a backward born child, until tears turn him into an adult, thoughtful, intelligent person. Only those who weep or have wept, know how to love and can understand. They know how to love their weeping brothers, how to understand them in their grief, how to help them with their goodness, which is fully aware how bitter it is to weep alone. And they know how to love God, because they have realised that everything is grief except God, because they have understood that sorrow can be soothed if tears are shed on God's heart and they have also realised that resigned tears, which do not cause faith to be lost or prayer to become barren and which loathe rebellion, such resigned tears change nature and instead of sorrow they become comfort.

Yes. Those who weep loving the Lord will be comforted.

170.9 [9] *"Blessed I shall be if I hunger and thirst for justice".*

From the moment he is born to the moment he dies, man

craves eagerly for food. He opens his mouth at his birth to get hold of his mother's nipple, he opens his lips to swallow some refreshment in the throes of death. He works to feed himself. He makes a huge nipple of the world from which he sucks insatiably for that which is perishable. But what is man? An animal? No, he is a son of God. He is in exile for a few or many years. But his life does not come to an end when he changes his dwelling.

There is a life in life as there is a kernel in a nut. The shell is not the nut, but it is the kernel inside the shell that is the nut. If you sow a shell nothing will come up, but if you sow the shell with the kernel inside it, a big tree will grow. The same applies to man. It is not his flesh that becomes immortal, but his soul. And it is to be nourished to take it to immortality, to which the soul, out of love, will take the body in the blessed resurrection. Wisdom and Justice are the nourishment of the soul. They are taken as food and as drink and they strengthen and the more one takes of them, the more grows the holy eagerness to possess Wisdom and know Justice. But the day will come when the holy insatiable hunger of the soul will be satisfied. It will come. God will give Himself to His child, and will suckle him and the child destined for Paradise will be satisfied with the admirable Mother Who is God Himself, and man will never be hungry again but will rest happily on God's divine bosom. No human science is equal to this divine science. The curiosity of the mind can be gratified, but the necessities of the spirit cannot. And more than that, the spirit is disgusted by the difference in taste and makes a wry mouth at the bitter nipple, preferring to suffer the pangs of hunger, rather than be filled with a food that does not come from God.

Be not afraid, o men thirsting or starving for God! Be faithful and you will be satisfied by Him Who loves you.

10 *"Blessed I shall be if I am merciful".* 170.10

Who amongst men can say: "I do not need mercy"? No one.
* Now, if the Old Law states: "Eye for eye, tooth for tooth", why should we not say in the New Law: "Who has been merciful shall find mercy"? Everybody needs forgiveness.

Well, then: forgiveness is not achieved by formulae or by the form of a rite, which are external symbols granted to man's dull

* **Eye for eye...**, in *Exodus 21:2425*; *Leviticus 24:19-20*; *Deuteronomy 19:21.*

mentality, it is instead obtained through the internal rite of love, which is still mercy. If the sacrifice of a goat or a lamb and the offer of a few coins were prescribed, the reason is that every evil is founded in two roots: greed and pride. Greed is punished through the expense for the purchase of the offering, pride by the open confession of the rite: "I am making this sacrifice because I have sinned". It is also done to anticipate the times and the signs of the times, and in the blood which is shed is symbolised the Blood which will be shed to cancel the sins of men.

Blessed therefore are those who are merciful to those who are hungry, naked, homeless, to those who suffer from the greatest misery, which is to have a bad disposition, as it causes grief both to those who have it and to those who live with them. Be merciful. Forgive, bear with people, help them, teach them, support them. Do not conceal yourselves in a crystal tower saying: "I am pure and I will not descend amongst sinners". Do not say: "I am rich and happy and I will not hear of other people's miseries". Remember that your richness, your health, your family wealth may vanish quicker than smoke blown away by a strong wind. And remember that crystal acts as a lense and consequently what may be unnoticed if you were mixed among the crowds, cannot be concealed if you place yourselves in a crystal tower where you are alone, isolated and illumined on all sides.

Mercy is necessary to offer a continuous, secret, holy sacrifice of expiation and to obtain mercy.

170.11 11 *"Blessed I shall be if I am pure in heart"*.

God is purity. Paradise is the Kingdom of Purity. Nothing impure can enter Paradise where God is. Therefore, if you are impure, you will not be able to enter the Kingdom of God. Oh! But what a joy the Father grants to His children in advance! He who is pure has in this world an advance of Heaven because God bends over a pure soul and man from the earth can see his God. He is not familiar with the taste of human love, but relishes the flavour of divine love, to the point of being enraptured, and can say: "I am with You and You are in me, I therefore possess You and I recognise You as the most loving spouse of my soul". And believe Me, he who has God enjoys substantial changes, of which he himself is unaware, and thus becomes holy, wise, strong; words embellish his lips and his actions acquire a strength that is not of the creature, but comes from God Who lives in it.

What is the life of those who see God? A beatitude. And do you wish to deprive yourselves of such a gift for the sake of fetid impurities?

[12] *"Blessed I shall be if I am peaceful in spirit".* 170.12

Peace is one of God's characteristics. God is to be found only in peace. Because peace is love, whereas war is hatred. Satan is hatred. God is peace. No man can say that he is the son of God, neither can God call son a man who has an irascible soul always ready to stir up a storm. Not only. Neither can he be called the son of God who, although not a trouble-maker himself, by means of his own great peace does not help to calm the storms stirred up by other people. He who is peaceful propagates peace also without uttering any words. Master of himself and, I dare say, master of God, he divulges Him as a lamp spreads its light, as a thurible exhales its perfume, as a wineskin holds wine, and this sweet oil, which is the spirit of peace issuing from the children of God, gives light in the foggy gloominess of ill-feelings, and purifies the air from the miasmas of malice and calms the raging waves of quarrels.

Let God and men say that you are so.

[13] *"Blessed I shall be if I am persecuted in the cause of right".* 170.13

Man has become so devilish that he hates good wherever it is, and he hates who is good, as if he who is good, even when silent, accuses and reproaches him, in fact the goodness of one person makes the wickedness of a wicked person appear even more wicked... In fact the faith of a true believer makes the hypocrisy of a false believer appear more clearly. In fact, he who by his way of living continuously bears witness to justice can but be hated by the unjust. And then the unjust are pitiless towards the lovers of justice.

The same applies here as in wars. Man makes more progress in the satanic art of persecution than in the holy art of love. But he can persecute only what has a short life. What is eternal in man eludes the snare, and more than that, it achieves a more energetic vitality than persecution itself. Life escapes through the bleeding wounds or because of the privations that consume those who are persecuted. But the blood makes the purple of the future king and the privations are as many steps to ascend the thrones that the Father has prepared for His martyrs, for whom are reserved the royal seats in the Kingdom of Heaven.

170.14 [14] *"Blessed I shall be if I am accused and abused falsely".*

Strive to have your names written in the celestial books, where names are not written according to human falsehood, which is accustomed to praise those who less deserve praise, where, instead, with justice and love are written the deeds of good people in order to give them the reward promised to the blessed ones by God.

In the past, the Prophets were calumniated and abused. But when the gates of Heaven are opened, they will enter the City of God, like imposing kings, and the angels will bow singing out of joy. You, too, who have been abused and accused falsely for being the children of God, will have a heavenly triumph and when the time comes to an end and Paradise is full, then every tear will be dear to you, because through it you will have conquered the eternal glory, which I promise you in the name of the Father.

Go. I will speak to you again tomorrow. Only the sick people should remain that I may relieve them from their pains. Peace be with you and may the meditation on salvation lead you, through love, on to the road at the end of which is Heaven.»

171. The Sermon of the Mount. Part Three: Jesus Has Come to Complete and Fulfill the Law.

25th May 1945.

171.1 [1] The Sermon of the Mount continues.

It is the same place and the same time. The crowd is larger. In a corner, near a path, there is a Roman, who seems anxious to hear but does not want to upset the crowd. I recognise him from his short tunic and the different style of his mantle. Stephen and Hermas are still there.

Jesus walks slowly to His place and resumes speaking.

«What I told you yesterday must not cause you to think that I have come to abolish the Law. No. But since I am the Man, and I understand the weakness of man, I wanted to encourage you to comply with it, turning your spiritual eyes not to the dark abyss, but to the bright Sublimity. Because if the fear of punishment can hold you back three times out of ten, the certainty of a reward will urge you seven times out of ten. Trust is therefore more efficient than fear. And I want you to be fully and firmly confident, so that you accomplish not seven parts of good out of ten, but ten out of ten and thus gain the most holy prize of Heaven.

I will not change one iota of the Law. And Who gave it amongst the peals of thunder on Sinai? The Most High. Who is the Most High? God One and Triune. Where did He take it from? From His Thought. How did He give it? By His Word. Why did He give it? Out of His Love. You can thus see that the Trinity was present. And the Word, obedient as ever to the Thought and Love, spoke on behalf of the Thought and Love. Could I give Myself the lie? No, I could not.

But since I can do everything, I can complete the Law, make it divinely complete, not what men did throughout centuries, as they did not make it complete, but incomprehensible and impossible to be fulfilled. In fact they superimposed precepts and laws taken from *their own* thoughts, according to *their own* gain, and they thus lapidated and suffocated, sterilised and buried the most holy Law given by God. Can a tree survive if it is continuously struck by avalanches, rubble and floods? No, it will die. The Law dies in many hearts, suffocated by the avalanches of too many superstructures. I have come to remove them all, and after unearthing and reviving the Law, I will make it no longer a law, but a queen.

[2] Queens promulgate laws. The laws are the work of queens, 171.2
but they are not above queens. I instead make the Law a queen: I complete it, I crown it, putting on its top the wreath of the evangelic counsels. Before it was order. Now it is more than order. Before it was the necessary thing. Now it is more than the necessary thing: now it is perfection. He who weds it, as I present you with it, becomes immediately a king, because he has reached "perfection", because he has not been only obedient, but also heroic, that is, holy, as holiness is the sum of virtues carried to the greatest height attainable by a creature, heroically loved and practised through a complete detachment from every human desire and consideration.

I could say that he is a saint, whom love and desire prevent from seeing everything but God. As his attention is not distracted by inferior sights, his eyes and heart are fixed on the Most Holy Brightness, which is God and in which, since everything is in God, he can see his distressed brothers stretching out their hands suppliantly. And without taking his eyes away from God, the saint devotes himself to his suppliant brothers. Against the flesh, against wealth, against comforts, he pursues his ideal: to serve. Is a saint poor or disabled? No, he is not. He has succeeded in achieving true wisdom and wealth. He therefore possesses everything. And he never tires because while it is true that he is always active, it is also true that he is continuously nourished. And while he understands the sorrows of the world, he feeds on the delights of Heaven. He is nourished by God and delights in God. He is a creature who has understood the meaning of life.

As you can see I neither change nor mutilate the Law, neither do I corrupt it by superimposing human fomenting theories. I complete it. The Law is what it is and shall be such until the last day: not one word will be changed, not one precept will be abolished. It is crowned with perfection. To reach salvation it is sufficient to accept it as it was given. To obtain immediate union with God it is necessary to live it according to My advice. But since heroes are an exception, I will speak to common souls, to the mass of souls, so that no one may say that I have made what is necessary unknown, in order to reach perfection. But of everything I tell you, remember this: he who takes the liberty of infringing one of the least of these commandments, will be considered one of the least in the Kingdom of Heaven. And he who will induce others to infringe them, will be considered one of the least both with regards to himself and to those whom he led to the infringement. He, instead, who through his life and deeds, rather than by words, has convinced others to abide by the Law, will be great in the Kingdom of Heaven and his greatness will be increased by each of those whom he has led to obey and thus sanctify themselves.

171.3 [3] I know that what I am about to say will taste bitter to many tongues. But I cannot tell lies, even if the truth I am about to speak will procure Me many enemies.

I solemnly tell you that unless you create anew your justice, detaching it completely from the poor and unfairly defined justice which the Pharisees and Scribes have taught you; unless you are *really* more just than the Pharisees and Scribes, who think they are just because they increase the number of formulae without any subtantial change of their spirits, you shall not enter the Kingdom of Heaven.

Beware of false prophets and erring doctors. They come to you clad as lambs, and they are rapacious wolves; they come clad with holiness and they deride God; they say they love the truth and they feed on falsehood. Study them before following them.

Man has a tongue and speaks with it, he has eyes and sees with them, he has hands and makes signs with them. But he has something else which is a more truthful witness of his real being: his deeds! And what are two hands joined in prayer, if a man is a thief and fornicator? And what are two eyes, which pretending to be inspired, roll in all directions, if after the farce, they greedily stare at a woman or an enemy, out of lust or for murder? And what is a tongue expert in whistling a false song of praise and in seducing by means of honeyed words, if behind your back it calumniates you and is capable of swearing falsely if only it could pass you off as a mean fellow? What is a tongue that says long hypocritical prayers and is then quick in killing the reputation of a neighbour or seducing his good faith? It is disgusting! And disgusting are untruthful hands and eyes. But the deeds of men, the *true* deeds, that is, his behaviour at home, in business, towards his neighbour and servants, are the things that testify: "This man is a servant of the Lord". Because holy deeds are the fruit of true religion.

A good tree does not bear bad fruit and a bad tree does not bear good fruit. Will these thorny bushes ever be able to give you tasty grapes? And those even more stinging thistles, will they ever be able to mature sweet figs for you? No, they will not. In actual fact you will be able to pick only a few sour blackberries from the former and uneatable fruits will come from the latter, which although flowers, are still thorny.

The man who is not just will be able to command respect by his appearance, and only by it. Also the downy thistle looks like a tuft of thin silvery threads adorned with diamonds by the dew. But if inadvertently you touch it, you can see that it is not a tuft, but a bundle of thorns, painful to man, harmful to sheep, so that shepherds uproot them from their pastures and burn them on the fire they light at night so that not even the seed may be spread. A just and provident step. I do not say to you: "Kill the false prophets and hypocritical believers". On the contrary, I say to you: "Leave the task to God". But I say to you: "Be careful, keep away from them that you may not be poisoned by their juices".

171.4 [4] I told you yesterday how God is to be loved. I will insist on how our neighbour is to be loved.

Once it was said: "You shall love your friend and hate your enemy". No, not so. That was all right for the times when man did not have the comfort of God's smile. But now new times have come, when God has loved man so much as to send His Word to redeem him. Now the Word is speaking. And it is already an effusion of Grace. Later the Word will consummate the sacrifice of peace and redemption and there will be not only an effusion of Grace, but Grace will be given to every soul believing in Christ. It is therefore necessary to elevate the love for our neighbour to a perfection that unifies friend and enemy. *

Have you been slandered? Love and forgive. Have you been struck? Love and offer the other cheek to him who smacked you, considering that it is better that he gives vent to his wrath on you who can put up with it, rather than on somebody else who would take vengeance for the insult. Have you been robbed? Do not think: "This neighbour of mine is greedy", but charitably say: "This poor brother of mine is needy" and give him also your tunic if he has stolen your mantle. You will make it impossible for him to steal twice, because he will have no need to rob another person of his tunic. You may say: "It may be a vice and not a need". Well, give just the same. God will reward you for it and the wicked man pay for it. But many times, and this should remind you of what I told you yesterday on lowliness, when he sees how he has been dealt with, his vice will drop from his heart and the sinner will redeem himself making amends for the theft by handing back what he had stolen.

Be generous towards those, who being more honest, ask you for what they need, instead of robbing you. If the rich were really

---

* **Once it was said**, in *Leviticus 19:18* and in *Sirach 12:1-7*, then repeated in *Matthew 5:43*.

poor in spirit, as I explained yesterday, there would be no painful social inequalities, the cause of so many human and superhuman calamities. Always consider: "If I were in need, how would I feel if I were denied help?" and act according to the reply of your *ego*. Do to others what you would like done to yourself and do not do to others what you would not like done to yourself.

The old saying: "Eye for eye, tooth for tooth", which is not one of the ten commandments, but was added because man, devoid of Grace, is such a beast that he only understands vengeance, the old saying has been canceled. It has indeed been canceled by the new word: "Love him who hates you, pray for him who persecutes you, justify him who slanders you, bless him who curses you, help the one who harms you, be pacific with quarrelsome people, be compliant with bothersome people, willingly help those who have recourse to you without practising usury, do not criticise, do not judge". You do not know the particular reason for men's actions. Be generous and merciful in all kinds of assistance. The more you give the more you will be given and a full and pressed measure will be poured by God on to the lap of he who has been generous. God will not give you only according to what you have given, but He will give you much more. Endeavour to love and be loved. Quarrels are more costly than friendly settlements and a good grace is like honey, the flavour of which lasts for a long time on one's tongue.

[5] Love, love. Love friends and enemies, to be like your Father, 171.5
Who allows the rain to fall on the good and the wicked and lets the sun shine on the just and unjust and will grant eternal sunshine and dew, and hellish fire and hail, when the goodwill be chosen, like selected ears of corn, amongst the sheaves of the harvest. It is not enough to love those who love you and from whom you expect reciprocation. That is no merit: it is a joy and also naturally honest men can do it. Also the publicans and the gentiles do it. But you must love according to God and out of respect for God, Who is also the Creator of those who are your enemies or are not very fond of you. I want the perfection of love in you and I therefore say: "Be perfect as your Father, Who is in Heaven, is perfect".

So great is the precept of love for your neighbour, the perfecting of the precept of love for your neighbour, that I no longer say, as used to be said: "Do not kill" because he who kills will be condemned by men. But I say to you: "Do not get angry" because a higher judgement is above you and takes into account immaterial actions. He who insults his brother will be condemned by the Sanhedrin. But he who treats him as a madman, and consequently has harmed him, will be condemned by God. It is useless to make offers at the altar, unless you, for the sake of God, first sacrifice your ill-feelings in your hearts and you fulfill the most holy rite of forgiveness. Therefore, when you are about to make an offering to God and you remember that you have wronged your brother and you bear him a grudge because of a fault of his, leave your offer before the altar, make first the sacrifice of your self-esteem, by becoming reconciled to your brother, then come to the altar and only then your sacrifice will be holy. Full agreement is always the best thing. The judgement of man is precarious and he who stubbornly challenges it, may lose the cause and have to pay the opponent down to the last coin or languish in jail.

In everything turn your eyes to God. Ask yourselves: "Am I entitled to do what God does not do to me?". Because God is not so stubborn and implacable as you are. Woe to you if He were! No one would be saved. Let that consideration induce you to mild, humble, pitiful feelings. And then you will certainly receive a reward from God, both here and in the next world.

171.6 [6] Here, in front of Me, there is also one who hates Me and dare not say to Me: "Cure me" because he knows that I am aware of his thoughts. But I say: "Let it be done as you wish. And as the scales fall from your eyes, so may ill-feelings and darkness fall from your heart".

You may all go with My peace. I will speak to you again tomorrow.»

The crowds disperse slowly, waiting perhaps for the cry of a miracle, which, however, is not heard.

Also the apostles and the first disciples, who remain on the mountain, ask: «Who was it? Has he not been cured?» and they insist with the Master, Who is standing, with folded arms, watching the crowd descending the mountain.

Jesus at first does not reply; He then says: «His eyes are cured, but his soul is not. It cannot be cured because it is full of hatred.»

«But who is it? That Roman, perhaps?»

«No. A poor wretch.»

«Why did You cure him, then?» asks Peter.

«Should I strike by lightning all the people like him?»

«Lord... I know that You do not want me to say: "yes", and so I will not say it... but that is what I think... and it is the same...»

«It is the same, Simon of Jonah. You should know then... Oh! How many hearts covered with scales of hatred there are around Me! Come. Let us go up there, to the top, to look from above at our beautiful sea of Galilee. Only you and I.»

172. The Sermon of the Mount. Part Four: the 'Swearing of Oaths', Secrecy in Praying or Fasting. Old Ismael and Sarah.

26th May 1945.

[1] The Sermon of the Mount continues. 172.1

The same place and the same time. The people, with the exception of the Roman, are the same. Perhaps the crowd is larger because many people are standing at the beginning of the paths leading to the little valley.

Jesus is speaking:

«One of the errors easily made by man is to be lacking in honesty, even towards himself. And since man is rarely sincere and honest, he has created a curb-bit for himself in order to be compelled to go along his way. This curb-bit which, after all, as he is a fiery horse, he soon slackens or gives a pull at, as he wishes, and thus changes his gait; or he removes it completely and does as he likes, without considering what reproach he may receive from God, from men and from his own conscience. That bit is the oath. But no oath is necessary amongst honest people and God never taught you it. On the contrary He commanded you: "You shall not bear false witness", without any further addition. Because man ought to be frank without the need for anything except the loyalty of his word.

When in Deuteronomy mention is made of vows, also of the vows that are something which originated from a heart considered to be united to God, either through a feeling of need or a sentiment of gratitude, it states: "Whatever word passes your lips, you must stick to it, and the vow that you have freely made with your own mouth to the Lord your God must be fulfilled". Mention is always made of the word given, without anything else but the word. He who feels the need of taking an oath is neither sure of himself nor of the opinion his neighbour has of him. And he who makes other people take an oath testifies thereby that he distrusts the frankness and honesty of the swearer. As you can see, the habit of taking an oath is one of the consequences of man's moral dishonesty. And it is a shame for man. It is a double shame because man is not even faithful to the shameful thing which an oath is and by deriding God as easily as he derides his neighbour, he swears falsely with the greatest ease and calmness.

172.2 [2] Can there be a more contemptible man than a perjurer? A perjurer in fact convinces his neighbour to believe him, often by using a sacred formula, thus calling God to be his accomplice and to stand surety for him, or by invoking his dearest affections: his father, mother, wife, children, his dead relatives, his very life and most essential organs, to support his false statements. He thus deceives his neighbour. He is an impious person, a thief, a traitor, a murderer. Of whom? Of God, of course, because he contaminates the Truth with his disgraceful lies and jeers at Him, daring Him: "Strike me, give me the lie, if You can. You are there, I am here and I laugh at it". Of course, you may laugh, liars and gibers! But the moment will come when you will not laugh and that will happen when He, to Whom all power is entrusted, will appear to you, dreadful in His majesty, and simply by His appearance will make you stand to attention and will strike you with the lightning of His eyes, before His voice hurls you to your eternal destiny branding you with His curse. He is a thief because he takes possession of a reputation he does not deserve. His neighbour, impressed by his oath, grants it to him, and the serpent adorns himself with it, pretending to be what he is not. He is a traitor because by his oath he promises something he does not want to keep. He is a murderer: he either kills the honour of his fellow man depriving him of his reputation through false witness or he kills his own soul because a perjurer is a vile sinner in the eyes of God, Who sees the truth, also when no one else sees it.

God can be deceived, neither by means of false words, nor by means of hypocritical deeds. He sees. He does not lose sight of each man for a moment. And there is no fortified stronghold or deep cellar which His eyes cannot penetrate. Also within you, God penetrates the stronghold every man has around his heart. And He judges you not according to what you swear, but to what you do.

* [3] I will therefore substitute another order for the one given to 172.3
you, when the oath enjoyed great favour to put a restraint on lies and on the easiness of failure to keep a promise. I do not say as the ancients said: "Do not swear falsely, but keep your oath", but I say to you: "Never swear". Neither by Heaven, which is the throne of God, nor by the earth, which is the stool of His feet, nor for Jerusalem and her Temple, which are the City of the Great King and the House of the Lord our God.

Do not swear either by the graves of the deceased or by their souls. Graves are full of the dross of the inferior part of man, which is also common to animals, and with regard to their souls, leave them in their dwellings. Do not cause them to suffer or to be struck with horror, if they are the souls of just people already in the foreknowledge of God. And although they are in such foreknowledge, which is partial knowledge, because they will not possess God in the fullness of His brightness until the moment of Redemption, they can but suffer seeing you sinners. And if they are just, do not increase their torture by reminding them of their sin through yours. Leave the holy deceased in their peace, and the unholy ones in their pains. Do not deprive the former of anything, do not add anything to the latter. Why appeal to the dead? They cannot speak. The saints because charity prevents them from speaking: they would have to give you the lie too many times. The damned because hell does not open its gates and the damned only open their mouths to curse, and their voices are suffocated by the hatred of Satan and of the demons, because the damned are like demons.

Do not swear by the head of your father or of your mother, or by the head of your wife or of your innocent children. You have no right to do so. Are they perhaps money or merchandise? Are they a signature on a document? They are more and they are less

---

* **given**, in *Leviticus 19:12*.

than such things. They are blood and flesh of your own blood, man, but they are also free creatures and you cannot use them as slaves to guarantee your false statements. And they are less than your own signature, because you are intelligent, free and grown up, you are not interdicted, neither are you a child who does not know what he is doing and must be represented by his parents. You are a man gifted with reason and consequently responsible for your actions and you must act by yourself, employing, as a guarantee for your own deeds and words, *your own* honesty and *your own* frankness, the reputation that *you* enjoy with your neighbour, not the honesty, the frankness of your relatives and the reputation they enjoy. Are fathers responsible for their children? Yes, they are, but only as long as they are under age. Afterwards, everybody is responsible for himself. Not always just children are born of just parents, nor is it so that a holy woman is married to a holy man. Why then use the justice of a relative as a guarantee? Likewise, holy children may be born of a sinner, and as long as they are innocent, they are holy. Why then appeal to a pure soul for an impure act of yours, such as oaths which you wish to swear falsely?

Do not swear by your own head, your eyes, your tongue, your hands. You have no right to. Everything you have belongs to God. You are only the temporary guardians, the bankers of the moral or material treasures that God granted you. Why then make use of what does not belong to you? Can you add one hair to your head or change its colour? And if you cannot do that, why do you use your sight, your word, the freedom of your limbs to corroborate your oath? Do not challenge God. He could take you at your word and dry up your eyes as He can dry up your orchards, or take your children away from you, or crush your houses to remind you that He is the Lord and you His subjects, and that he who idolizes himself and thinks he is above God, challenging Him with his falsehood, is cursed.

172.4 [4] Let your speech be simply: yes, it is; no, it is not. Nothing else. Any addition is suggested by the Evil one, who later will laugh at you, because you cannot remember everything and you will contradict yourself and you will be jeered at and recognised as a liar.

Be sincere, My children, both in your words and in your

prayers. Do not behave like the hypocrites, who, when praying, love to stand in synagogues or in the corners of squares where they may be seen by people and praised as just and pious men, whereas, within their families, they are guilty towards God and towards their neighbour. Do you not consider that is like a form of perjury? Why do you want to maintain as true what is not true, in order to win a reputation which you do not deserve? A hypocritical prayer aims at saying: "I am truly a saint. I swear it in the presence of those who see me and cannot deny they saw me praying". Like a veil laid on existing wickedness, a prayer said for such purposes becomes blasphemy.

Let God proclaim you saints and live in such a way that your whole life may shout on your behalf: "Here is a servant of God". But you must be silent for your own sake. Do not allow your tongue to be urged by pride and thus become an object of scandal in the angels' eyes. It would be better for you to become mute at once if you do not have the power to control pride and tongue, and you proclaim yourselves just and pleasing to God. Leave that poor glory to proud and false people. Leave that fleeting reward to haughty and deceitful people! A poor reward! But that is what they want and they will not have any other, because you cannot have more than one. Either the true reward, the Heavenly one, which is eternal and just, or the sham one, the earthly one, which lasts as long as the life of man, and even less, and which is paid for, after this life, with a truly mortifying punishment, because it is an unjust reward.

[5] Listen how you must pray with your lips and with your work 172.5
and with your whole selves, urged by your hearts which do love God and feel He is your Father, but they always remember who the Creator is and what the creature is, and in the presence of God they are always full of reverential love, whether you are praying or are busy, whether you are walking or resting, earning or helping.

I said urged by your hearts. It is the first and essential feature. Because everything comes from your hearts and your minds: your words, your eyes, your deeds are like your hearts. A just man draws good from his just heart and the more he draws the more he finds, because the good done creates more good, like blood that is renewed circulating in the veins and flows back to the heart enriched with new elements taken from the oxygen, which it had absorbed or from the food juices, which it had assimilated. Whereas a wicked man can draw but fraud and poison from his gloomy heart full of fraud and poison, which grow more and more because they are corroborated by accumulating sins, while the blessings of God accumulate in a good man. You may be sure that it is the exhuberance of the heart that overflows from lips and reveals itself in deeds.

Make your hearts humble, pure, loving, trustful and sincere and love God with the chaste love of a virgin for her bridegroom. I solemnly tell you that each soul is a virgin married to the Eternal Lover, to God Our Lord; this world is the time of engagement during which the guardian angel of every man is the spiritual paranymph, and all the hours and contingencies of life are as many maids preparing the nuptial trousseau. The hour of death is the hour for the accomplished wedding when the introduction, embrace and union take place and the soul can raise the veil of the bridal dress and throw itself into the arms of God and the Spouse will not cause scandal by loving so.

But for the time being, o souls still victimised in the bonds of the engagement to God, when you wish to speak to the Spouse, withdraw to the peace of your abode, above all to the peace of your inner abodes and, angels of flesh helped by your guardian angels, speak to the King of angels. Speak to your Father in the secrecy of your hearts and of your inner rooms. Leave outside everything that belongs to the world: eagerness to be noted and to edify, and the scruples of long prayers full of words, of monotonous, tepid words lacking love.

172.6 [6] For God's sake, get rid of standards in your prayers. There are really some people who waste many hours reciting a monologue only with their lips and which is a real soliloquy because not even the guardian angels listen to it; it is such a vain noise that they become absorbed in fervent prayer for the silly men guarded by them, in an effort to find a remedy. There are in fact some men who would not spend those hours in a different way, not even if God appeared to them saying: "The salvation of the world depends on your leaving such soulless manner of speech and going, shall we say, just to draw water from a well and pour it onto the ground for My sake and the sake of your fellow men".

There are indeed many who believe that their monologue is more important than the kindness in receiving a visitor or the charity in helping a person in need. They are souls which have fallen into the idolatry of prayer.

Prayer is an act of love. And one can love praying or baking bread, meditating or assisting a sick person, making a pilgrimage to the Temple or looking after the family, sacrificing a lamb or sacrificing one's desires, even the honest desire to concentrate on the Lord. It is sufficient for you to have your wholeselves and all your actions impregnated with love. Be not afraid! The Father sees, understands, listens, grants. How many graces are granted for one single, true perfect sigh of love! How much wealth for an intimate sacrifice made with love. Do not be like the Gentiles. God does not need to be told what He has to do for your needs. The pagans may tell their idols, who cannot understand. But you cannot tell God, the True Spiritual God, Who is not only God and King, but also your Father and knows what you need, even before you ask Him.

[7] Ask and it will be given to you, look and you will find, knock 172.7
and the door will be opened to you. Because whoever asks, will receive, whoever looks, will find and the door will be opened to whoever knocks. When your child stretches his little hand towards you saying: "Father, I am hungry" do you perhaps give him a stone? Will you give him a snake if he asks for a fish? No, you will give him bread and fish, and caresses and blessings over and above, because it is pleasant for a father to nourish his son and see his happy smiles. If therefore you, whose hearts are imperfect, are capable of giving gifts to your children, out of a natural love that is also common to animals for their offspring, how much more will your Father, Who is in Heaven, grant to those who ask Him for the good and necessary things for their welfare. Do not be afraid to ask and do not be afraid not to receive!

However, I wish to warn you against an easy error: do not behave like those who are weak in their faith and in their love. Also amongst believers there are pagans whose poor religion is a mixture of superstition and faith, a building tampered with, into which all kinds of parasitic herbs have penetrated, so much so that it falls to pieces, and they, weak and pagans as they are, feel their faith is dying if they are not heard.

You ask. And you think it is fair to ask. And for that particular moment a certain grace may be right. But life does not end at *that* moment. And what is good today may *not* be good tomorrow. You do not know that, because you know only the present, and that is a grace of God, too. But God knows the future as well. And God, to save you a greater pain, does not hear your prayer.

During My year of public life more than once I heard hearts moaning: "How much I suffered then, when God did not hear me. But now I say: 'It was better thus, because that grace would have prevented me from reaching this hour of God'". I heard others say to Me: "Why, Lord, do You not hear me? You grant it to everybody but not to me?" And yet, although I was sorry to see them suffer, I had to say: "I cannot", because to hear them would have meant hindering their flight towards a perfect life.

Also the Father sometimes says: "I cannot". Not because He cannot satisfy the request immediately, but because He does not want to satisfy it because of future consequences. Listen. A child is suffering from intestinal trouble. His mother calls a doctor and the doctor says: "He must fast to be cured". The child cries, yells, implores, seems to be languishing. The mother, always pitiful, joins her moaning to her son's. She thinks that the doctor's order is severe and hard. She feels that such fasting and crying may be detrimental to her son. But the doctor does not change his opinion. At last he says: "Woman, I know, you don't. Do you want to lose your son or do you want me to save him?". The mother shouts: "I want him to live". "In that case" says the doctor "I cannot let him have any food. It would kill him". Also the Father sometimes says so. You, pitiful mothers of your own *egos,* do not want to hear it weep because some grace has been denied. But God says: "I cannot. It would do you harm". The day will come, or eternity will come, when you will say: "Thank You, my God, for not listening to my foolishness!"

172.8 [8] What I said with regard to prayers, I say with regard to fasting. When you fast, do not look sad, as hypocrites do, who on purpose disfigure their faces that the world may know and believe that they are fasting, even if it is not true. They too have received their reward with the praise of the world, and will not receive another one. Instead, when you fast, look happy, wash your faces thoroughly so that they may look fresh and smooth, put oil on your heads and scents on your hair and smile like one who has been well fed. Oh! Truly there is no food that nourishes as much as love does! And he who fasts with a loving spirit, feeds on love! I solemnly tell you that even if the world calls you "vain" and "publicans", the Father will see your heroic secret and will give you a double reward. One for your fasting and the other for the sacrifice of not being praised for it.

And now go and feed your bodies, since your souls have been
nourished. 9Those two poor people may stay here with us. They 172.9
will be blessed guests who will give flavour to our bread. Peace be with you.»

And the two poor people stay. One is a very lean woman, the other a very old man. They are not together. Chance had joined them, as they were standing dejected in a corner, stretching out their hands in vain towards those who passed in front of them.

Jesus goes straight towards them since they dare not come forward and takes them by the hand leading them to the middle of the group of the apostles, under a kind of tent that Peter has put up in a corner and under which they perhaps take shelter at night and they gather during the hot hours of the day. It is a shed formed by branches and... mantles. But it serves its purpose, although it is so low that Jesus and the Iscariot, the tallest of the group, have to bend to enter.

«Here a father and a sister. Bring what we have. While taking our food we will hear their story.» And Jesus personally serves the two shy old souls and listens to their sorrowful stories. The old man is alone, after his daughter went far away with her husband and forgot her father. The woman is also alone, after a fever killed her husband and, in addition, she is ill.

«The world despises us because we are poor» says the old man. «I wander about begging for alms to scrape together some money to celebrate Passover. I am eighty years old. I have always kept Passover and this may be the last time. But I do not want to go to Abraham's bosom with any regret. As I forgive my daughter, so I hope to be forgiven. And I want to keep my Passover.»

«It is a long way, father.»

«The way to Heaven is even longer, if one is not present at the rite.»

«Are you going by yourself? And if you feel ill on the way?»

«The angel of God will close my eyes.»

Jesus caresses his white trembling head and asks the woman: «And what about you?»

«I am looking for work. If I were better fed I would get rid of my fever. And if I were cured I could work at the corn.»

«Do you think that food alone could cure you?»

«No, You could, too. But I am a poor thing, too poor to ask You for mercy.»

«And if I cured you, what would you like afterwards?»

«Nothing else. I would already have had more than I could hope for.»

Jesus smiles and hands her a piece of bread dipped into some water and vinegar, which I think is their drink. The woman eats it without speaking and Jesus continues smiling.

172.10 [10]The meal is over. It was so frugal! The apostles and disciples look for a shady place along the slopes and among the thickets. Jesus remains under the tent. The old man is lying on the grass and tired as he was, has fallen asleep.

After a short time the woman, who had gone away looking for some shade to rest, comes towards Jesus Who smiles at her to cheer her up. She comes forward looking shy, but happy, almost as far as the tent. She is then overcome by joy, she walks with a vigorous stride and falling flat on her face with a choked cry exclaims: «You have cured me! May You be blessed! At this time I used to shiver with fever, but I am not now... Oh!» and she kisses Jesus' feet.

«Are you sure that you have been cured? I did not tell you. It might be by chance...»

«Oh! no! Now I understand Your smile when You handed me the bread. Your virtue entered me with that morsel. I have nothing to give You in exchange, except my heart. Order Your maid, Lord, and she will obey You until she dies.»

«Yes. See that old man? He is all alone and he is just. You had a husband and death took him away. He had a daughter and selfishness took her away. And that is worse. And yet he does not curse. But it is not fair that he should go about alone in his last hours. Be a daughter to him.»

«Yes, my Lord.»

«Mind you, it means working for two.»

«I am strong now, and I will do it.»

11 «Go up there, then, to that cliff and tell the man who is resting there, the one wearing a grey tunic, to come to Me.» 172.11

The woman goes away quickly and comes back with Simon Zealot.

«Come, Simon, I want to speak to you. Woman, wait here.»

Jesus walks away for a few yards.

«Do you think that Lazarus would find it difficult to take on another worker?»

«Lazarus? I do not think that he even knows how many servants he has! One more, one less!... But who is it?»

«That woman. I cured her and...»

«That is enough, Master. If You cured her it means that You love. What You love is sacred to Lazarus. I commit myself for him.»

«That is true. What I love is sacred to Lazarus. You are right. And that is why Lazarus will become a saint, because by loving what I love he will love perfection. I want to join that old man to that woman and let that patriarch keep his last Passover in great joy. I am very fond of old holy people and I am happy if I can give them a serene sunset.»

«You love too children...»

«Yes, and sick people...»

«And those who weep...»

«And those who are alone...»

«Oh! My Master! Don't You realise that You are fond of everybody? Of Your enemies as well?»

«I do not realise it, Simon. To love is My nature. There... the patriarch is waking up. Let us go and tell him that he will be keeping Passover with a daughter beside him, and without any more need for bread.»

They go back to the tent where the woman is waiting for them and the three of them go towards the old man who has sat up and is tying his sandals.

«What are you going to do, father?»

«I am going down to the valley. I hope to find some shelter for the night and tomorrow I will beg on the road and then down, down, in a month's time, if I am not dead, I will be in the Temple.»

«No.»

«Must I not?... Why!»

«Because God does not want it. You will not go alone. This woman will come with you. She will take you where I tell her and you will be made welcome for My sake. You will keep your Passover, but without any trouble. You have already carried your cross, father. Put it down now. All you have to do is to concentrate on prayer thanking the good Lord.»

«But why... why... I... I do not deserve so much... You... a daughter... It is more than if You gave me twenty years... And where, where are You sending me?...» The old man is weeping into his long beard.

«I am sending you to Lazarus of Theophilus. I do not know whether you know him.»

«Oh!... I come from the border of Syria and I remember Theophilus. But... Oh! Blessed Son of God, allow me to bless You!»

And Jesus, sitting on the grass, in front of the old man, does bend His head to let him impose his hands solemnly on it, thundering out in a very deep voice the old blessing: «May the Lord bless You and keep You. May the Lord let His face shine on You and be gracious to You. May the Lord uncover His face to You and bring You to peace.» *

Jesus, Simon and the woman reply together: «Amen.»

173. The Sermon of the Mount. Part Five: the Right Use of Riches and Possessions, Secrecy on the Deeds of Charity.

27th May 1945.

173.1 [1] The Sermon of the Mount continues.

The crowd is growing larger and larger as the days go by. There are men, women, old people, children, rich and poor alike. The couple, Stephen and Hermas, is always present, although not yet associated with the old disciples led by Isaac. And there is also the new couple formed yesterday: the old man and the woman. They are at the very front, near their Comforter and they look much more cheerful than yesterday. The old man, to make up for

* **old blessing**, in *Numbers 6:24-26*.

the many months or years during which he was neglected by his daughter, has laid his wrinkled hand on the knees of the woman and she is caressing it out of the inborn instinct of a morally sound woman to be maternal.

Jesus passes near them to climb up to His rustic pulpit, and while passing He caresses the head of the old man who looks at Him as if he already saw Him as God.

Peter says something to Jesus Who makes a gesture as if He wanted to say: «It does not matter.» But I do not understand what the apostle says. Peter remains near Jesus and Judas Thaddeus and Matthew join him. The other apostles are scattered among the crowd.

[2] «Peace be with you all! 173.2

Yesterday I spoke of prayer, of swearing, of fasting. Today I want to instruct you in other perfections. They are also prayer, trust, sincerity, love, religion.

The first thing I will speak to you of is the right use of riches, changed into as many treasures in Heaven by the goodwill of the faithful servant. The treasures of the earth do not last. But the treasures of Heaven are eternal. Are you fond of what is yours? Are you sorry to die because you will no longer be able to look after your property and you will have to leave it? In that case transfer them to Heaven. You may say: "What is of the earth will not enter Heaven and You have taught us that money is the filthiest thing on earth. How can we transpose them to Heaven?" No. You cannot take money, material as it is, into the Kingdom where everything is spiritual. But you can take the fruit of money.

When you give a banker your money, why do you do it? That he may make it bear interest. You do not deprive yourselves of it, not even temporarily, so that he may give you back the same amount. But out of ten talents you want him to give you back ten plus one or even more. Then you are happy and you praise the banker. Otherwise you say: "He is honest, but he is a fool". And, if instead of ten plus one, he should give you nine, saying: "I lost the rest", you would denounce him and send him to prison. What is the fruit of money? Does the banker sow your money and water it to make it grow? No. The fruit is given by a skillful handling of business, so that by means of mortgage deeds and interest loans, the money is increased by the premium rightly requested for the loan of the gold. Is it not so?

Now listen. God gives you earthly riches. To some people he grants a great deal, to some only as much as they need to live, and He says to you: "Now it is up to you. I have given them to you. Gain by these means an end as My love wishes for your own good. I have entrusted you with them, but not that you may turn them into evil. Make your wealth bear interest, for this real Fatherland, both because of the reputation I hold you in, and out of gratitude for My gifts".

173.3 [3] And here is the method to reach this end.

Do not accumulate your treasures on the earth, living for them, being cruel for them, cursed by your neighbour and by God on account of them. It is not worth it, They are never safe in this world. Thieves can always rob you. Fire can always destroy your houses. Diseases of plants and animals can exterminate herds and orchards. How many things undermine your property! Whether it is real estate and unassailable, such as houses and gold; whether its nature is liable to be damaged, such as all living things, vegetables and animals, or precious cloths, they can be ruined. Thunderbolts, fire and floods can destroy houses; thieves, blight, dry weather, rodents and insects can damage fields; catching diseases, fever, crippling, murrain can destroy cattle; moths and mice can ruin valuable pieces of cloth and precious pieces of furniture; oxidization can corrode vases, chandeliers and artistic gates; everything is subject to destruction.

But if you turn earthly welfare into supernatural good, then it becomes free from all damage by time, men and calamities. Store your treasures in Heaven, where thieves cannot break them, and where no calamities occur. Work with merciful love for *all* the miseries of the earth. You may caress your money and kiss it if you wish so, you may rejoice at the plentiful crops, at the vineyards laden with grapes, at the countless number of olives which bend the branches of the olive-trees, and at your prolific sheep with turgid udders. You may rejoice at all that, but not in a sterile or human way. Rejoice with love and admiration, with supernatural delight and foresight.

"Thank You, my God, for this money, for these crops, plants, sheep and for this business! Thank you, sheep, plants, meadows, business, which serve me so well. May you all be blessed, *because* through Your goodness, o Eternal Father, and through yours, o things of mine, I can do so much good to those who are hungry, or are naked, homeless, sick, alone... Last year I did it for ten. This year — as I have more money, although I gave away much as alms, and the crops are more plentiful and the flocks larger — I will give twice, three times as much as last year. So that everybody, also those who have no wealth of their own, may partake of my joy and bless with me the Eternal Lord". That is the prayer of a just man. A prayer, which joined to your deeds, transfers your wealth to Heaven, and not only keeps it eternally for you, but you will find it increased by the holy fruit of love.

Store your treasure in Heaven so that your heart may also be there, above and beyond the risk that not only your gold, your houses, fields and herds may suffer damage, but that your very heart may be attacked and robbed, corroded, burnt and killed by the spirit of the world. If you do that, you will have your treasure in your heart because you will have God within you until the blessed day when you will be in Him.

[4]But in order not to diminish the fruit of charity, take care to 173.4
be charitable in a supernatural spirit. What I said with regards to prayer and to fasting applies also to charity and to any other good action you may do.

Keep the good you may do free from the violating sensation of the world, keep it immune from human praise. Do not profane the scented rose of your charity and of your good deeds, as it is a true censer of perfumes agreeable to the Lord. Good is profaned by a proud spirit, by the desire to be noted when doing good and by the quest for praise. The rose of charity is then dribbled and eaten away by the big slimy snails of satisfied pride and the censer is filled with the fetid straw of the litter on which the proud man basks like a well fed animal.

Oh! Those deeds of charity accomplished to be pointed out by people! It would be better, much better, if they had not been performed at all! He who does not do them, commits a sin of harshness. He who does them, letting people know both the amount given and the name of the person to whom it was given, and begging for praise, commits a sin of pride by making the offer known, as he says: "See how much I can afford?", he sins against charity because he humbles the beneficiary by making his name known, and commits a sin of spiritual avarice as he wants to accumulate human praises... It is straw, nothing but straw. Let God and His angels praise you.

When you give alms do not have it trumpeted before you, to draw the attention of passers-by and win their praise, as the hypocrites do, who want to be praised by men and thus give alms only where they can be seen by many people. They, too, have received their reward and will not have another one from God. Do not commit the same sin and do not be so presumptuous. But when you give alms your left hand must not know what your right is doing, so secret and modest is your almsgiving and then *forget about it*. Do not linger admiring your deed, swelling with it like the toad that contemplates itself with its veiled eyes in the pond and sees also the clouds, trees and a chart near the bank reflected in the still water and when it sees that it is so small as compared to them, which are so large, it swells up with air until it bursts. Also your charity is nothing as compared to the Infinite, which is the Charity of God, and if you wanted to become like Him and make your small charity so big as to be equal to His, you would fill yourselves with the wind of pride and would end up by perishing.

Forget about it. Forget about the action itself. A light, a sweet voice will always be present with you and will make your day bright, sweet and happy. Because that light will be the smile of God, the honey will be the spiritual peace, which still comes from God, and the voice will be the voice of God, the Father Who will say to you: "Thank you". He sees the hidden evil and the concealed good and will give you a reward for them. I can...»

173.5 [5] «Master, You lie with Your own words!»

The sudden resentful remark comes from the centre of the crowd. They all turn around in the direction of the voice. There is some confusion.

Peter says: «I told You! Eh! When there is one of those over there... everything goes wrong!» Many people in the crowd hiss and grumble against the reviler.

Jesus is the only one who remains calm. He has folded His arms and is standing, tall as He is, on His rock, with the sun in front of Him, in His dark blue tunic.

The reviler, heedless of the reaction of the crowd, goes on: «You are a bad Master because You teach what You do not do and...»

«Be quiet! Go away! Shame!» shout the crowd. And again: «Go back to your Scribes! The Master is quite enough for us! Let the hypocrites go with the hypocrites! You false masters! Usurers!...» and they continue but Jesus thunders out: «Silence! Let him speak» and the crowds no longer shout but they whisper their insults glaring at him at the same time.

«Yes. You teach what You do not do. You told us that we should give alms without being seen, and yesterday in the presence of a whole crowd You said to two poor people: "Stay and I will appease your hunger".»

«I said: "Let the two poor people stay here. They will be the blessed guests who will give flavour to *our* bread". Nothing else. I did not say I wanted to satisfy their hunger. Which poor man has not at least some bread? It was My joy to extend our good friendship to them.»

«Of course! You are cunning and You can play the part of the lamb!...»

The old man stands up, turns around and raising his walking stick he shouts: «Infernal tongue who are accusing the Holy One, do you think that you know everything and that you can accuse Him of what you know? As you do not know who God is and who He is Whom you are insulting, so you do not know His deeds. Only the angels and my overjoyed heart know. Listen, men, listen everybody and see whether Jesus is the liar and the proud man as this traitor to the Temple is saying. He...»

«Be quiet, Ishmael! Be quiet for My sake! If I made you happy, please make Me happy by being silent» Jesus begs him.

«I obey You, Holy Son. But let me say only this: the blessing of an old faithful Israelite is on Him Who assisted me in the name of God and God put that blessing on my lips for me and for Sarah, my new daughter. But there will be *no* blessing on your head. I will not curse you. I will not foul, with a curse, my mouth which must say to God: "Receive me". I did not do it to her who disowned me, and I have already received a divine reward for it. But there is One who will take the place of the Innocent you are accusing and of Ishmael, the friend of God, Who assists Him.»

A chorus of shouts closes the speech of the old man who sits down again, while a man sneaks away, followed by insults. The crowds then shout to Jesus: «Go on, go on, Holy Master! We will listen only to You. Listen to us, not to those cursed birds of evil omen! They are jealous, because we love You more than we love them! But You are holy, they are wicked. Go on, speak to us. You can see that we have no other wish but to hear You. Our homes, our business? They are nothing, we left them to hear You.»

«I will speak to you. But do not be upset by what happened. Pray for those poor people. Forgive them as I do. Because if you forgive men their faults, your Father Who is in Heaven will forgive you your sins as well. But if you bear men a grudge and do not forgive them, neither will your Father forgive you your shortcomings. And everybody needs to be forgiven.

173.6 [6] I was saying to you that God will give you a reward, even if you do not ask to be rewarded for the good you have done. But do not do good to be rewarded, to have a security for tomorrow. Do not do good restricted within narrow limits by fear: "And after, shall I have enough for myself? And should I have nothing, who will help me? Shall I find anyone who will do what I did? And when I shall no longer be able to give, shall I still be loved?".

Look: I have mighty friends among rich people and I have friends amongst the poor people of the earth. And I solemnly tell you that the mighty ones are not the most loved. I go to them not for My own sake or profit. But because they can give Me much for those who have nothing. I am poor. I have nothing. I would like to have all the treasures in the world and change them into bread for those who are hungry, into homes for the homeless, into clothes for the naked and into medicines for the sick. You may say: "You can cure people". Yes, I can do that and other things. But I do not always find faith in men, and I cannot do what I would do and would like to do, if the hearts of men had faith in Me. I would like to help also those who have no faith. And as they do not ask the Son of man for miracles, I would like, as a man to man, to help them. But I have nothing. That is why I stretch out My hand to those who are rich and I ask them: "Give Me some alms, in the name of God". That is why I have high-placed friendships. Tomorrow, when I am no longer on the earth, there will still be poor people, but I shall not be there to work miracles for those who have faith, nor to give alms to lead to faith. But then My rich friends, who are in touch with Me, will have learned how to help, and My apostles, after their experience with Me, will have learned how to give alms out of love for their brothers. And the poor will always receive assistance.

Yesterday, I received from one who has nothing, more than all those who are rich have given Me. He is a friend, and as poor as I am. But he gave Me something that no money can buy, and which made Me happy, bringing back to Me so many serene hours of My childhood and youth, when every evening the hands of a Just One were laid on My head and I went to rest with his blessing as the guardian of My sleep. Yesterday this poor friend of Mine made Me king with his blessing. You thus see that none of My rich friends has given Me what he gave Me. Therefore, be not afraid. Even if you no longer have the power of money, providing you have love and holiness, you can still assist those who are poor, tired and distressed.

[7] And I therefore say to you: do not worry too much because you 173.7
are afraid of having too little. You will always have what is necessary. Do not worry too much about your future. Nobody knows how much future there is ahead of him. Do not worry about what you will eat to support yourselves in life or what clothes you will put on to keep your bodies warm. The life of your souls is by far more precious than your stomachs and your limbs, it is much more valuable than your food and your clothes, exactly as material life is more valuable than food and the body more precious than its clothes. And your Father knows. You ought to know, too. Look at the birds in the sky. They do not sow or reap or gather into barns, and yet they do not starve to death because the heavenly Father feeds them. And you men, the favourite creatures of the Father, are worth much more than they are.

Which of you, with all his talent, can add one single cubit to his height? If you cannot raise your height even by a span, how can you possibly change your future conditions, increasing your wealth, to ensure that you will live to a long and happy old age? Can you say to death: "You shall come for me when I want"? You cannot. Why, then, worry about your future? And why go to so much trouble lest you should be left without clothes? Think of the lilies growing in the fields: they do not work or spin, they do not buy any cloth from vendors, yet I assure you that not even Solomon in all his regalia was robed like one of them. Now if that is how God clothes the grass in the field, which is there today and will be thrown into the furnace tomorrow or used to feed the cattle and will thus end up in ash or dung, how much more He will see to you, His children?

Do not be of little faith. Do not worry about an uncertain future saying: "What shall I eat when I am old? What shall I drink? How will I clothe myself?". Leave such worries to the Gentiles, who do not have the lofty certainty of the divine paternity. You have it and you know that the Father is aware of your needs and loves you. Therefore trust Him. Seek first what is really necessary: faith, goodness, charity, humility, mercy, purity, justice, meekness, the three and four main virtues, and all the others as well, in order to be the friends of God, and have a right to His Kingdom. And I can assure you that all the rest will be given to you as well, without having to ask for it. There is no rich man richer than a saint or any man safer than he is. God is with the saint and the saint is with God. He does not ask anything for his body, and God supplies what is necessary. But he works for his soul, and God gives Himself to him in this world, and Paradise in the next one.

So do not go to any trouble for what is not worth your trouble. Let your imperfections grieve you, not your scanty earthly means. Do not worry about tomorrow. Tomorrow will take care of itself, and you will take care of it when you live it. Why worry today? Is life not already quite full of yesterday's sad memories and of today's troubles, that we should feel the need to add the nightmares of tomorrow's uncertainties? Leave to each day its own trouble! There will always be in life more pains than we would wish, without adding the present pains to future ones! Always say the great word of God: "Today". You are His children, created to His likeness. So say with Him: "Today".

And today I give you My blessing. May it accompany you until the beginning of a new today: of tomorrow, that is when, I will once again give My peace in the name of God.»

174. The Sermon of the Mount.
Part Six: Adultery, Divorce and Temptations.
Encounter with the Magdalene.

29th May 1945.

174.1 [1] It is a glorious morning and the air is clearer than usual. Distances seem to be shortened and remote things seem to be seen through a magnifying lens, so clear and neat are the tiniest details. The crowds are getting ready to listen to the Master. Day by day the country is becoming more beautiful in its luxurious dress at the height of the spring season, which in Palestine I think is at the end of March and beginning of April, because later it has the typical look of summer, with ripe crops and thick fully developed foliage.

The whole country is now in bloom. From the height of the mountain, which is adorned with its own flowers even in spots which would appear least suitable for blossom growth, one can see the flexuous corn undulating down in the plain, blown by the breeze making it look like sea-green waves, with a pale golden hue at the top of the ears now seeding in their bristly awns. The fruit trees, completely covered with petals stand straight above the crops undulating in the light breeze, and look like as many huge powder-puffs or balls of white, pale pink, dark pink, bright red gauze. The olive-trees by contrast, in their dress of penitent ascetics seem to be praying and their prayers are already changing into an attempted snowfall of tiny white flowers.

The top of Mount Hermon is like pink alabaster and is kissed by the sun. Two diamond threads — they look like threads from here — run down from the alabaster top twinkling in an unbelievable fashion in the sun, and disappear into the green woods; they appear once again down in the valley where they form water-courses which flow towards Lake Merom, which cannot be seen from here. They then flow out with the beautiful waters of the Jordan and later drop into the light sapphire sea of Galilee, which twinkles like chips of precious stones set in and lit up by the sun. The sails moving on the lake, calm and splendid in its frame of gardens and wonderful countryside, seem driven by the small light clouds sailing in the sea of the sky.

Nature really seems to be smiling in this early hour of a spring day.

174.2 [2] And the crowds throng incessantly. They come up from all directions: old, healthy, sick, children and young couples who wish to start their married life with the blessing of God's word. There are beggars and wealthy people who call the apostles and give them offerings for those who are poor and they are so anxious to find a concealed place in which to do it that they seem to be going to confession. Thomas has taken one of the traveling bags and calmly pours all the money into it as if it were chicken-feed, and then takes it to the rock where Jesus is speaking, and he laughs happily saying: «Rejoice, Master! You have enough for everybody today!»

Jesus smiles and says: «And we shall start at once, so that those who are sad may be happy immediately. You and your companions will select the poor and sick people and bring them here.»

That takes a comparatively short time, although they have to listen to the cases of many people and it would have taken much longer without the practical help of Thomas, who, standing on a stone to be seen by everybody, shouts in his powerful voice: «All those suffering from physical trouble go to my right hand side, over there, in the shade.» The Iscariot follows his example as he, too, is gifted with an exceptionally powerful and beautiful voice, and he shouts: «And all those who think they are entitled to alms should come here near me. And make sure you are not telling lies because the eyes of the Master can read your hearts.»

The crowds start moving about to form three groups: those who are sick, those who are poor, and those who are anxious only to hear Jesus teaching.

174.3 [3] But two people, and then three of the last group seem to be in need of something which is neither health nor money, but is more necessary than both: a woman and two men. They look at the apostles but dare not speak. The severe looking Simon Zealot passes by; also Peter passes by; he is busy speaking to a dozen little children to whom he promises some olives if they keep quiet until the end of the sermon, and a thrashing if they disturb while the Master is speaking; the elderly serious Bartholomew passes by; Matthew and Philip pass carrying a cripple who would have to struggle too much to open his way through the crowd; also the cousins of the Lord pass by helping an almost blind beggar and a very old poor woman — I wonder how old she is — who weeps telling James all her troubles; James of Zebedee passes by holding in his arms a poor girl, who is certainly ill, and whom he has taken from her mother to ensure that she does not get hurt by the crowds, while the panting mother follows him; the last to pass by are Andrew and John, whom I would call the indivisible ones, because while John, in his serene simplicity of a holy child, is willing to go with his companions, Andrew, on account of his reservedness, prefers going with his old fishing companion and fellow disciple of the Baptist. They had stayed at the junction of the two main paths, to show people to their places, but there being no more pilgrims on the stony path of the mountain, the two have come together to go to the Master with the last offerings received.

Jesus is already bending over sick people and the hosannas of the crowds punctuate each miracle.

The woman, who appears to be completely distressed, dares to pull John's tunic, while he is speaking to Andrew and she smiles.

He bends and asks her: «What do you want, woman?»

«I would like to speak to the Master...»

«Are you not well? You are not poor...»

«I am well and I am not poor. But I need Him... because there are evils without any fever and there is misery without poverty and mine... mine...» and she weeps.

«Listen, Andrew. This woman is sick in heart and would like to speak to the Master. What shall we do?»

Andrew looks at the woman and says: «It is certainly something which is painful to tell...» The woman nods assent. Andrew goes on: «Do not weep... John, try and take her behind our shed. I will take the Master there.»

And John, smiling, begs people to let him pass, while Andrew goes in the opposite direction towards Jesus.

But they are noticed by two distressed men, and one of them stops John, and the other Andrew, and shortly afterwards they are both with John and the woman behind the shed of branches which is part of the tent.

[4] Andrew reaches Jesus when the Latter is curing the cripple 174.4

who raises his crutches like two trophies, as brisk as a skilled dancer, shouting his blessing. Andrew whispers: «Master, behind our shed there are three people weeping. But it is their hearts that ache and their grief cannot be made known...»

«All right. I still have this girl and this woman. Then I will come. Go and tell them to have faith.»

Andrew goes away while Jesus is bending over the little girl who is being held once again by her mother. «What is your name?» Jesus asks her.

«Mary.»

«And what is My name?»

«Jesus» replies the child.

«And Who am I?»

«The Messiah of the Lord Who has come to bring good to bodies and souls.»

«Who told you?»

«My mother and father who hope in you for my life.»

«Live and be good.»

The child, whose spine I think was affected by a disease, because although she is about seven years old, or perhaps older, she only moved her hands and was all wrapped in thick stiff bandages from her armpits down to her hips — they can be seen because her mother has lifted her dress to show them — remains as she was for a few minutes, then begins to slide down from her mother's lap on to the ground and runs towards Jesus Who is curing the woman, whose case I do not understand.

All the sick people have been satisfied and they are the ones who shout most in the crowd applauding «the Son of David, glory of God and ours.»

174.5 [5] Jesus goes towards the shed.

Judas of Kerioth shouts: «Master! What about these?»

Jesus turns around and says: «Let them wait where they are. They will be comforted, too» and He walks fast to the back of the shed where the three people in anguish are with Andrew and John.

«The woman first. Come with Me into these hedges. Speak without any fear.»

«My Lord, my husband wants to leave me for a prostitute. I have five children and the last one is two years old... Great is my grief... and I am worried about my children... I do not know whether he will take them or leave them to me. He will certainly want the boys, at least the oldest one... And I who bore him will no longer have the joy of seeing him? And what will they think of their father and of me? They must think evil of one of us. And I would not like them to judge their father...»

«Do not weep. I am the Master of Life and of Death. Your husband *will not marry* that woman. Go in peace and continue to be good.»

«But... You will not kill him? Oh! Lord, I love him.»

Jesus smiles: «I will not kill anyone. But there is someone who will do his work. You must know that the demon is not greater than God. When you go back to your town you will find out that someone killed that evil creature and in such a way that your husband will realise what he was doing and will love you again with revived love.»

The woman kisses the hand that Jesus had laid on her head and goes away.

[6] One of the men comes: «I have a daughter, Lord. Unfortunately she went to Tiberias with some girl friends and it was as if she had taken some poison. When she came back to me she was like a mad woman. She wants to go away with a Greek man... and then... Why was she born? Her mother is heartbroken and perhaps will die of grief... I... only Your words, which I heard last winter, keep me from killing her. But, I tell You, my heart has already cursed her.» 174.6

«No. God, Who is a Father, only curses an accomplished and obstinate sin. What do you want from Me?»

«That You get her to mend her ways.»

«I do not know her and she will certainly not come to Me.»

«But You can change her heart also from far away! Do You know who sent me to You? Johanna of Chuza. She was leaving for Jerusalem when I went to her mansion to ask her whether she knew that wretched Greek. I was afraid she might not know him, because she is good, although she lives at Tiberias, but since Chuza has contacts with the Gentiles... She does not know him. But she said to me: "Go to Jesus. He called my soul back from very far away and He cured me, by that call, of my phthisis. He will cure your daughter's heart as well. I will pray and you must have faith". I have faith. You can see it. Have mercy on me, Master.»

«Your daughter this evening will weep on her mother's knees asking to be forgiven. You must be as good as her mother and forgive her. The past is dead.»

«Yes, Master. As You wish and may You be blessed.»

He turns around to go away... but retraces his steps: «Forgive me, Master... But I am so afraid. Lust is such a demon! Give me a thread of Your tunic. I will put it in my daughter's pillow. The demon will not tempt her while she is asleep.»

Jesus smiles and shakes His head... but satisfies the man saying: «That your mind may be quieter. But you must believe that when God says: "I want it" the demon goes away without any further need. So keep this as a souvenir of Mine», and He gives him a small tuft from His fringe.

174.7 [7] The third man comes: «Master, my father died. We thought he had some money. But we did not find any. That would not matter as my brothers and I are not short of bread. But I lived with my father as I am the eldest. The other two brothers are now accusing me of stealing the money and they want to sue me for theft. You can see my heart. I did not see one single coin. My father kept his money in a coffer in a metal case. When he died we opened the coffer but the case was no longer there. They say: "Last night, while we were sleeping, you took it". It is not true. Help me to restore peace and esteem among us.»

Jesus stares at him and smiles.

«Why are you smiling, Master?»

«Because your father is the guilty one, the guilt of a child who hides his toy lest someone should take it.»

«But he was not a miser. Believe me. He was charitable.»

«I know. But he was very old... It is the disease of old people... He wanted to preserve things for you, and out of too much love, he caused you to fall out with one another. But the case is buried at the foot of the cellar steps. I am telling you so that you may be aware that I know. While I am speaking to you, by pure chance. your younger brother, by striking the ground angrily, caused it to vibrate and so they discovered it and they are now embarrassed and sorry for blaming you. Go back home with a quiet mind and be good to them. Do not reproach them for their lack of esteem.»

«No, my Lord. I will not. But I am not going home, I am staying here to hear You. I will go tomorrow.»

«And if they take that money?»

«You say that we must not be greedy. I do not want to be so. It is enough for me if there is peace amongst us. On the other hand... I did not know how much money there was in the case and thus will not suffer for any information contrary to the truth. And consider that that money might have been lost... I will live now, as I lived before, should they deny me it. It is enough if they do not call me a thief.»

«You are well advanced on the way of God. Proceed and peace be with you.»

And also that man goes away happily.

[8] Jesus goes back to the crowds, towards the poor people and 174.8
gives them alms according to His own judgement. Everybody is now happy and Jesus can speak.

«Peace be with you.

I explain the ways of the Lord to you, that you may follow them. Could you follow the path that goes down on the right hand side, and at the same time follow the one on the left hand side? You could not. Because if you take one you must leave the other. Even if the two paths were close together you could not walk any length with one foot in one and one in the other. You would end up by being tired and making a mistake, even if there was a wager. But between the path of God and Satan's there is a great distance, which becomes greater and greater, just like the two paths that come out up here, but as they run down the valley they become farther and farther from each other, as one goes towards Capernaum and the other towards Ptolomais.

Such is life, it bestrides past and future, good and evil. Man is in the centre with his willpower and free will; at the ends, on one side there is God and His Heaven, on the other side Satan and his Hell. Man can choose. Nobody forces him. Do not say to Me: "Satan tempts us" as an excuse for descending towards the low path. Also God tempts with His love, which is very strong, with His words, which are most holy, with His promises, which are most alluring! Why then should you allow yourselves to be tempted by one only of the two, by the most undeserving one to be listened to? Are God's words, promises, love not sufficient to counteract Satan's poison?

Consider that that is not to your favour. When a man is physically very healthy, he is not immune from contagion, but overcomes it quite easily. Whereas if a man is already ill and consequently weak, he will almost certainly die in the event of catching a new infection, and if he survives, he is more seriously ill than previously because his blood lacks the strength to kill the contagious germs completely. The same applies to the superior part. If a man is morally and spiritually healthy and strong, you may be sure that he is not free from temptations, but evil does not strike roots in him. When I hear anyone say to Me: "I approached this man and that one, I read this book and that one, I endeavoured to persuade this person and that one to do good, but in actual fact the evil which was in their minds and in their hearts, the evil which was in the book, entered my heart", I conclude: "Which proves that you *had already created* within yourself a suitable ground for penetration. Which proves that you are a weakling lacking in moral and spiritual strength. Because we must derive some good also from our enemies. By watching their errors we must learn not to fall into the same. An intelligent man does not become the laughing stock of the first doctrine he hears. A man saturated with a doctrine cannot make room in his mind for any other. This explains the difficulties met when one endeavours to convince those, who are persuaded of other doctrines, to follow the true Doctrine. But if you admit that you change your mind like a weathercock, I can see that you are thoroughly empty, that your spiritual stronghold is full of breaches, that the dam of your mind is leaking in hundreds of places, through which good water runs out and foul water runs in and you are so stupid and listless that you are not even aware of it and you do not see it. You are a wretch".

Of the two paths, therefore, choose the good one and proceed along it resisting to the allurements of senses, of the world, of science, of the demon. Leave half faiths, compromises, pacts with two people, one opposed to the other, to the men of the world. They, too, should avoid them, if they are honest. At least you, men of God, must shun them. You cannot have them either with God or with Mammon. You must not have them with yourselves either because they would be of no value. If your actions are a mixture of good and evil, they are of no value whatsoever. The entirely good ones would be cancelled by the bad ones. The evil ones would lead you straight into the Enemy's arms. Therefore do not indulge in them. Be loyal in your service. No one can serve two masters with two different minds. He will either love one and hate the other or viceversa. You cannot be both of God and of Mammon. The spirit of God cannot be conciliated with the spirit of the world. The former ascends, the latter descends. The former sanctifies, the latter corrupts. And if you are corrupt, how can you act with purity. Senses light up in corrupt people and other lusts follow senses.

[9] You already know how Eve was corrupted and how Adam became corrupt through her. Satan kissed the woman's eyes and bewitched them, so that every aspect, so far pure, became impure for her and aroused strange curiosities. Then Satan kissed her ears and opened them to the words of a new science: his own. Eve's mind also wanted to know what was not necessary. Then Satan showed her eyes and mind, now awake to Evil, things that previously they had not seen or understood, and everything in Eve became sharp and corrupt. And the Woman went to the Man, revealed her secret and persuaded Adam to taste the new fruit, so beautiful to the eye and so strictly forbidden so far. And she kissed him and looked at him with mouth and eyes already fouled by Satan's gloomy disorder. And corruption penetrated Adam who saw, and through his eyes he craved for what was forbidden and he bit it with his helpmate and fell from such height into mud. 174.9

A corrupt person will draw another person to corruption, unless the latter is a saint in the true sense of the word.

Watch your eyes, men. Both the eyes of your bodies and the eyes of your minds. If they are corrupt, they can but corrupt all the rest. The eye is the light of the body. Your thought is the light of your heart. But if your eye is not pure — because since the organs are subject to thought, a corrupt thought will corrupt also senses — everything in you will become obscure, and a seducing haze will create impure phantasms in you. Everything is pure in him who has a pure thought which causes a pure look, and the light of God descends as a master where there is no obstruction of senses. But if out of ill will you have accustomed your eyes to disorderly visions, everything will become darkness in you. In vain you will look at the most holy things. In the darkness they will be nothing but blackness and blackness will be the deeds accomplished by you.

174.10 [10] Therefore, o children of God, defend yourselves against yourselves. Look after yourselves diligently against all temptations. There is no evil in being tempted. An athlete prepares himself for victory fighting. But it is evil to be overcome because you are not prepared and you are negligent. I know that everything serves as a temptation. I know that defence is exhausting. I know that it is tiring to have to struggle. But think of what you will gain through these things. And for one hour of pleasure, whatever kind it may be, would you like to lose an eternity of peace? What does the pleasure of the flesh, of gold, of thoughts leave you? Nothing. What do you gain by rejecting them? Everything. I am speaking to sinners, because man is a sinner. Well, tell me the truth: after satisfying your senses, your pride, your greed, have you felt fresher, happier, safer? In the hour following your satisfaction, which is always the time of meditation, have you sincerely felt that you were happy? I have never tasted the bread of sensuality. But I will reply in your stead: "No. Languor, unhappiness, uncertainty, nausea, fear, restlessness: that was the juice squeezed out of the hour spent in pleasure".

But I beg you: while I say to you: "Never do that", I also say to you: "Do not be inflexible with those who make mistakes". Remember that you are all brothers, made of one flesh and one soul. Consider that there are many reasons why one is led to sin. Be merciful towards sinners and kindly help them and take them back to God, showing them that the path they have followed is full of dangers for the flesh, the mind and the spirit. Do that and you will receive a great reward... Because the Father Who is in Heaven is merciful to good people and He knows how to give you one hundredfold to one. Now I say to you...

(And here Jesus tells me that you must copy the vision dated 12th August 1944, from line 35 to the end, that is to the departure of Mary Magdalene.)

12th August 1944.

174.11 [11] Jesus says: «Look and write. It is the Gospel of Mercy that *

I give to everybody and in particular to those women who will recognise themselves in the sinner and whom I invite to follow her in her redemption.»

Jesus is standing on a rock and is speaking to a large crowd. It is a mountainous place. A lonely hill, between two valleys. The top of the hill is shaped like a yoke, or rather, like a camel's hump, so that a few yards from the top there is a natural amphitheatre where voices resound clearly as in a well-built concert hall.

The hill is all in flower. It must be summer. The crops down in the plain are beginning to ripen and are getting ready to be cut. The glacier of a high mountain in the north is shining in the sun. Directly below, to the east, the Sea of Galilee looks like a mirror broken into numerous fragments, each of which is a sapphire lit up by the sun. Its blue-gold twinkling is dazzling and it reflects a few fluffy clouds in a very clear sky and the shadow of some swift sails. Beyond the lake of Gennesaret there is a vast extent of plain ground, which because of a light mist near the earth, caused perhaps by evaporation of dew — in fact it must be early morning as the grass on the mountain still has a few dewy diamonds glittering on its stems — looks like a continuation of the lake with an opal-like hue veined with green. Further back there is a chain of mountains, the side of which is so bizarre as to give the impression of clouds sketched on the clear sky.

Some of the people are sitting on the grass, some on large stones, some are standing. The apostolic college is not complete. I can see Peter and Andrew, John and James, and I can hear the other two being called Nathanael and Philip. Then there is one who is and is not one of the group. Perhaps he is the last one who arrived: they call him Simon. The others are not there, unless they are among the crowds and I cannot see them.

The sermon has already started. I understand that it is the Sermon of the Mount. But the Beatitudes have already been proclaimed. I would say that the sermon is drawing to an end be-

* **It is the Gospel of Mercy**: a section of visions and lessons regarding the conversion of Mary of Magdala. The were received from 12th to 14th August 1944. Following Jesus' instructions to M.V., they were placed in different points of the Work. They are in chapter 174 (here), 183, 233, 234, 377.

cause Jesus says: «Do that and you will receive a great reward. Because the Father Who is in Heaven is merciful to good people and He knows how to give you one hundredfold to one. So I say to you...»

174.12 [12]There is much excitement amongst the people who crowd around the path leading to the tableau. The people closest to Jesus turn their heads around. Everybody's attention is distracted. Jesus stops speaking and turns His eyes in the same direction as the others. He is serious and handsome in His dark blue tunic, His arms folded on His chest while the first rays of the sun rising above the eastern peak of the hill shine on His head.

«Make room, you plebeians» shouts the angry voice of a man. «Make room for the beauty who is passing...» and four dandies. smartly dressed, come forward, one of whom is certainly Roman, because he is wearing a Roman toga; they are carrying Mary of Magdala, still a great sinner, triumphantly on their hands, crossed to form a seat.

And she smiles with her beautiful mouth, throwing back her head and her golden hair, which is all plaits and curls held by precious hair-pins and a pale gold leaf strewn with pearls, which encircles the upper part of her forehead like a diadem, from which small light curls hang down to veil her splendid eyes, made larger and more seductive by a refined make-up. The diadem disappears behind her ears, under the mass of plaits at the back of her snow-white completely bare neck. And her nakedness extends much farther than her neck. Her shoulders are bare down to her shoulder-blades and her breast is even more so. Her dress is held on her shoulders by two little gold chains. It is completely sleeveless. Her body is covered, so to say, by a veil the only purpose of which is to protect her skin from sunburn. The dress is of a very light fabric and when she throws herself back, out of affection, against one or the other of her lovers, she seems to be doing so completely naked. I am under the impression that the Roman is the one she prefers because she glances and smiles at him more frequently and rests her head on his shoulder.

«The desire of the goddess has been satisfied» says the Roman. «Rome has acted as a mount for the new Venus. Over there, there is the Apollo you wanted to see. Seduce Him, therefore... But leave some crumbs of your charm to us as well.»

Mary laughs and with an agile provoking movement she jumps to the ground, showing her small feet shod in white sandals with golden buckles, as well as a good length of her leg. Then her dress covers her whole body. It is in fact a very wide one of snow-white wool as thin as a veil, held tight at the waist, very low, near her sides, by a large belt made of supple gold bosses. And she stands on the green tableland, where there is a vast amount of lilies of the valley and wild narcissi, like a flower of flesh, an impure flower, which has opened there by witchcraft.

She is more beautiful than ever. Her tiny purple lips seem a carnation opening on the whiteness of her perfect set of teeth. Her face and body would satisfy the most exacting painter or sculptor both because of her complexion and her figure. With her broad breast, her perfectly sized sides, her naturally supple slender waist, as compared with her sides and breast, she does look like a goddess, as the Roman said, a goddess sculptured in a light pinkish marble on the sides of which a fabric is draped and then hangs in the front in a mass of folds. Everything has been devised to please.

Jesus stares at her. And she defiantly resists His look while she smiles and twists lightly as the Roman tickles her, running on her bare shoulders and breast a lily picked among the grass. Mary with affected indignation, lifts her veil saying: «Have respect for my innocence» which causes the four to burst into a guffaw.

Jesus continues staring at her. As soon as the noise of the laughter fades away, Jesus carries on speaking, as if the apparition of the woman had kindled the flame of the sermon, which was losing intensity in its conclusion, and *no longer looks at her.* He looks instead at His audience who seem embarrassed and scandalised at the event.

[13] Jesus says: «I told you to be faithful to the Law, to be humble 174.13
and merciful, to love not only your brothers by the flesh but also those who are brothers because they were born, like you, of man. I told you that forgiveness is better than hostility, that compassion is better than stubbornness. But now I tell you that you must not condemn unless you are free from the fault you wish to condemn. Do not behave like the Scribes and Pharisees who are severe with everybody except themselves, who call impure what

is exterior and can only contaminate what is exterior and then they receive impurity in the very depths of their hearts.

God does not stay with the impure. Because impurity corrupts what is the property of God: souls, and in particular the souls of children who are angels spread over the earth. Woe to those who tear off their wings with the cruelty of devilish beasts and throw those flowers of Heaven into the mire, by letting them taste the flavour of material things! Woe... It would be better if they died struck by thunderbolts rather than commit such sin!

Woe to you, rich and fast living people! Because it is amongst you that the greatest impurity thrives and idleness and money are its bed and pillow! You are now sated. The food of concupiscence reaches your throats and chokes you. But you will be hungry. And your hunger will be terrible, insatiable and unappeasable forever and ever. You are now rich. How much good you could do with your wealth! Instead you do so much harm both to yourselves and to other people. But you will experience a dreadful poverty on a day that will have no end. You now laugh. You think you are triumphing. But your tears will fill the ponds of Gehenna. And they will never cease.

Where does adultery nestle? Where does the corruption of young girls hide? Who has two or three licentious beds, in addition to his own matrimonial one, on which he squanders his money and wastes the strength of a healthy body given to him by God that he may work for *his* family and not to wear himself out through filthy unions which place him below unclean beasts? You heard what was said: "You shall not commit adultery". But I tell you that he who looks at a woman lustfully, that she who wished to go with a man, has already committed adultery in his or her heart, *simply by that*. There is *no* reason which can justify fornication. *None*. Neither the abandonment nor the repudiation of a husband. Nor pity for the repudiated woman. You have one soul *only*. When it is joined to another soul by a pact of faithfulness, it must not lie. Otherwise the beautiful body for which you sin will go with you, o impure souls, into the inexhaustible fire. Mutilate your body, rather than kill it forever by damning it. Come to your moral senses, o rich men, verminous sinks of vice, so that you may not disgust Heaven...»

174.14 [14] Mary, who at the beginning listened with a face which was a dream of allurement and irony, sneering now and again, at the end of the sermon becomes livid with rage. She realises that although Jesus does not look at her, He is speaking to *her*. She becomes more and more livid and rebellious and at last can resist no longer.

She spitefully wraps herself in her veil and followed by the glances of the crowds jeering at her and by Jesus' voice which pursues her, she runs down the slope of the mountain, leaving strips of her dress on the thistles and dogrose bushes growing on the edges of the path, laughing out of anger and mockery.

I see nothing else. But Jesus says: «You will see more.»

29th May 1945.

[15] Jesus resumes: «You are indignant at what happened. For two 174.15
days our shelter, which is well above the mud, has been upset by Satan's hiss. It is therefore no longer a shelter and we will leave it. But I wish to conclude this code of the "most perfect" in this wide and bright horizon. God really appears here in the majesty of the Creator and watching His marvels we can firmly believe that He and not Satan is the Master. The Evil One could not create even a blade of grass. But God can do everything. This should comfort us. But you are all already in the sun. And that is harmful. Spread out on the slopes where there is shade and it is cool. Have your meals, if you wish so. I will speak to you again on the same subject. Many things have delayed us. But do not be sorry about it. You are with God here.»

The crowds shout: «Yes, we are. With You» and they move under the thickets spread on the eastern side so that the slope of the hill and the tree branches shelter them from the sun, which is already too warm.

In the meantime Jesus tells Peter to take the tent down.

«Are we really going away?»

«Yes, we are.»

«Because she came?...»

«Yes, but do not tell anybody, especially the Zealot. He would be upset because of Lazarus. I cannot allow the word of God to be mocked at by heathens...»

«I see, I see...»

«Well, there is another thing you must understand.»

«Which, Master?»

«That it is necessary to be silent in certain cases. Please do not forget. You are so dear, but you are also so impulsive as to burst out into biting criticism.»

«I understand... You do not want for Lazarus and Simon...»

«And for others as well.»

«Do You think there will be any today?»

«Today, tomorrow, the day after tomorrow, always. It will always be necessary to watch the rashness of My Simon of Jonah. Go now and do what I told you.»

Peter goes away calling his companions to help him.

174.16 [16] The Iscariot is pensive in a corner. Jesus calls him three times, but he does not hear. At last he turns around: «Do You want me. Master?» he asks.

«Yes, go and take your food and help your companions.»

«I am not hungry. Neither are You.»

«Neither am I, but for different reasons. Are you upset, Judas?»

«No, Master. I'm tired...»

«We are now going to the lake and then to Judaea, Judas. To your mother's, as I promised you...»

Judas cheers up. «Are You really coming only with me?»

«Of course. Love Me, Judas. I would like My love to be such in you as to preserve you from all evil.»

«Master... I am a man. I am not an angel. At times I feel tired. Is it a sin to feel the need of sleep?»

«No, providing you sleep on My chest. Look over there how happy the people are and how beautiful the scenery is from here. All Judaea must be lovely in springtime.»

«Most beautiful, Master. But spring, there, on the mountains, which are higher than here, is later. But there are beautiful flowers. The apple-orchards are magnificent. Mine, which is looked after by my mother, is one of the most beautiful ones. And when she moves about in it, with the doves following her to get some corn, believe me, it is a sight that soothes your heart.»

«I believe you. If My Mother is not too tired, I would like to take Her to see yours. They would love each other, because they are both good.»

Judas, drawn by this idea, cheers up and forgetting that «he was not hungry and he was tired» runs happily to his companions and tall as he is, he undoes the highest knots without any trouble and eats his bread and olives, as happy as a child.

Jesus looks at him pitifully and then goes towards the apostles.

17 «Here is some bread, Master. And an egg. I got that rich man 174.17
over there, the one wearing the red tunic, to give me it. I said to him: "You listen and you are hungry. He speaks and is exhausted. Give me one of your eggs. It will do Him much more good than it would do you".»

«Peter!»

«No, Lord. You are as pale as a baby sucking from an empty breast, and You are becoming as thin as a fish after the mating season. Let me see to it. I do not want to have to reproach myself. I will put it under these warm ashes of the faggots I burnt, and You will eat it. Don't You know it is... how many? most certainly weeks that we have been feeding on bread and olives and a little milk. H'm!... One could say that we are purging ourselves. And You eat less than everybody and speak for everybody. Here is the egg. Take it while it's warm, it will do You good.»

Jesus obeys and seeing that Peter is eating bread only, He asks: «And what about you? Where are your olives?»

«Sss! I need them for after. I promised them.»

«To whom?»

«To some children. But if they are not quiet until the end, I will eat the olives and give them the stones, that is slaps.»

«Very good indeed!»

«Eh! I will never do that. But if we don't say so... I got so many blows myself, and if they had given me all the ones I deserved for all my pranks, I should have had ten times as many! But they do you good. I am like this because I received them.»

They all laugh at the apostle's sincerity.

«Master, I would like to remind You that today is Friday and that these people... I do not know whether they will be able to get food in time for tomorrow or reach their homes» says Bartholomew.

«That's true. It is Friday!» several of them say.

«It does not matter. God will provide. But we will tell them.»

Jesus stands up and goes to His new place, in the middle of the crowds spread in the thickets. «First of all I wish to remind you that today is Friday. I say that those who are afraid they cannot reach their homes in time and are not in a position to believe that God will provide food for His children tomorrow, should go away at once, so that they will not be still on the road at sunset.»

Of all the crowd there, about fifty people get up. All the others stay where they are.

174.18 [18] Jesus smiles and begins to speak.

«You heard that in the old days it was said: "You shall not commit adultery". Those who among you have heard Me in other places know that I have spoken about that sin several times. Because, look, as far as I am concerned, it is a sin not for one person only, but for two or for three. I will make Myself clear. An adulterer sins with regards to himself, he sins with regards to his accomplice, and sins causing the betrayed wife or husband to sin, they may in fact be led to despair or to commit a crime. That with regards to the accomplished sin. But I will say more. I say: "Not only the accomplished sin, but the desire to accomplish it is already a sin". What is adultery? It is to crave for him, who is not ours, or for her, who is not ours. One begins to sin by wishing, continues by seduction, completes it by persuasion, crowns it by the deed.

How does one begin? Generally with an impure glance. And that is connected with what I said before. An impure eye sees what is concealed from a pure eye and through the eye thirst enters the throat, hunger enters the body and fever the blood. A carnal thirst, hunger, fever. Delirium begins. If the person looked at is honest, the delirious looker-on is left alone on tenterhooks, or will denigrate in revenge. If also the person looked at is dishonest, he will reply to the look and the descent into sin begins.

I therefore say to you: "If a man looks at a woman lustfully, he has already committed adultery with her because his thought has accomplished the deed of his desire". If your right eye should cause you to sin, tear it out and throw it away. It is better for you to be without one eye than to be thrown into the infernal darkness forever. And if your right hand should cause you to sin, cut it off and throw it away, for it will do you less harm to lose one part, than you to have your whole body sent to hell. It is true that

* it is stated that deformed people cannot serve God in the Temple. But after this life, the deformed by birth who are holy and those who are deformed out of virtue, will become more beautiful than angels and will serve God, loving Him in the happiness of Heaven.

19 It has also been said to you: "Anyone who divorces his wife, must give her a writ of dismissal". But that is to be condemned. for it does not come from God. God said to Adam: "This is the helpmate I made for you. Be fruitful, multiply, fill the earth and conquer it". And Adam, full of superior intelligence, because Sin had not yet dimmed his reason made perfect by God, exclaimed: "This at last is bone from my bones, and flesh from my flesh. This is to be called woman, that is: another I, because this was taken from man. This is why a man leaves his father and mother and joins himself to his wife and the two become one body". And in an increased splendour of light the Eternal Light approved smiling Adam's word, which became the first *indelible* law. Now, if owing to the ever increasing hardness of man, the human lawgiver had to give a new law; if owing to the ever increasing inconstancy of man. the lawgiver had to put a restraint and say: "If you have dismissed her you cannot take her back", that does not cancel the first genuine law, passed in the Earthly Paradise and approved by God. 174.19

I say to you: "Whoever divorces his wife, except for the case of fornication, exposes her to adultery". Because what will the divorced woman do in ninety per cent of situations? She will get married again. With what consequences? Oh! How much there is to be said about that! Do you not know that you can cause involuntary incests by such system? How many tears are shed because of lust. Yes: lust. There is no other name for it. Be frank. Everything can be overcome when the spirit is righteous. But everything is an excuse to satisfy sensuality when the spirit is lustful. Woman's frigidity, dullness, inability for housework, shrewish tongue, love for luxury, everything can be overcome, also diseases and irascibility, if one loves holily. But as after some time one does not love as on the first day, what is more than possible

---

* **it is stated**: *Leviticus 21:16-23*.

is considered impossible and a poor woman is thrown onto the road and to perdition.

He who rejects her commits adultery. He who marries her after divorce, commits adultery.

Death only dissolves a marriage. Remember that. And if your choice is an unhappy one bear the consequences as a cross, being both of you unhappy but holy, without making also the children unhappy, as they are innocent and suffer more because of such unfortunate situations. The love for your children should cause you to ponder one hundred times, also in the case of death of your partner. Oh! I wish you could be satisfied with what you already have had and to which God said: "Enough!" I wish you, widows and widowers, realised that death is not an attenuation but an elevation to the perfections of parents! To be a mother instead of a dead mother. To be a father instead of a deceased father. To be two souls in one and receive the love for the children from the cold lips of the dying partner and say: "Go in peace, without worrying for those who were born of you. I will continue to love them, on my own and on your behalf, I will love them twice and will be their father and mother and they will not suffer the unhappiness of orphans, neither will they feel the inborn jealousy that the children of a remarried consort experience with regards to him or her who takes the sacred place of mother or father called by God to a new abode".

174.20 [20] My children, My sermon is drawing to its end, as the day is nearing its end while the sun is setting in the west. I want you to remember the words of this meeting on the mountain. Engrave them in your hearts. Read them over and over again and very often. Let them be your everlasting guidance. And above all be good to those who are weak. Do not judge that you may not be judged. Remember that the moment might come when God could remind you: "That is how you judged. So you knew that that was bad. You therefore committed a sin, knowing what you were doing. You must now pay for it".

Charity is an absolution. Be charitable to everybody and in everything. If God gives you much assistance to keep you good, do not be proud of it. But endeavour to climb the full length of the ladder of perfection and give a hand to those who are tired or unaware and to those who are easily disappointed. Why do you observe the splinter in your brother's eye so diligently if first you do not go to the trouble of taking the plank out of your own eye? How dare you say to your brother: "Let me take the splinter out of your eye" while the plank in your eye is blinding you? Son, do not be a hypocrite. Take the plank out of your own eye first and then you will be able to take the splinter out of your brother's eye, without ruining him.

As you avoid being uncharitable, avoid also being imprudent. I said to you: "Give a hand to those who are tired or unaware and to those who are easily disappointed". But if it is charity to teach the ignorant, to encourage the tired, to give new wings to those whose old ones are broken, it is imprudence to reveal the eternal truths to those affected by satanism, who take possession of them to pretend they are prophets, to insinuate themselves among simple people, to corrupt, lead astray and sacrilegiously foul the things of God. Absolute respect, to be able to speak, to be silent, to ponder to act, are the virtues of the true disciple in order to make proselytes and serve God. You are gifted with the faculty of reason and, if you are just, God will grant you all the light to make a better use of your reason. You must consider that the eternal truths are like pearls, and no one has ever seen pearls thrown in front of pigs, who prefer acorns and rank broth to precious pearls, which they could crush under their feet and then, furious at being mocked at, they would turn against you to tear you to pieces. Do not give dogs what is holy. That is for the present and the future.

[21] I have told you much, My children. Listen to My words; he 174.21
who listens to them and puts them into practice, can be compared to a thoughtful man, who wishing to build a house, choses a rocky place. He certainly worked hard to lay the foundations. He had to work with pick and stone chisel, he got callous hands and broke his back. But he was able to put lime in the fissures of the rock and lay bricks one close to the other, like the wall of a fortress, and the house was as solid as a mountain. The house was exposed to the inclemency of the weather and to downpours, the rain caused the rivers to overflow their banks, the winds whistled, the waves beat it, but the house resisted everything. Such is he who has a sound faith. Instead he who listens superficially and does not strive to engrave My words in his heart, because he

is aware that to do so he would have to work hard, suffer and extirpate too many things, is like a man who out of indolence and foolishness builds his house on sand. As soon as the inclement weather comes, the house quickly built, quickly collapses and the forlorn fool contemplates the rubble of the house and the ruin of his capital. And in that case the ruin can be repaired with expenses and work. But if the edifice of the spirit crashes, because it was badly built, there is no way to rebuild it. One cannot build in future life. Woe to those who present themselves there with rubble!

174.22 [22] I have finished. I am now going down towards the lake and bless you in the name of the One and Triune God. May peace be with you.»

But the crowds shout: «We are coming with You. Let us come. No one has words like Yours!» And they begin to follow Jesus Who goes down on the opposite side from which He came up and which is in the direction of Capernaum.

The descent is steeper but faster and they soon reach the foot of the mountain on a green flowery plain.

(Jesus says: «Enough for today. Tomorrow... »)

175. The Leper Cured at the Foot of the Mountain. The Generosity of the Scribe John.

30th May 1945 (40 years ago I was confirmed by the Cardinal Andrea Ferrari).

175.1 [1] Amongst the many flowers which perfume the earth and delight our eyes, I see the horrible spectre of a revolting, corroded leper, completely covered with sores.

The crowds shout with fear and rush back to the lower slopes of the mountain. Some of them gather stones to throw at the rash man.

But Jesus turns around with His arms fully stretched out and shouts: «Peace! Stay where you are: be not afraid. Put the stones down. Have mercy on a poor brother. He is a son of God, too.»

The crowds obey, overwhelmed by the power of the Master, Who moves forward through the tall grass in bloom to a few steps from the leper, who, as far as he is concerned, has understood that Jesus is protecting him, and has come nearer.

When he reaches Jesus, he prostrates himself, and the blooming grass wraps him like cool scented water. The flowers undulate and gather together, forming a veil over the miserable man concealed amongst them. Only the mournful voice that can be heard reminds people of the wretched creature lying there. It says: «Lord, if You want, You can cure me. Have mercy on me too!»

Jesus replies: «Raise your head and look at Me. A man who believes in Heaven must be able to look at it. And you do believe, because you are asking for a grace.»

The grass is shaken and opens out once again. Like the head of a shipwrecked person emerging from the sea, the head of the leper appears, stripped of hair and beard. His head is a skull not yet entirely deprived of all flesh.

And yet Jesus does not disdain touching that forehead with the tips of His fingers, where there are no sores on the skin. But the skin on that spot is ashen-grey, scaly, and lies between two putrid erosions, one of which has destroyed his scalp, and the other has opened a hole where his right eye was, so that I could not say whether the ball of his eye is still in the huge socket, which, between his temple and his nose, lays bare his cheek-bone and his nasal cartilage, full of corruption. And Jesus, holding the fingertips of His lovely hand there, says: «I want it. Be cleansed.»

And as if the man were not eaten away and covered with sores, but only covered with dirt on which cleansing waters were poured, the leprosy disappears at once. First the wounds heal; then his skin becomes clear, his right eye appears between fresh eyelids, his lips close around his yellowish teeth. Only his hair and beard are missing, that is, there are only scanty tufts of hair where previously there was only a tiny piece of wholesome skin.

The crowds shout in amazement. And their joyful shouts tell the man that he is cured. He lifts his hands, so far concealed by the grass, he touches his eye, where the huge hole was; he touches his head, where the large sore showed the skull and feels his fresh skin. He stands up, looks at his chest, his hips... He is all wholesome and clean... He collapses once again on the flowery meadow weeping out of joy.

«Do not weep. Stand up and listen to Me. Go back to life according to the rite and do not tell anybody until you have accomplished it. Show yourself to the priest as soon as possible, make the offering prescribed by Moses as evidence of your miraculous cure.»

«It's for You that I should witness, my Lord!»

«You will witness for Me by loving My doctrine! Go.»

175.2 [2] The crowd has come close once again and they congratulate the man miraculously healed, although from due distance. There are some people who feel they ought to give him some provisions for his journey and throw some coins to him. Others throw bread and foodstuffs, and a man, seeing that the leper's clothes are nothing but torn rags, through which his entire body is visible, takes his mantle off, ties it in a knot, as if it were a large handkerchief, and throws it to the leper who can thus cover himself decently. Another man, as charity is contagious when it is in common, cannot resist his desire to supply him with sandals, takes off his own and throws them to the leper.

«And what about you?» asks Jesus Who saw the gesture.

«Oh! I live nearby. I can walk barefooted. He has to go a long way.»

«May God bless you and all those who have helped our brother Man: you will pray for them.»

«Yes, I will, I will pray for them and for You; that the world may have faith in You.»

«Goodbye. Go in peace.»

The man walks away a few yards, then turns around and shouts: «Can I tell the priest that You have cured me?»

«It is not necessary. Just say: "The Lord had mercy on me". It is the whole truth and nothing else is required.»

175.3 [3] The people throng around the Master, forming a circle which does not want to open at any cost. But the sun has set and the Sabbath rest begins. The villages are far away. But the people do not pine for their villages, their food or anything else. But the apostles are worried about it and they tell Jesus. Also the elder disciples are worried. There are women and children, and while the night is mild and the grass of the meadow is soft, the stars are not bread. Neither do stones become food.

Jesus is the only one who does not trouble. The people in the meantime eat the remains of their food without any worry and Jesus points it out to His apostles: «I solemnly tell you that these people are worth more than you are! Look how thoughtlessly they are finishing everything. I said to them: "Those who cannot believe that God will provide food for His children tomorrow, may go away", and they stayed. God will not belie His Messiah and will not disappoint those who hope in Him.»

The apostles shrug their shoulders and do not show concern for anything else.

It is nightfall after a placid, beautiful red sunset and the silence of the country spreads over everything after the last choir of birds. There is a light whispering of the wind and then the first mute flight of a night bird, the first star appears and a frog croaks.

The children are already asleep. The adults are talking among themselves and now and again someone goes to the Master asking for clarification of some point or other. [4]So no one is sur- 175.4
prised when a person, imposing by look, garments and age, is seen coming from a path between two corn fields. Some men are following him. Everybody turns around to look at him and they point him out to one another whispering. The whispering spreads from one group to another, it revives and fades away. The groups that are farther away come near drawn by curiosity.

The noble looking man reaches Jesus, Who is sitting at the foot of a tree listening to some men, and bows down before Him. Jesus stands up at once and responds with equal respect to the greeting. The people present are watching attentively.

«I was up on the mountain and perhaps You thought that I did not have faith as I went away for fear of having to fast. But I went away for another reason. I wanted to be a brother among brothers, the eldest brother. I would like to speak to You aside. Can You listen to me? Although a scribe, I am not Your enemy.»

«Let us move away a little...» and they go into the corn field.

«I wanted to provide some food for the pilgrims and I came down to tell the baker to bake bread for a large crowd. You can see that I am at a legal distance, because these fields belong to me, and it is lawful to walk from here to the top on a Sabbath. It was my intention to come up tomorrow with my servants. But I found out that You are here with the crowd. I beg You to allow me to provide for the Sabbath. Otherwise I would be very sorry that I had to forego Your words for nothing.»

«For nothing, no, never, because the Father would have compensated you with His light. But I thank you and will not disappoint you. I only wish to point out that the crowd is very large.»

«I asked them to heat all the ovens, also the ones used to dry foodstuffs and I will succeed in having bread for everybody.»

«I did not mean that. I was referring to the quantity of bread...»

«That does not trouble me. Last year I had a good crop of corn. You have seen what the ears of corn are like this year. Let me do it. It will be the greatest protection for my fields. After all, Master... You gave me such bread today... You really are the Bread of the spirit!...»

«Let it be done as you wish. Let us go and tell the pilgrims.»

«No. You said so.»

«Are you a scribe?»

«Yes, I am.»

«May the Lord take you where your heart deserves.»

«I understand what You mean but do not say, You mean: to the Truth. Because great are our errors... and our ill-will.»

«Who are you?»

«A son of God. Pray the Father for me. Goodbye.»

«Peace be with you.»

175.5 [5] Jesus goes slowly back to His apostles while the man goes away with his servants.

«Who was he? What did he want? Did he say something unpleasant to You? Has he sick people?» Jesus is flooded with questions.

«I do not know who he is. Or rather, I know that he is good-hearted and that...»

«He is John, the scribe» says one of the crowd.

«Well, I know now, because you said so. He only wanted to be the servant of God with His children. Pray for him because tomorrow we shall all have food, thanks to his goodness.»

«He is really a just man» says one.

«Yes, indeed. I do not know how he can be the friend of others» remarks another one.

«He is swathed in scruples and rules like a baby, but he is not a bad man» concludes a third one.

«Do these fields belong to him?» ask many who are not from this part of the country.

«Yes, they do. I think that the leper was one of his servants or peasants. But he allowed him to stay around here and I think that he also fed him.»

The comments continue but Jesus does not pay attention to them. He calls the Twelve near Him and asks them: «And what should I say now with regards to your incredulity? Did the Father not put bread for all of us into the hands of one who, by caste, is an enemy of Mine? Oh! men of little faith!... Go into the soft hay and sleep. I am going to pray the Father that He may open your hearts and to thank Him for His kindness. Peace be with you.»

And He goes to the lower slopes of the mountain. He sits down and collects His thoughts in prayer. When He raises His eyes He sees the myriad of stars crowding the sky, when He lowers them. He sees the crowd of people sleeping on the meadows. Nothing else. But such is the joy in His heart that His face seems to become transfigured by a bright light...

176. At the Foot of the Mountain, the Last Sermon During the Sabbath Rest. 'Those Who Do the Will of My Father Will Enter the Kingdom of Heaven'.

1st June 1945.

[1] Jesus has delayed somewhat up on the mountain during the night, so that at dawn He can be seen standing on the edge of an escarpment. 176.1

Peter, who sees Him, points Him out to his companions and they go up towards Him. «Master, why did You not come with us?» many of them ask.

«I needed to pray.»

«But You also need to rest very badly.»

«My friends, during the night a voice came from Heaven asking for prayers for the good and the wicked and also for Myself.»

«Why? Do You need it?»

«As much as anybody. My strength is nourished with prayer

and My joy with doing what My Father wants. My Father told Me the names of two people and a sorrow for Myself. The three things He mentioned need prayer so much.» Jesus is very sad and He looks at His apostles with eyes which seem to be begging or asking for something. His eyes rest on one, then on another and at last on Judas Iscariot and Jesus stares at him.

The apostle notices it and asks: «Why do You look at me like that?»

«I was not looking at you. My eyes were contemplating something else...»

«That is?.»

«The nature of a disciple. All the good and all the evil that a disciple can do and give to his Master. I was thinking of the disciples of the Prophets and of John. And I was thinking of My own. And I was praying for John, for the disciples and for Myself...»

«You are sad and tired this morning, Master. Tell those who love You what Your trouble is» begs James of Zebedee.

«Yes, tell us, and if there is anything we can do to relieve Your grief, we will do it» says His cousin Judas.

Peter speaks to Bartholomew and Philip, but I do not understand what they say.

Jesus replies: «Be good, endeavour to be good and faithful. That is the only relief. There is no other one, Peter. Have you understood? Forget your suspicion. Love Me and love one another, do not allow those who hate Me to seduce you, above all love the will of God.»

«Eh! If everything is within its control, also our errors are within it» exclaims Thomas in a philosophical tone.

176.2 [2] «Do you think so? But it is not so. But many people have woken up and are looking here. Let us go down and sanctify this holy day with the word of God.»

They go down while the people who wake up are more and more numerous. The children, as merry as little sparrows, are already prattling, running and jumping in the meadows, getting wet with dew, so that a few smacks begin to fly with consequent tears. Then the children run towards Jesus Who caresses them and begins to smile once again as if He reflected their innocent cheerfulness. A little girl wants to put a little bunch of flowers on His belt, flowers she picked in the meadow «because His tunic is more beautiful like that» she says and Jesus lets her do it, although the apostles grumble. But Jesus says: «You ought to be happy that they love Me! The dew removes the dust from flowers. The love of children removes all sadness from My heart.»

Jesus coming from the mountain arrives in the midst of the pilgrims at the same time as John, the scribe, who is coming from his house with many servants carrying baskets of bread, olives, cheese and a little lamb or little kid, whatever it may be, roasted for the Master. Everything is laid at His feet and He sees to the distribution giving everybody some bread, a slice of cheese and a handful of olives. But He gives a piece of the roasted lamb with bread to a mother who is still holding at her breast a plump baby who laughs showing his milk teeth, and He does likewise with two or three more people who He thinks need special attention.

«But it's for You, Master» says the scribe.

«I will have some, do not worry. But see... if I know that many take part in your goodness, it will taste better to Me.»

The distribution is over and the people nibble at their bread. leaving some for later. Jesus drinks some milk which the scribe wishes to pour for Him into a precious cup from a little flask held by a servant and which looks like a little pitcher.

«But You must satisfy me and give me the joy of hearing You» says John, the scribe, who is greeted by Hermas with equal respect and with greater respect by Stephen.

«I will not deny you that satisfaction. Come over here» and Jesus leans against the mountain and begins to speak.

3 «God's will has held us in this place because had we gone any 176.3
further, after the distance we had walked, we would have infringed the precepts and caused scandal. And may that never happen until the New Pact is written. It is right to sanctify feast days and praise the Lord in places of prayer. But the whole creation can be a place of prayer if man can make it thus through his elevation to the Father. Noah's Ark adrift on the water was a place of prayer and likewise the belly of Jonah's whale. Places of prayer were the house of the Pharaoh when Joseph lived in it, and the tent of Holofernes for the chaste Judith. And was not the corrupt place where the prophet Daniel lived as a slave, so sacred to the Lord, because of the holiness of His servant who so sanc-

tified the place as to deserve the high prophecies of Christ and * of the Antichrist, which are a key to present and future times? All the more reason this place is holy as with its hues and scents, with its pure air and rich crops, with its dewy pearls it speaks to us of God, the Father and Creator and says: "I believe. And you ought to believe because we bear witness to God". Let it therefore be our synagogue for this Sabbath and let us read the eternal pages on corollas and ears, with the sun as our lamp.

I mentioned Daniel. I said to you: "Let this place be our synagogue". That reminds us of the joyful "bless the Lord" of the three holy young men in the flames of the furnace: Heavens and waters, dew and frost, ice and snow, fire and colours, light and darkness, lightning and clouds, mountains and hills, all germinated things, birds, fish and animals, praise and bless the Lord with humble holy-hearted men. We can pray and deserve Heaven everywhere. We deserve it when we do the Father's will.

176.4 [4] At daybreak they pointed out to Me that if everything is controlled by the will of God, also the errors of men are wanted by that will. That is an error and a widespread one. Can a father ever wish his son to be blameworthy? No, he cannot. And yet we see that in some families some sons become blameworthy, although they have a just father who points out to them the good to be done and the evil to be avoided. And no righteous person will accuse a father of urging his sons to do evil things.

God is the Father, men are the sons. God points out the good and says: "Behold, I put you in this situation for your own good". Also when the Evil One and the men who serve him bring misfortunes to men, God says: "Behold, this is how you must behave in this painful hour; by doing so, this misfortune will serve for an eternal good". He advises you, but does not force you. So if a man, knowing what the will of God is, prefers to do the very opposite, can we say that this very opposite is the will of God? We cannot.

Love God's will. Love it more than your own and follow it against the enticements and power of the world, of the flesh, of the demon. Also those things have a will. But I solemnly tell you that he who submits to such wills is most unhappy.

---

* **prophecies**, in *Daniel 7:12.*

You call Me Messiah and Lord. You say you love Me and you praise Me. You follow Me and that seems love. But I solemnly tell you that not everyone amongst you will enter the Kingdom of Heaven with Me. Also amongst My earliest and latest disciples there are some who will not enter the Kingdom, because many will do their own will or the will of the flesh, of the world, of the demon, but not My Father's. Not those who say to Me: "Lord! Lord!" will enter the Kingdom of Heaven, but those who do the will of My Father, They will be the only ones to enter the Kingdom of God.

[5]The day will come when I, Who am now speaking to you, after 176.5
being the Shepherd, will be the Judge. Do not let the present appearance deceive you. Now My shepherd's staff gathers together all the scattered souls and kindly invites you to come to the pastures of Truth. Later the staff will be replaced by the sceptre of the Judge King and My power will be quite different. It will not be with kindness but with implacable justice that I will separate the sheep fed with Truth from those which mixed Truth and Error or fed only on error. I will do that a first time and then once again. And woe betide those who between the first and the second appearance before the Judge will not have purged themselves because they will not be able to purge themselves of their poisons. The third category will not purge itself. No pain could purge it. They wanted nothing but Error, so let them be in Error.

And yet among them there will be someone moaning: "What, Lord! Did we not prophesy in Your name, and in Your name did we not cast out demons and work many miracles?". And then I will say very clearly to them: "Yes, you dared to clothe yourselves with My name that you might appear what you are not. You wanted your satanism to be considered as living with Jesus. But you are accused by the fruit of your deeds. Where are the souls you saved? When were your prophecies fulfilled? What was the result of your exorcisms? Who was the accomplice of your deviations? Oh! My Enemy is really powerful! But not more than I am. He helped you only to plunder more souls, and thanks to you, the circle of those swept away by heresy has widened. Yes, you have worked wonders, which apparently looked even greater than those of the true servants of God, who are not historians who astonish crowds, but are so humble and obedient as to amaze angels. My true servants, through their sacrifices do not create phantasms, but wipe them out of hearts; they do not impose themselves on men, but show God to the souls of men. They do nothing but the will of the Father and lead others to do it, like a wave that pushes the wave preceding it and draws the one following it, without putting themselves on a throne and saying: 'Look'. My true servants do what I tell them, without thinking of anything else, and their deeds bear the sign of My unmistakable peace, kindness and order. I can therefore say to you: they are My servants, but I do not know you. Go away from me all of you, workers of iniquity".

That is what I will say. And it will be a dreadful word. Take care you do not deserve it and proceed along the safe, although painful way of obedience, towards the glory of the Kingdom of Heaven.

176.6 [6] Enjoy your Sabbath rest praising God with your wholeselves, Peace be with you.»

And Jesus blesses the crowds before they scatter seeking shade, one group speaking to another, commenting on the words they have just heard.

Jesus is left with His apostles and John, the scribe, who does not speak but is absorbed in deep meditation, watching every gesture of Jesus.

And the cycle of the Mount is over.

177. At Capernaum, the Healing of the Centurion's Servant.

2nd June 1945.

177.1 [1] Jesus enters Capernaum coming from the country. Only the Twelve are with Him, or rather, only eleven apostles, as John is not there. The usual greetings of the crowd form a vast range of expressions, from the entirely simple ones of children, to the rather shy ones of women, to the enraptured ones of people cured miraculously, and those which are either curious or ironical. There are enough to satisfy all tastes. And Jesus replies to everybody according to how He is greeted: caressing the little ones, blessing the women, smiling at those cured miraculously, and with deep respect for the others.

But this time the series is completed by the greeting of a centurion of the town, I think. He greets Him: «Hail, Master!» to which Jesus replies: «May God come to you.»

While the crowd draws close to see the outcome of the meeting, the centurion continues: «I have been waiting for You for several days. You do not recognise me as one of those who were listening to You on the Mount. I was wearing plain clothes. Are You not asking me why I went there?»

«No, I am not, but what do you want from Me?»

«I have instructions to follow those who hold meetings, because too often Rome has had to regret having granted permission for apparently honest meetings. But seeing and listening to
You, I thought of You as a... as a... [2]I have a servant who is ill, 177.2
Lord. He is lying in my house, in his bed, paralyzed by a disease of the bones and he suffers dreadfully. Our doctors cannot cure him. Your doctors refuse to come. I invited them to come because it is a disease caused by the corrupt air of this area and they know how to cure it with the herbs of the feversome soil of the shore where the water stagnates before being absorbed by the sand of the sea. I am very sorry because he is a faithful servant.»

«I will come and cure him.»

«No, my Lord. I am not asking You to go to all that trouble. I am a heathen, filth, as far as you are concerned. If the Jewish doctors are afraid of becoming contaminated by coming to my house, all the more reason it would contaminate You, Who are divine. I am not worthy that You should enter under my roof, but if You say only one word here, my servant will be cured because You rule over everything. Now if I, who am subject to my authorities, the first being Caesar, for whom I must act, think and behave as I am told, can in turn order soldiers under me, and if I say to one: "Go" to another: "Come" and to a servant: "Do that", the first one will go where I send him, the other will come because I call him, and the third will do what I tell him, You, as You are Who You are, will be immediately obeyed by the disease, which will vanish.»

«But the disease is not a man...» objects Jesus.

«Neither are You a man, You are the Man. You can therefore give orders to elements and fevers, because everything is subject to Your power.»

177.3 [3] Some elders of Capernaum take Jesus aside and say to Him: «He is a Roman, but listen to him because he is an honest man who respects and helps us. It was he who built our synagogue and he has given strict instructions to his soldiers not to gibe at us on Sabbaths. Grant him, therefore, the grace, for the sake of Your town so that he may not be disappointed and irritated, and his fondness for us may not turn into hatred.»

And Jesus, after listening to them, turns around smiling at the centurion and says: «Go ahead and I will come after you.»

But the centurion says once again: «No, my Lord, I have told You: it would be a great honour if You entered under my roof, but I do not deserve so much; say only one word and my servant will be cured.»

«Let it be so. Go and have faith. This very moment the fever is leaving him and life is flowing back into his limbs. Endeavour to get Life to come also to your soul. Go.»

The centurion salutes, then bows and goes away.

177.4 [4] Jesus watches him go away, then turns to the people present and says: «I solemnly tell you that I did not find so much faith in Israel. Oh! It is quite true! "The people that walked in darkness saw a great light; on those who live in a land of deep shadow a light has shone", and also "The Messiah will hoist His flag over the nations and gather them together". Oh! My Kingdom! They will really flow to you in immense numbers! More numerous than all the camels and dromedaries of Madian and Ephah, than those who bring the gold and incense of Sheba, more numerous than all the flocks of Kedar and the rams of Nebaioth, will be those who come to you and My heart will exult with joy seeing all the peoples of the sea and the wealth of the nations coming to Me. The islands are waiting for Me to adore Me, and the children of foreigners will build the walls of My Church, the gates of which will lie open continually to receive the kings and the wealth of the nations and sanctify them in Me. What Isaiah saw, will be accomplished! I tell you that many will come from the east and the west and will sit with Abraham, Isaac and Jacob in the Kingdom of Heaven, whereas the children of the Kingdom

* **It is quite true**; what is said in *Isaiah 9:1; 11:12; 60:6-11.*

will be thrown out into the dark, where there will be weeping and grinding of teeth.»

«You therefore foretell that the gentiles will be equal to the children of Abraham?»

«Not equal, but *greater*. You can only regret that it is due to your fault. Not I, but the Prophets say so, and the signs already confirm it. [5]Now some of you should go to the house of the cen- 177.5
turion and ascertain that his servant is cured as the faith of the Roman deserved. Come. Perhaps in the house there are some sick people waiting for Me.»

Jesus with the apostles and a few more people turns His steps towards the usual house where He stays when in Capernaum, while most of the people, driven by curiosity, rush towards the centurion's house making a great noise.

178. Three Different Men Who Wish to Follow Jesus.

3rd June 1945.

[...].

[1]I see Jesus heading towards the lake with eleven apostles, 178.1
as John is still absent. Many people press around Him: among them there are many who were on the Mount, mainly men, who have reached Him at Capernaum to hear His words once again. They would like to detain Him. But He says: «I belong to everybody. And there are many who are entitled to have Me. I will come back. You will join Me. But let Me go now.» He has difficulty in walking through the crowd who throng the little narrow street. The apostles push with their shoulders to make room for Him. But it is like pushing a spongy substance that immediately springs back again. They get angry, too, but to no avail.

[2]They are already in sight of the lake, after a fierce struggle, 178.2
when a middle-aged refined looking man goes near the Master and touches His shoulder to attract His attention.

Jesus turns around and stops, asking: «What do you want?»

«I am a scribe. But our precepts can in no way be compared to Your word and I am fascinated by it. Master, I do not want to leave I will follow You wherever You go. Which way are You going?»

«The way to Heaven.»

«I do not mean that. I am asking You where are You going now. In which houses will You stop after the present one, so that I may always find You?»

«Foxes have holes and the birds of the air have nests, but the Son of Man has nowhere to lay His head. The world is My home, wherever there are spirits to be taught, distress to be relieved, sinners to be redeemed.»

«Everywhere, then.»

«You are right. Can you, a doctor in Israel, do what these simple men do for My sake? This is what is required here: sacrifice, obedience, charity for everybody, a mind adaptive for everything and with everybody. Because compliance is alluring. Because he who wishes to cure must bend over all sores. Afterwards there will be the purity of Heaven. But here we are in mud and we have to pull out of the mud, on which we walk, the victims already submerged in it. We cannot lift our clothes and move to one side because the mud is deeper there. Purity must be *within us*. We must be filled with it so that nothing else can enter. Can you do all that?»

«At least let me try.»

«Try. I will pray that you may succeed.»

178.3 [3] Jesus begins to walk again and His attention is drawn by two eyes staring at Him, the eyes of a tall strong young man who has stopped to let the train of followers pass, as he seems to be going in a different direction. Jesus says to him: «Follow Me.»

The young man starts, changes colour, blinks as if he were dazzled by light, then opens his mouth to speak but cannot find an immediate reply. At last he says: «I will follow You. But my father died at Korazim and I must bury him. Let me do that and then I will come.»

«Follow Me. Leave the dead to bury their dead. You have already been attracted by Life. On the other hand, you aspired that. Do not weep over the gap Life opened around you to make you a disciple. The maiming of affection is the root of the wings which are born of a man who has become a servant of the Truth. Leave corruption to its own fate. Rise towards the Kingdon of the incorrupt. You will also find the incorruptible pearl of your father there. God calls and passes by. Tomorrow you would no longer find your heart of today or God's invitation. Come. Go and announce the Kingdom of God.»

The man is leaning against a low wall with his arms hanging by his sides: he is holding two bags, full of perfumes and bandages, his head is lowered in thought, wavering between two loves: for God and for his father.

Jesus waits and looks at him, he then gets hold of a little child clasps him to His heart saying: «Say with Me: "I bless You, o Father, and I invoke Your light for those who weep in the haze of life. I bless You, o Father, and I invoke Your strength for those who are like a child in need of support. I bless You, o Father, and I invoke Your love that it may cause men to forget everything which is not Yourself, as they can find all good in You, both here and in Heaven, although they cannot believe it".» And the child, an innocent boy about four years old, repeats in his thin voice the holy words with his hands held in prayer by the right hand of Jesus, Who holds them by their plump, wrists as if they were two flower stems.

The man makes up his mind. He hands the two bundles to a companion and comes towards Jesus, Who puts down the child after blessing him, and embraces the young man, proceeding thus with him, to comfort him and support him in his effort.

[4] Another man questions Him: «I would like to come with You, 178.4
too. But before following You I would like to take leave of my relatives, Will You allow me?»

Jesus stares at him and replies: «There are too many roots in your human being. Uproot them and if you cannot, cut them off. One must come to God's service with spiritual freedom. He who gives himself, must have no ties.»

«Flesh and blood are always flesh and blood. I will slowly reach the freedom You refer to...»

«No, you would never reach it. God is as exacting as He is infinitely generous in rewarding. If you wish to be a disciple you must embrace your cross and follow Me. Otherwise one remains a simple believer. The way of the servant of God is not strewn with petals of roses. And it is absolute in its demands. No one who has put his hand to the plough to furrow the fields of hearts and spread there the seed of God's doctrine, can look back to see what he left, what he lost and what he could have had if he had followed another common way. He who does that is not fit for the Kingdom of God. Work upon yourself. Make a man of yourself and then come. Not now.»

They reach the shore. Jesus goes on board Peter's boat and whispers a few words to him. I see Jesus smile while Peter makes a gesture expressing amazement. But He does not say anything. Also the man who did not go to bury his father in order to follow Jesus, gets into the boat.

179. The Parable of the Sower. In Korazim with the New Disciple Elias.

4th June 1945.

179.1 [1] Jesus says to me showing me the course of the Jordan, or rather, the mouth of the Jordan where it flows into Lake Tiberias, that is where the town of Bethsaida lies on the right bank of the river, with respect to those facing north: «The town nowadays no longer appears to be on the shore of the lake, but a little inland. And that puzzles scholars. The explanation is to be found in the earth that filled this part of the lake, as it was deposited there throughout twenty centuries by the river, by alluvia and landslides from the hills of Bethsaida. The town was then just at the mouth of the river and in fact the smaller boats, particularly in seasons rich in water, used to sail upstream, almost as far as Korazim; the river, however, was always used as a harbour and shelter for the boats of Bethsaida when the lake was very rough. I am not saying this for you, to whom it is of no interest, but for difficult doctors. And now go on.»

179.2 [3] The boats of the apostles, after crossing the short stretch of the lake between Capernaum and Bethsaida, land in the latter town. Other boats have followed them and many people come off them to join the people of Bethsaida who have come to greet the Master. Jesus enters Peter's house where his wife is staying once again. I suppose she has preferred to be alone rather than live with her mother who continuously grumbles about her husband.

Outside the crowds claim Jesus at the top of their voices, which disturbs Peter very much, so much so that he goes up to the roof terrace and harangues the citizens telling them that they ought to have respect and manners. He would like to enjoy the company of his Master for a little while, in peace, now that he has Him in *his* house, whereas he has neither the time nor the pleasure to offer Him some water and honey among the many things he asked his wife to offer. And he grumbles...

Jesus looks at him smiling and shakes His head saying: «You would think that you never see Me and that we have just met by chance!»

«But it is so! When we are in the world are You and I ever together? Never in your life! Between You and me there is the world with its sick people, its distressed people, its listeners, its curious people, its slanderers, its enemies, and You and I are never together. Here instead You are with me, in my house, and they ought to understand that!» He is really upset.

«But I do not see the difference, Simon. My love is the same and My word is the same. Whether I tell you privately, or I tell everybody, what difference does it make?»

[3] Peter then confesses his great grief: «The trouble is that I am 179.3
a blockhead and my mind wanders easily. When You speak in a square, on a mountain, amongst a large crowd, I understand everything, but I do not know why, I remember nothing. I told also my companions and they say that I am right. Other people, I mean the people who listen to You, understand You and remember what You say. How often have we heard someone say: "I have no longer done that because You told us", or: "I came because once I heard You say so and so I was impressed by it". We instead... hum! it's like a water course which passes by and does not stop. The river bank no longer has the water that has passed by. It is true that other water comes, a great deal of it, but it passes by, it passes by... And I am terrified at the thought that, if what You say will come true, the moment will come when You will no longer be there to play the part of the river and... and I... What will I give to those who are thirsty if I cannot save even one drop of the great lot You give me?»

Also the others support Peter's moaning, complaining that they are left with nothing of what they hear, whilst they would like to remember everything to reply to those who ask them questions.

Jesus smiles and replies: «I do not think so. People are very satisfied with you as well...»

«Certainly... of course! For all we do! Make room for You, by elbowing our way through the crowds, carrying sick people, collecting alms and saying: "Yes, that is the Master!". Wonderful, isn't it?»

«Do not defame yourself too much, Simon.»

«I am not defaming myself. I know myself.»

«*That is the most difficult wisdom*. But I wish to relieve you of your great fear. When I speak and you cannot understand and remember everything, ask Me without any fear of boring or discouraging Me. We always have some hours of privacy, when you can open your hearts to Me. I give so much to so many. And what would I not give you whom I love so much that God could not love you more? You spoke of waves that pass by and nothing is left on the bank. The day will come when you will realise that every wave has deposited a seed and that a plant has grown from every seed. You will find in front of you flowers and plants for all occasions and you will be amazed at yourself saying: "What has the Lord done to me?" because you will then be redeemed from the slavery of sin and your present virtues will have reached a great height of perfection.»

«You say so, my Lord, and I rest upon Your word.»

179.4 [4] «Now let us go to those who are waiting for us. Come. Peace to you, woman. I will be your guest this evening.»

They go out and Jesus directs His steps towards the lake to avoid being oppressed by the crowds. Peter is quick in moving the boat a few yards from the shore, so that Jesus' voice may be heard by everybody, but with a space between Him and those listening.

«Coming here from Capernaum I was thinking what I should tell you and I found an indication in the events of this morning.

You saw three men come to Me. One came spontaneously, the second because I urged him, the third came because of a sudden enthusiasm. And you also saw that I took only two of them. Why? Did I perhaps see a traitor in the third one? No, in truth. But I saw that he was unprepared. To all appearances, this one here beside Me, the one who was going to bury his father, seemed more unprepared. Instead the most unprepared was the third one. This one was so prepared, without being aware of it, that he was able to make a really heroic sacrifice.

Heroism in following God is always evidence of strong spiritual preparation. And that is the explanation of certain surprising events that take place around Me. Those who are most prepared to receive Christ, whichever their caste and education might be, come to Me with absolute promptitude of faith. Those who are less prepared examine Me as an exceptional man or they study Me with suspicion or curiosity, or they attack and defame Me accusing Me in various ways. The different ways of behaviour are proportional to the unprepared nature of spirits.

Among the chosen people it should be possible to find everywhere spirits ready to receive the Messiah in Whose expectaion Patriarchs and Prophets were consumed by anxiety, the Messiah Who at last has come, preceded and accompanied by all the prophesied signs, the Messiah, Whose spiritual personality becomes clearer and clearer through the visible miracles worked on bodies and elements, and through the invisible ones worked on consciences which are converted and on Gentiles who turn to the True God. But it is not so. The promptitude in following the Messiah is strongly hindered by the children of that people and, what is sad to be said, it is more hindered the more one climbs to its higher classes. I am not saying this to scandalise you, but to induce you to pray and meditate. Why does that happen? Why do Gentiles and sinners proceed farther on My way? Why do they accept what I say and the others do not? Because the children of Israel are anchored, or rather, they are stuck like pearl-oysters to the bank where they were born. Because they are filled, overwhelmed and obese with *their* wisdom and they cannot make room for Mine by throwing away what is superfluous to make room for what is necessary. The others do not suffer from such slavery. They are poor heathens or poor sinners, unimpeded like a boat which is adrift, they are poor people, who have no treasures of their own, but only heaps of errors or sins, of which they gladly strip themselves as soon as they understand what the Gospel is and they taste its fortifying honey, which is quite different from the nauseating mixture of their sins.

[5] Listen, and perhaps you will understand better how the same 179.5
action can bear different fruits.

A sower went out to sow. He owned many fields of various kinds. He had inherited some from his father, on which his carelessness had allowed thorny plants to proliferate. Other fields had been purchased by him: he had bought them from a neglectful man and he had left them as they were. In other fields there were many intersecting roads, as the man loved comfort and did not like to travel a long way when going from one place to another. Finally, there were some fields, the closest to his house, which he had looked after to have a pleasant sight in front of his house. They were free from stones, thorns, couch-grass and so on.

So the man took his sack of seed-corn of the best quality, and began to sow. The seed fell on the good soft soil, which had been ploughed, weeded, fertilized, in the fields near the house. It was spread in the fields with many roads and paths, which divided into small portions, and caused also the fertile soil to be covered by ugly arid dust. Some of the seed fell on the fields where the foolishness of the man had allowed the thorny plants to proliferate. The plough had turned them upside down, it looked as if they were not there, but they were, because only fire, the radical destructor of weeds, prevents them from growing again. The last seed fell on the fields which he had recently bought and had left as they were, without ploughing them and without removing all the stones, which had sunk into the ground forming a hard surface on which no plant could take root. After scattering all the seed, he went back home and said: "Very well! All I have to do is to wait for the harvest".

179.6 [6] And he was delighted because, as months went by, he saw the corn come up thick in the fields near the house and grow... oh! what a beautiful sea! and it turned gold and it sang hosannas to the sun, as one ear rubbed against another. The man said to himself: "All the fields are like these ones! Let us prepare sickles and granaries. How much bread! How much gold!" And he was delighted...

He cut the corn in the nearest fields and after that he went to the ones which he had inherited from his father and which he had left in a wild state. And he was taken aback. The corn had come up, because the fields were good and the soil cultivated by the father was rich and fertile. But its fertility had affected also the thorny plants, which had been overturned but not destroyed.

They had grown again and had formed a really thick ceiling of bramble, through which the corn had not been able to emerge, with the exception of a few ears, and it was completely suffocated.

The man said: "I neglected this place. But there was no bramble in the other fields, so it should be all right". And he went to the fields which he had purchased shortly before. His surprise and grief were greater. The thin withered corn leaves were strewn all over like dry hay. Nothing but dry hay. "How come?" moaned the man. "And yet there are no thorns here! And it was the same seed! And it had come up thick and beautiful. It can be seen by the well formed and numerous leaves. Why then did it all wither before coming into ear?" And with real regret he began to dig the ground to see whether there were any mole burrows or other pests. There were no insects or rodents. But how many stones! A stone-pit! The fields were literally paved with chips of stone and the scanty earth covering them was deceiving. Oh! if he had ploughed deep at the right time! Oh! if he had dug the ground before accepting the fields and buying them as good ones! Oh! if, after the mistake he had made in buying what he had been offered without making sure of its goodness, if at least he had improved them by working hard! It was now too late and all regret was useless.

The man stood up, and, downhearted as he was, he went to the fields where he had built many roads for his comfort... and mad with grief he tore off his clothes. There was absolutely nothing there... The dark soil of the field was covered with a thin layer of white dust... The man collapsed to the ground moaning: "But why here? There are no stones, no bramble here, because these are our fields. My grandfather, my father and I have always owned them and in many many years we made them fertile. I built the roads, have taken some of the earth away, but that could not make them so sterile..." He was still weeping when he received the answer to his grief from a swarm of birds, which flew eagerly from the paths to the field and back to the paths in search of seeds... The field. which had been turned into a network of paths, on the edges of which the corn had fallen, had attracted many birds, which first had eaten the corn on the paths and then the seeds in the field. down to the last grain.

So the same seed, sown in all the fields, had yielded one hundred to one in some, sixty, thirty, nothing in others. Listen, anyone who has ears. The seed is the Word: the same for everybody. The places where the seed fell: your hearts. Meditate the parable and understand it. Peace be with you.»

179.7 [7] He then turns towards Peter and says: «Go up the river as far as you can and stop on the other side.» And while the two boats sail a short distance up the river and then stop near the bank, Jesus sits down and asks the new disciple: «Who is left at home now?»

«My mother and the eldest brother, who has been married for five years. My sisters are in various parts of the region. My father was very good and my mother mourns his death broken-heartedly.» The young man stops all of a sudden, stifling heartfelt sobs.

Jesus grabs his hand and says: «I experienced that sorrow Myself and I saw My Mother weep. So I can understand...»

The rubbing of the boat on the pebbly river-bed causes the conversation to be interrupted to allow them to go ashore. The low hills of Bethsaida, which almost reach down to the lake, have come to an end here, instead a plain rich in crops extends from the shore, on the other side of Bethsaida, northwards.

«Are we going to Merom?» asks Peter.

«No, let us take this path among the fields.»

The lovely and well kept fields show ears of corn still tender but well formed, all of the same height; and, while lightly undulating in the cool northern breeze, they look like another small lake, the sails of which are the trees growing here and there full of whistling birds.

«These fields are not like the ones of the parable» remarks Jesus' cousin James.

«Not really! The birds have not devastated them, there are no stone, no bramble. The corn is beautiful! In a month's time it will be golden... and in two it will be ready for the sickle and the granary» says Judas of Kerioth.

«Master... I remind You of what You said in my house. You spoke so well. But I am beginning to have ideas in my head that are as confused as those ruffled clouds up there...» says Peter.

179.8 «This evening I will explain it to you. [8]Now we are in sight of Korazim.» And Jesus stares at the new disciple saying: «Much is given to those who give. And possessions do not deprive the gift of its merits. Take Me to the sepulchre of your family and to your mother's house.»

The young man kneels down kissing Jesus' hand and weeping.

«Get up. Let us go. My spirit has perceived your weeping. I want to fortify you in your heroism through My love.»

«Isaac the Elder had told me how good You were. Isaac, You know? You cured his daughter. He was my apostle. But I see that Your Kindness is much greater than I was told.»

«We shall call also on the Elder to thank him for giving Me a disciple.»

They reach Korazim and Isaac's house is the first one they find. The old man, who is on his way back home, when he sees Jesus with His apostles and the young man from Korazim among them, raises his arms, holding his walking stick in his hand, and is speechless and dumbfounded. Jesus smiles and His smile gives speech back to the old man.

«May God bless You, Master! Why so much honour to me?»

«To say "Thanks" to you.»

«But what for, my God? I have to say that word to You. Come in. Oh! I am sorry that my daughter is absent, assisting her mother-in-law. Because she got married, You know? I have received nothing but blessings after I met You! After she was cured that rich relative of ours came from far away, a widower, with the little ones needing a mother... Oh! But I have already told You all that! My head is old! Forgive me!»

«Your head is wise and forgets to be proud of the good it does for its Master. To forget the good done is wisdom. It shows humility and trust in God.»

«But I... I would not know...»

«And this disciple... have I not had him through you?»

«Oh!... But I have done nothing, You know? I only told him the truth... and I am happy that Elias is with You.» He turns towards Elias and says: «Your mother, after the first moment of astonishment, was relieved when she heard that you were with the Master. The last honours rendered to your father were really solemn. He has not been long buried.»

«And what about my brother?»

«He is quiet... you know... he was rather upset by your absence... because of the village people... He still has that mentality...»

The young man turns to Jesus: «You said so. But I would not like him to be dead... Let him become alive as I am, and at Your service.»

The others do not understand and they look at one another inquisitively, but Jesus replies: «Do not despair, but persevere.» He blesses Isaac and goes away, notwithstanding he entreats Him to stay.

179.9 [9] They stop first near the sepulchre and pray. After, through still semi-bare vineyards, they go to Elias' house.

The meeting of the two brothers is rather a cold one. The elder feels offended and wants people to notice it. The younger feels guilty from a human point of view and does not react. But the arrival of their mother, who without saying anything prostrates herself and kisses the hem of Jesus' tunic, brightens the atmosphere and their spirits. And they want to honour the Master But Jesus does not accept anything, He only says: «Let your heart be just, one towards the other, as just was he whom you are mourning. Do not give a human sense to what is super-human: death and the election to a mission. The soul of your just father was not upset seeing that this son was not present at the burial of his body, but it rested quietly on the certainty of Elias' future. Do not let worldly thoughts disturb the grace of the election. If the world was surprised at not seeing him near his father's coffin, the angels exulted seeing him beside the Messiah. Be just. And may that comfort you mother. You brought him up wisely and he has been called by Wisdom. I bless you all. Peace be with you now and always.»

They go on the road which takes them back to the river, and from there to Bethsaida. Elias did not delay even for one moment on the threshold of his father's house. After kissing his mother goodbye, he followed the Master with the simplicity of a child who follows his real father.

180. At Bethsaida in Peter's Kitchen. Explanation of the Parable of the Sower. News of the Baptist's Second Capture.

7th June 1945.

[1] We are in Peter's kitchen once again. The meal must have 180.1
been a hearty one because dishes with leavings of meat, fish, cheese dried fruit and honey cakes are being piled up on a kind of cupboard, which reminds me of our Tuscan kneading troughs. Pitchers and chalices are still on the table.

Peter's wife must have worked miracles to satisfy her husband, and she must have worked all day. Now, tired but happy, she is in her little corner listening to what her husband and the others are saying. She watches her Simon, who, as far as she is concerned, must be a great man, even if he is somewhat exacting, and when she hears him speak new words, whereas before he could only talk of boats, nets, fish and money, she begins to blink as if she were dazzled by a bright light. Peter, both because of his joy in having Jesus at his table and because of the hearty meal he has had, is in the best of spirits this evening, and the future Peter, preaching to the crowds, is disclosed.

I do not know which remark of a companion originated the clearcut reply of Peter who says: «It will happen to them what happened to the founders of the Tower of Babel. Their own pride will provoke the collapse of their theories and they will be crushed.»

Andrew objects to his brother: «But God is Mercy. He will prevent the collapse to give them time to mend their ways.»

«Do not believe that. They will crown their pride with false accusations and persecutions. Oh! I can already see it. They will persecute us to disperse us as unpleasant witnesses. And since they attack the Truth by laying snares for it, God will take revenge and they will perish.»

«Shall we have the strength to resist?» asks Thomas.

«Well… as for me, I would not have it. But I put my trust in Him» and Peter nods to the Master Who is listening and is silent, His head slightly inclined, as if He wished to hide His understanding countenance.

«I think that God will not put us to tests beyond our strength» says Matthew.

«Or He will at least increase our strength in proportion to the tests» concludes James of Alphaeus.

180.2 «He is already doing that. [2]I was rich and powerful. If God had not decided to preserve me for a purpose of His, I would have surrendered myself to despair and perished when I was persecuted and a leper. I would have acted harshly against myself... Instead a new wealth, which I had never possessed before, descended upon my desolation: the wealth of a conviction: "God exists". First... God... Yes, I believed, I was a faithful Israelite. But mine was a faith of formalism. And I thought that the reward of my faith was always inferior to my virtue. I took the liberty of debating with God because I felt that I was still something on the earth. Simon Peter is right. I, too, was building a tower of Babel by praising myself and satisfying my *ego*. When * everything collapsed around me and I was like a worm crushed by the weight of all this human futility, then I no longer debated with God, but with myself, with my stupid self and I ended up by demolishing it. And as I did so, by making room for what I think is the God immanent in our earthly beings, I gained a new strength and wealth: the certainty that I was not alone and that God was watching over man defeated by men and by evil.»

«According to you, what is God, "the God immanent in our earthly beings" as you said? What do you mean? I do not understand you and I think it is a heresy. God is the One we know through the Law and the Prophets. There is no other God» says rather sternly Judas of Kerioth.

«If John was here he would tell you better than I can. But I will tell you as best I can. God is the One we know through the Law and the Prophets. That is true. But in what do we know Him? And how?»

Judas of Alphaeus exclaims: «Little and badly. The Prophets, who described Him for us, knew Him. The idea we have is a muddled one, as we can just see through a mound of explanations piled up by sects...»

«Sects? What do you mean? We have no sects. We are the children of the Law. We all are» the angry aggressive Iscariot says.

---

* **tower of Babel**, in *Genesis 11:1-9.*

«The children *of the laws*. Not of the Law. There is a slight difference. Plural, not singular. In actual fact, we are the children of what we created, no longer of what God gave us» retorts Thaddeus.

«The laws derive from the Law» says the Iscariot.

«Also diseases originate in our bodies, but that does not mean that they are good» replies Thaddeus.

«But let me hear what this immanent God of Simon Zealot is.» The Iscariot, who cannot argue against the remark of Judas of Alphaeus, endeavours to take the discussion back to where it started.

[3] Simon Zealot says: «Our senses need a term to catch an idea. 180.3
Each of us, I am referring to us believers, believes, by the virtue of faith, in the Most High Lord and Creator, Eternal God, Who is in Heaven. But every being needs more than such bare, pure, incorporeal faith, which is fit and sufficient for the angels who see and love God spiritually, as they share with Him a spiritual nature and can see God. We have to create a "picture" of God for ourselves, which picture is made with the essential features that we ascribe to God, to give a name to His infinite absolute perfection. The more a soul concentrates, the more it succeeds in achieving an exact knowledge of God. That is what I say: the immanent God. I am not a philosopher. Perhaps I have applied the word wrongly. In short, I think that the immanent God is to feel, to *perceive* God in our spirits, to feel and perceive Him no longer as an abstract idea, but as a real presence, bestowing strength and a new peace upon us.»

«All right. But, to sum up, how did you feel Him? What is the difference between feeling by faith and feeling by immanence?» asks the Iscariot somewhat ironically.

«God is safety, boy. When you perceive Him, as Simon says, by means of that word, which I do not understand literally, but I understand its spirit — and believe me, the trouble is that we understand only literally and we do not understand the spirit of God's words — it means that you are able to grasp the idea of the terrible majesty, but also of the most sweet paternity of God. It means that, should all the world judge and condemn you unjustly, you would feel that One only, He, the Eternal One, Who is your Father, does not judge you, but absolves and comforts you.

It means that if all the world should hate you, you would feel over you a love greater than any this world can offer. It means that if you were isolated in jail or in a desert you would always hear One speak to you and say: "Be holy, that you may be like your Father". It means that for the true love for this Father and God, Whom at last you perceive as such, you accept, work, take and leave without any human consideration, as you are concerned only to return love for love and to copy God as much as possible in your actions» says Peter.

«You are proud! To copy God! You are not entitled to» declares the Iscariot.

«It is not pride. Love leads to obedience. To copy God seems to me a form of obedience because God said that He made us in His own image and likeness» replies Peter.

«He made us. We must not go higher up.»

«You are a poor wretch, my boy, if that is what you think! You are forgetting that we fell and that God wants to take us back to what we were.»

180.4 [4]Jesus begins to speak: «Even more, Peter, Judas and you all. Even more than that. Adam's perfection was still susceptible of improvement through love, which would have made him a more precise image of his Creator. Adam without the stain of sin would have been a most shining mirror of God. That is why I say: "Be perfect as your Father Who is in Heaven is perfect". Like your Father. Therefore like God. Peter is quite right. And so is Simon. I ask you to remember their words and apply them to your souls.»

Peter's wife almost faints from joy on hearing her husband being praised thus. She weeps behind her veil: she is quiet but happy.

Peter blushes so much that he seems to be having a stroke of apoplexy. He remains dumb for a few moments, then says: «Well, then, give me my reward. The parable of this morning...»

Also the others join Peter saying: «Yes, You promised. Parables serve very well to make people understand the comparison. But we know that they have a higher meaning than the compari-
180.5 son. [5]Why do You speak to them in parables?»

«Because they are not to understand more than I explain. You are granted much more, because as My disciples, you must be acquainted with the mystery; and you are therefore given to understand the mysteries of the Kingdom of Heaven. That is why I say to you: "Ask Me if you do not understand the spirit of the parable". You give everything and everything is given to you, that you, in your turn, may give everything. You are giving everything to God: love, time, interests, freedom, lives. And God gives you everything to reward you and to enable you to give everything in the name of God to those who come after you. Thus, to him who has given will be given abundantly. But he who gave only partly or did not give at all, will be deprived also of what he has.

I speak to them in parables, so that, while seeing, they may see only what is illuminated by their will to adhere to God, and while listening, always through the same will of adherence, they may hear and understand. See! Many hear My word, few adhere to God. Their spirits lack goodwill. Isaiah's prophecy is fulfilled * in them: "You will hear with your ears and will not understand, you will look with your eyes and will not see". Because these people are hard-hearted; their ears are hard and their eyes are closed, so that they may not see and hear, that they may not understand with their hearts and convert, that I may cure them. But you are blessed because your eyes see and your ears hear, and because of your goodwill! I solemnly tell you that many Prophets and many just people were anxious to see what you see and they did not see it, and to hear what you hear and they did not hear it. They pined away with the desire to understand the mystery of the words, but as soon as the light of the prophecy went out, the words remained like burnt out coals, also for the holy man who had received them.

Only God reveals Himself. When His light fades out, as soon as the purpose of illuminating the mystery comes to its end, the inability to understand envelops the regal truth of the word received, like the bandages of a mummy. That is why I said to you this morning: "The day will come when you will find everything I have given you". Now you cannot remember. But later light will come upon you, not just for a moment, but for an inseparable union of the Eternal Spirit with yours, whereby your teaching concerning what pertains to the Kingdom of God will be infallible.

---

* **prophecy** in *Isaiah 6:9-10.*

And what applies to you, will also apply to your successors, *if they live of God as of one bread only.*

180.6 [6] Now listen to the spirit of the parable.

We have four kinds of fields: the fertile ones, the thorny ones, the stony ones and the ones full of paths. We also have four types of spirits.

There are the honest spirits, the spirits of goodwill, prepared by their own will and by the work of an apostle, of a "true" apostle; because there are apostles who have the name but not the spirit of an apostle and they are more lethal for the will in formation, than birds, thorns and stones, They upset in such a way, through their intolerance, their haste, their reproaches and their threats, as to drive people away from God forever. There are others who, on the contrary, through an excess of benignity, utterly out of place, cause the seed to rot in too soft a soil. Because of their lack of vigour, they kill the vigour of the souls they cure. But let us consider true apostles, that is, the shining mirrors of God. They are paternal, merciful, patient, and at the same time they are strong, as their Lord is strong. Now: the souls prepared by them and by their own will can be compared to the fertile fields, free from stones and brambles, from couch-grass and darnel, in which the word of God thrives and every word, that is every seed, bears a bundle of ears, yielding in some places one hundred, in others sixty per cent. Are there any like that among those who follow Me? There certainly are. And they will be holy. They come from all castes and countries. And there are Gentiles among them and they will yield one hundred per cent because of their goodwill, only because of that, or because of their goodwill and that of an apostle or disciple who prepares them for Me.

The thorny fields are those in which thorny tangles of personal interests, which suffocate the good seed, have been allowed to grow by carelessness. You must watch yourselves all the time. Never say: "Oh! I am well formed, I have been sown, I can rest assured that I will bear seeds of eternal life". Watch yourselves; the struggle between Good and Evil is still on. Have you ever watched a colony of ants that install themselves in a house? There they are, near the fireplace. The housewife takes all foodstuff away from there and puts it on the table. They sniff the air and attack the table. The housewife puts the food in a cupboard and they get into the cupboard through the keyhole. The woman hangs her food supply from the ceiling, and they go a long way along walls and beams, down the rope and reach the food. The woman burns them, scalds them, poisons them. And thinking that she has destroyed them she is happy. But if she does not watch, what a surprise she gets! The new hatched ones come out and she has to start all over again. And that is what happens while you live; you must be careful and uproot the evil weeds as soon as they come up. Otherwise they will form a ceiling of brambles which suffocate the corns. Worldly cares, deceiving wealth form the tangle, suffocate the seed of God and prevent it from coming into ears.

And here are the fields full of stones. How many there are in Israel! They are the ones that belong to the "children of the laws" as My cousin Judas quite rightly said. In them there is not the one Stone of Witness, nor the Stone of the Law. There is the quarry poor petty human laws made by men. They are so many that with their weight they have broken also the Stone of the Law into chips. A disaster which does not allow the seed to take root. The root is no longer nourished because there is neither soil nor sap. The water stagnating on the stone pavement causes the seed to rot, the sun makes the stones hot and parches the little plants. Such are the spirits of those who put complicated human doctrines in place of the simple doctrine of God. They even receive My word with joy. At first it shakes and allures them. But later... They would need to be heroes and work hard to clean the field, their souls and minds of all rhetorical stones. The seed would then take root and bear long spikes. As it is... it bears nothing. The fear of human retaliation is enough. It is enough to say: "And after? What will the mighty ones do to me?" and the poor seed languishes without nourishment. It is enough for the whole quarry to stir with the vain sound of the hundreds of precepts, which have been put in place of the Precept, that man perishes with the seed received.. Israel is full of them. That explains why the coming to God is in inverse ratio to human power.

The last are the dusty barren fields full of roads. Those of worldly selfish people. Their comfort is their law, enjoyment their aim. Their ambitions: to do no work, to slumber, to enjoy themselves, to feast... The spirit of the world is their king. The dust of worldliness covers the soil which becomes mouldy. Birds, that dissipation, rush onto the thousand paths which have been built to make life easier. The spirit of the world, that is, of the Evil one, picks up and destroys all the seed that falls on this soil open to all sensuality and laxity...

180.7 [7] Have you understood? Have you any questions to ask? No? In that case we can go and rest and tomorrow we will leave for Capernaum. There is one place to which I must go before starting on My journey to Jerusalem for Passover.»

«Shall we go through Arimathea again?» asks the Iscariot.

«I am not sure. It depends on...»

There is a loud knocking at the door.

«Who can it be at this time?» asks Peter getting up to open the door.

John comes in. He is most upset, covered in dust, and he has obviously been weeping.

«You are here!» they all shout. «What's the matter?»

Jesus, Who has stood up, says only: «Where is My Mother?»

And John, coming forward and kneeling at the feet of the Master, holding his arms as if he were asking for help, says: «Your Mother is well, but She is weeping as I am, as many others are, and She begs You not to come following the Jordan on our side. That is why She sent me back, because Your cousin John has been captured...» And John weeps while everybody is bewildered.

Jesus turns very pale but does not become excited. He only says:

«Stand up and tell us.»

«I was going down with Your Mother and the other women. Isaac and Timoneus were also with us. We were three women and three men. I was carrying out Your instruction to take Mary to John... Ah! You knew it was their last farewell!... It was to be their last farewell... Because of the storm of a few days ago, we had to stop for a little while. But it was enough to make it impossible for John to see Mary... We arrived at noon and he had been captured at daybreak...»

«Where? How? By whom? In his cave?» they all ask, they all want to know.

«He was betrayed!... They used Your name to betray him!»
«How horrible! Who did that?» they all shout.

And John shuddering, whispering in a low voice what not even the air should hear, states: «It was one of his disciples...»

The confusion is at its highest pitch. Some curse, some weep, some are petrified with astonishment.

[8]John throws his arms around Jesus' neck and shouts: «I am 180.8
afraid for You!... for You! The saints have their traitors who sell themselves for gold and for fear of the mighty ones, yearning for reward, obeying Satan. For thousands of things! Oh! Jesus! Jesus! How dreadful! My first master! My John who gave me to You!»

«It is all right! Do not worry! Nothing will happen to Me for the time being.»

«But later? What will happen later? I look at myself, at these... I am afraid of everybody, also of myself. Will one of us be Your traitor?...»

«Are you mad? And do you think that we would not tear him to pieces?» shouts Peter.

And the Iscariot: «Oh! You really are mad! It will never be I! But if I should feel so weak as to eventually become so, I would kill myself. Better than be the murderer of God.»

Jesus frees Himself from John's grip, shakes Judas violently saying: «Do not swear! Nothing can make you weak, *unless you want!* And if that should happen, make sure you weep for it, and do not commit another crime in addition to deicide. He becomes
weak who cuts off his vital link with God.» [9]He then returns 180.9
to John, who is weeping with his head on the table and he says: «Speak calmly. It grieves Me, too. He was of My blood and was My Precursor.»

«I only saw some of the disciples, who were dismayed and furious with the traitor. The others accompanied John towards his prison to be near him at his death.»

«But he is not dead yet... the last time he managed to escape.» says the Zealot endeavouring to comfort John of whom he is very fond.

«He is not dead yet. But he will die» replies John.

«Yes, he will die. He knows as well as I do. Nothing and no one will save him this time. When? I do not know. I know that he will not come out of Herod's hand alive.»

«Yes, Herod. Listen. John went to the mountain gorge, between Mount Ebal and Gerizim, where we also passed coming back from Galilee, because the traitor said to him: "The Messiah is dying after being attacked by His enemies. He wants to see you to entrust a secret to you". And he went with the traitor and some other people. Herod's armed men were in the shade of the valley and they captured him. The others ran away and gave the news to the disciples who had remained near Hennon. They had just come when I arrived with Your Mother. And the dreadful thing is that he was one from our towns... and that the Pharisees of Capernaum are the leaders of the plot to catch him. They went to John saying that You had been their guest and that You were leaving from there to go to Judaea... he would not have left his refuge but for You...»

180.10 [10]Dead silence follows John's report. Jesus looks bloodless, His deep blue eyes are dimmed. He is standing with his head bowed, His hand still on John's shoulder, and His hand is trembling lightly. No one dare speak. Jesus breaks the silence: «We shall go to Judaea following a different route. But I must go to Capernaum tomorrow. As early as possible. Rest now. I am going up to the olive-grove. I need to be alone.» And He goes out without saying anything else.

«He is certainly going to weep» whispers James of Alphaeus.

«Let us follow Him, brother» says Judas Thaddeus.

«No. Let Him weep. But let us go out quietly and keep watch. I fear tricks everywhere» replies the Zealot.

«Yes, let us go. We fishermen to the shore. If anybody comes from the lake we will see him. You go to the olive-grove. He is certainly in the usual place, near the walnut-tree. At dawn we will have the boats ready to go away early. Those snakes! Ehi! I did tell you! Tell me, boy? But... is His Mother really safe?»

«Oh! Yes! The shepherd disciples of John have also gone with Her. Andrew... we will never see our John again!»

«Be quiet! It sounds like the song of the cuckoo... One precedes the other and... and...»

«By the Holy Ark! Be quiet! If you go on talking about misfortunes to the Master, I will start from you, letting your backs feel the weight of my oar!» shouts an enraged Peter. «You...» he then says to those who are to go to the olive-grove: «Get some clubs, some big branches, you will find some in the wood-shed...

and spread out, armed with them. The first one to come near Jesus to harm Him, kill him.»

«The disciples! We must be careful with the new ones!» exclaims Philip.

The new disciple feels hurt and asks: «Are you in doubt about me? He chose me and wanted me.»

«Not about you. I mean the scribes and Pharisees and their worshippers. That is where the trouble will come from, believe me.»

They go out, some towards the boats, some towards the olive-trees on the hills, and it all ends.

181. The Parable of the Wheat and the Darnel.

18th June 1945.

[1] A clear dawn causes the lake to sparkle like pearls and en- 181.1
velops the hills in a mist as light as a muslin veil, through which olive and walnut-trees, houses and the background of villages look prettier than usual. Boats are sailing smoothly and quietly towards Capernaum. All of a sudden Peter turns the tiller of the rudder, so abruptly that the boat heels to one side.

«What are you doing?» asks Andrew.

* «There is the boat of an owl. It is leaving Capernaum now. My eyes are good and since yesterday evening I have the scent of a hound. I do not want them to see us. I am going back to the river. We will go on foot.»

Also the other boat has followed the manouevre, but James, who is holding the rudder, asks Peter: «Why are you doing that?»

«I will tell you later. Follow me.»

Jesus, Who is sitting astern, rouses when they are almost off the Jordan. «What are you doing, Simon?» He asks.

«We are getting off here. There is a jackal about. It is not possible to go to Capernaum today. I want to go and find out what is happening first. I will go with Simon and Nathanael. Three worthy people against three unworthy ones… if the unworthy ones are not more.»

---

* The **owl** is considered the bird of evil-omen.

«You must not see traps everywhere, now! Is that not the boat of Simon the Pharisee?»

«It is just that one.»

«He was not present at John's arrest.»

«I don't know.»

«He has always shown respect to Me.»

«I don't know.»

«You make Me appear a coward.»

«I don't know.»

Although Jesus does not feel like laughing, He cannot help smiling at Peter's holy obstinacy. «But, after all, we must go to Capernaum. If not today, later...»

«I told You that I am going first, to see... and if necessary... I will also go... it will be a bitter pill to swallow... but I will do it for Your sake... I will go... to the centurion and ask his protection...»

«No! It is not necessary!»

The boat grounds on the little desert shore opposite Bethsaida. They all go ashore.

«You two come with me. You too, Philip. You younger ones, stay here. We will not be long.»

Elias, the new disciple, begs Jesus: «Come to my house, Master. I will be so happy to give You hospitality...»

«Yes, I will come. Simon: you will meet Me at Elias' house. Goodbye, Simon. Go. But be good, wise and merciful. Come here that I may kiss you and bless you.»

Peter does not guarantee that he will be good, patient and merciful. He is silent and kisses Jesus while being kissed by Him. Also the Zealot, Bartholomew and Philip kiss Jesus goodbye and the two groups go in opposite directions.

181.2 [2] They enter Korazim when it is broad daylight. All the stems twinkle with dewy gems. Birds are singing everywhere. The air is pure and cool, it seems to savour of milk, of a vegetable milk rather than animal milk. The scent of the corn coming into ears, of the almond-groves laden with fruit... is the scent I could smell in cool mornings in the rich fields in the Po Valley.

They soon reach Elias' house. Many people in Korazim already know that the Master has arrived, and while Jesus is about to enter the house, a mother rushes towards Him shouting: «Jesus, Son of David, have mercy on my daughter!» She is carrying in her arms a little girl, about ten years old, who is very thin and waxen, or yellowish rather than waxen.

«What is the matter with your daughter?»

«She is feverish. She caught a disease at the pastures along the Jordan. Because we are the shepherds of a rich man. Her father sent for me when she was taken ill. He has gone back to the mountains. But You know that with this kind of disease one cannot stay up in high places. But how can I stay here? Our master has allowed me so far. But I look after the wool and the litters. This is the busy season for shepherds. If I stay here we shall be dismissed or separated. And if I go back to the Hermon I will see my daughter die.»

«Do you believe that I can cure her?»

«I have spoken to Daniel, Elisha's shepherd. He said to me: "Our Child cures all diseases. Go to the Messiah". I have come from beyond Merom carrying her in my arms and looking for You. I was going to walk until I found You...»

«You need walk no farther, but go home, to your peaceful work. Your daughter is cured because that is what I want. Go in peace.»

The woman looks at her daughter and at Jesus. She is perhaps hoping to see her daughter become fat and rosy all at once. Also the girl stares at Jesus with her tired eyes wide open and smiles.

«Do not be afraid, woman. I am not deceiving you. Her fever has gone forever. Day by day she will become a healthy girl. Let her go. She will no longer stagger neither will she feel tired.»

The mother puts the child down and she stands upright. She becomes more and more cheerful and at last she trills in her silvery voice: «Bless the Lord, mother! I am cured! I can feel it» and with the naivety of a little shepherd girl, she throws her arms around Jesus' neck and kisses Him. Her mother, reserved as her age demands, prostrates herself and kisses His tunic blessing the Lord.

«Go. Remember the gift of God and be good. Peace be with you.»

[3] The crowds gather in Elias' little kitchen garden requesting 181.3
Jesus to speak to them. And although He is not inclined to do so, sad as He is because of the Baptist's capture and the way it hap-

pened, He yields and begins to speak in the shade of the trees.

«As we are still in the lovely season when the corn bursts into ears, I wish to tell you a parable taken from the corn. Listen.

The Kingdom of Heaven may be compared to a man who sowed good seed in his field. But while the man and his servants were asleep, his enemy came and sowed darnel seeds among the wheat and went away. At first no one noticed anything. Winter came with rain and frost, the end of the month of Tebeth came and the corn sprouted. The tiny little green leaves which had just come up, looked all alike in their innocent early days. The months of Shebat and Adar came and the plants grew and the spikes seeded. They then saw that it was not all wheat, and that there was also darnel, twisted with its thin strong bearbines round the corn stalks.

The servants of the master went to his house and said: "Lord, what seed did you sow? Was it not selected seed, free from every other seed?".

"It was certainly so. I picked all the grain and they were all of the same quality. I would have noticed any other seed".

"If so, why has so much darnel grown among your corn?".

The landlord became pensive and said: "Some enemy has done that to harm me".

The servants then asked: "Do you want us to go into the field and free the corn from the darnel, weeding it out patiently? Tell us and we will do it".

But the master said: "No. Because you might weed out also the corn and almost certainly you would damage the ears which are still tender. Let them both grow till the harvest. Then I will say to the reapers: 'Cut everything together, but before tying the sheaves, since the bearbines of the darnel are withered and friable, whereas the closed ears are stronger and harder, pick the darnel from the wheat and tie it into separate bundles. You will burn them and they will fertilize the soil. Take instead the good corn into the granaries and it will be used to bake good bread, to the great shame of my enemy who will have only gained to become despicable to God because of his envious malice' ".

Consider now how often and how plentifully the Enemy sows in your hearts. And you must understand that it is necessary to watch patiently and constantly to ensure that little darnel is mixed with the chosen wheat. The fate of the darnel is to be burnt. Do you wish to be burnt or to become citizens of the Kingdom? You say that you want to become citizens of the Kingdom. Well, endeavour to be so. The good God gives you the Word. The enemy is vigilant to make it harmful, because the flour of wheat if mixed with the flour of darnel makes a bitter bread, which is harmful to the stomach. If there is darnel in your souls, pick it with goodwill and throw it away, so that you may not be unworthy of God.

Go, My children. Peace be with you.»

[4] The crowds slowly disperse. The eight apostles, Elias, his brother and mother, old Isaac, whose soul rejoices seeing his Saviour, stay in the kitchen garden. 181.4

«Gather around Me and listen. I will explain the full meaning of the parable to you, as it has two more meanings, besides what I told the crowd.

In the universal sense the purport of the parable is as follows: the field is the world. The good seed is the children of the Kingdom of God sown by God in the world, while they wait to reach their end and be cut by the Mower and be taken to the Master of the world Who will store them in His granaries. The subjects of the Evil one are the darnel, which has also been spread in the field of God for the purpose of causing grief to the Master of the world and damage to the corn of God. The enemy of God has sown them deliberately, through witchcraft, because the demon really perverts the nature of man making him a creature of his own and then sows it to lead astray other people whom he has not been able to enslave otherwise. The harvest, that is the tying of the sheaves and carrying them to the granaries, is the end of the world and that is accomplished by the angels. They are given instructions to gather together the creatures which have been cut, to separate the corn from the darnel, and as in the parable the darnel is burnt, so the damned will be burnt in the eternal fire, at the Last Judgement.

The Son of man will have all scandalmongers and performers of iniquity removed from His Kingdom. Because the Kingdom then will be on the earth and in Heaven and many sons of the Enemy will be mixed among the citizens of the Kingdom on Earth. And, as prophesied also by Prophets, they will reach the perfection of scandal and abomination in every ministry on the earth and will be of great annoyance to the children of the spirit. The corrupt will have already been driven out of the Kingdom of God in Heaven, because no corruption will enter Heaven. And now the angels of the Lord, brandishing their sickles among the group of the last harvest, will mow down and separate the corn from the darnel and will throw the latter into the burning furnace, where there will be weeping and grinding of teeth. The just, instead, the chosen seed, will be taken to the eternal Jerusalem, where they will shine like the sun in the Kingdom of My Father and yours.

181.5 [5]That is the universal sense. But there is another sense, which is the answer to the question which you have been asking yourselves many times and particularly since yesterday evening. Your question is: "Can there be traitors in the mass of disciples?" and your hearts tremble with horror and fear. Yes, there may be some. There are certainly some.

The Sower sows the good seed. In this case, instead of sowing, we could say that He "picks". Because the master, whether it is I or the Baptist, choses his disciples. How were they, therefore, led astray? No, I did not use the right word saying that the disciples are the "seed". You may misunderstand. I will call them "field". As many disciples as fields, chosen by the master to form the area of the Kingdom of God, the wealth of God. The master tires himself cultivating them so that they may yield one hundred per cent. He takes care of everything with patience, love, wisdom, hard work and perseverance. He also sees their wicked inclinations, their barrenness and avidity, their stubbornness and weakness. But he hopes all the time, corroborating his hope through prayer and penance, because he wishes to lead them to perfection.

But the fields are open. They are not gardens enclosed in walls of protection, of which the only owner is the master, who is the only one who can go in. They are open. Placed as they are in the centre of the world, among the world, anyone can go near them and into them. Everybody and everything. Oh! darnel is not the only bad seed sown! Darnel could be the symbol of the bitter frivolity of the worldly spirit. But all the other seeds, scattered by the Enemy, come up in them. There are nettles, couch-grass, dodder, bearbines, and finally hemlock and poisonous herbs. Why? What are they?

Nettles: stinging untameable spirits which hurt through their excess of poison and cause so much trouble. Couch-grass: parasites who wear out the master as they can only creep and suck, taking advantage of his work and injuring the willing ones, who would make much more profit if the master were not upset and distracted by the cares required by the couch-grass. The sluggish bearbines rise from the ground only by making use of the efforts of other people. Dodders: they are a torture on the already painful road of the master and a torment to the faithful disciples who follow him. They twist, pierce, tear to pieces, scratch, cause mistrust and pain. The poisonous ones: the criminal disciples, who go as far as betraying and killing as hemlock and other poisonous plants do. Have you noticed how beautiful they are with their little flowers which later become white, red, blue-violet berries? Who would say that the white or pinkish star-shaped corolla, with its little gold heart, or the many-coloured corals, so much like other little fruits which are the delight of birds and children, can cause death, once they are ripe? No one. And the innocent ones fall into the trap. They believe that everybody is as good as they are... they pick and die.

They believe that everybody is as good as they are! Oh! The truth that makes the master sublime and condemns his traitor! How? Does goodness not disarm wickedness? Does it not make ill-will harmless? No, it does not, because the man who has fallen prey to the Enemy is indifferent to what is superior. And what is superior changes apperance, as far as he is concerned. Kindness becomes weakness on which it is lawful to tread and it stimulates his ill-will as the scent of blood stimulates a beast to slaughter.

Also the master is always innocent... and he lets his traitor poison him, because he cannot possibly believe that a human being can murder an innocent person.

[6] The enemies come into the fields of the Master, that is to His 181.6
disciples. They are many and Satan is the first one. The others are his servants, that is, men, passions, the world and the flesh. The disciple who is more easily struck by them is the one who is not *entirely* close to the Master, but is between the Master and the world. He is not capable and does not want to part completely

with the world, the flesh, passions and demons, to belong entirely to Him Who wants to take him to God. And the world, flesh, passions and the demon scatter their seed in him: gold, power, women, pride, the fear of an unfavourable opinion of the world, the spirit of utilitarianism. “The great ones are the strongest. I will serve them so that they will be friendly to me”. And they become criminals and damned for such miserable things!...

Why does the Master, Who sees the imperfection of a disciple, not cast him away at once, even if He is not prepared to submit to the thought: “He will be My murderer”? That is what you are asking yourselves. *Because it is useless to do so.* If He did so he would not avoid having him as an enemy, a double and more dangerous enemy, because of his anger and his sorrow at being found out or at being found out or at being driven away. Yes, because of his sorrow. Because sometimes a bad disciple does not realise that he is such. The demon's action is so subtle that he is not aware of it. He becomes wicked without even suspecting that he is subject to such action. And because of his anger, He is enraged at being known for what he is, when he is aware of Satan's work and of his followers: the men who tempt weak people in their weak points, to remove from the world a saint who offends them, wicked as they are, when compared with his goodness. The saint then prays and trusts in God. “Let what You allow be done” he says. He adds only the clause: “providing it serves Your purpose”. The saint knows that the time will come when the wicked darnel will be rejected from the harvest. By God Himself Who does not allow more than what is useful to the triumph of His loving will.»

181.7 [7] «If You maintain that Satan and his followers are always to be blamed... it seems to me that the responsibility of the disciple diminishes» says Matthew.

«Do not believe that. If there is Good there is also Evil and man is gifted with discernment and freedom.»

«You say that God does not allow more than what is useful to the triumph of His loving will. Therefore such an error is useful too, if He allows it, and it serves the triumph of the divine will» says the Iscariot.

«And you infer, as Matthew does, that that justifies the disciple's crime. God created the lion without ferocity and the snake without poison, now one is ferocious and the other poisonous. That is why God separated them from man. Ponder over that and draw conclusions. Let us go to the house. The sun is already too warm. It looks as if there is going to be a storm. And you are tired because of the sleepless night.»

«The rooms in the house are high, large and cool. You will be able to rest» says Elias.

They go up the outside staircase. But only the apostles lie down on the mats to rest. Jesus goes out onto the terrace, a corner of which is shaded by a very tall oak-tree, and becomes engrossed in thought.

182. While Going to Magdala, Jesus Speaks to Some Shepherds. Little Orphan Zacharias.

9th June 1945.

[1] Peter comes back only the following morning. And he is calmer than when he left, because he was made welcome at Capernaum and the town had been cleared of Eli and Joachim. 182.1

«They must have taken part in the plot. Because I asked some friends when they had left, and I understood that they had not come back after going to the Baptist as penitents. And I do not think that they will come back so soon, now that I mentioned that they were present at the arrest... There is much turmoil because of the Baptist's capture... I will ensure that the whole world knows about it... It is the best weapon we have. I also met Simon, the Pharisee... But if he really is what he appeared to me, I think he is favourably disposed towards us. He said to Me: "Tell the Master not to follow the Jordan along the western valley. The other side is safer" he said stressing the words. And he ended: "I have not seen you. I have not spoken to you. Don't forget. And mind what you do in mine, yours and everybody's interest. Tell the Master that I am a friend" and he kept looking up, as if he were speaking to the wind. They are always false, even when doing good things and... and I will say "strange", so that You will not reproach me. But... ehi!... but I went and I had a little chat with the centurion. Just... to ask: "Is your servant well?", and when I was told that he was, I said: "That is good!

Make sure you keep him healthy because they are laying snares for the Master. The Baptist has already been captured..." and the Roman grasped the idea immediately. A cunning fellow he is! He replied: "Where there is a vexillum, there will be a guard for Him, and there will be someone reminding the Jews that no plot is allowed under the sign of Rome, death or the galley being the punishment". They are heathens, but I could have kissed him. I like people who understand and *take action!* So we can go.»

«Let us go. But all that was not necessary» says Jesus.

«It was... it was necessary indeed!» Jesus says goodbye to the hospitable family and also to the new disciple, to whom He must have given some instructions.

182.2 [2] They are alone once again: the Master with His apostles and they walk along the cool country, along a road which Jesus has taken much to Peter's surprise, as he wanted to take a different one. «We are going away from the lake...»

«We will still arrive in time for what I have to do.»

The apostles become silent and go towards a little village, a handful of houses, spread out in the country. A loud ding-dong of sheep-bells can be heard as the flocks are driven towards the pastures on the mountains.

When Jesus stops to let a large herd pass, the shepherds point Him out and gather together. They consult with one another but dare no more. Jesus puts an end to their doubts by walking through the herd, which has stopped to graze the thick grass. He goes straight to caress a little shepherd, who is standing towards the centre of the woolly bleating mass of sheep. He asks the boy: «Are they yours?» Jesus knows very well that they are not the boy's, but He wants him to speak.

«No, Lord. I am with those men. And the herds belong to many owners. We are all together for fear of the bandits.»

«What is your name?»

«Zacharias, the son of Isaac. But my father died and I work as a servant because we are poor and my mother has three more sons younger than I am.»

«Has your father been long dead?»

«Three years, Lord... and since then I have never smiled because my mother always weeps and I have no one who caresses me any more... I am the first born and my father's death has made a man of me, while I was still a child... But I must not weep but earn some money... But it is so difficult!» Tears stream down his face which is too serious for his age.

The shepherds have drawn near and so have the apostles. A group of men in the midst of moving sheep.

«You are not fatherless, Zacharias. You have a holy Father in Heaven, Who always loves you, if you are good, and your father has not ceased loving you because he is in Abraham's bosom. You must believe that. And because of such faith you must endeavour to become better and better.» Jesus speaks kindly and caresses the boy.

[3] A shepherd dares to ask: «You are the Messiah, are You not?» 182.3

«Yes, I am. How do you know?»

«I know that You are about in Palestine and I know that You speak holy words. That is why I recognised You.»

«Are you going far?»

«Up to the high mountains. The hot weather is coming... Will You not speak to us? Up there, where we are, only the winds speak, and sometimes the wolf speaks and it slaughters... as it happened to Zacharias' father. During the whole winter we were hoping to see You, but we never found You.»

«Let us go under the shade of that thicket and I will speak to you.» And Jesus goes ahead of them, holding the little shepherd by the hand and caressing with the other hand the little lambs which raise their heads, bleating.

The shepherds gather the flock under a coppice and while the sheep lie down ruminating or grazing or rubbing themselves against tree trunks, Jesus speaks.

[4] «You said: "Up there, where we are, only the winds speak, 182.4
and sometimes the wolf speaks and slaughters". What happens up there, happens in men's hearts through the work of God, of men and of Satan. You may, therefore, have up there what you would have in any other place.

Do you know the Law well enough and its ten commandments? And you, too, boy? In that case you know enough. If you faithfully practise what God commanded, you will be holy. Do not complain of being far from the world. That will preserve you from much corruption. And God is not far from you, but closer in that solitude, where you can hear His voice in the winds, which

He created, in the herbs and in the water, whereas you would not hear it among men. Your flock teaches you a great virtue, or rather, many great virtues. It is meek and obedient. It is satisfied with little and grateful for what it has. It loves and knows those who take care of it and love it. Do likewise saying: "God is our Shepherd and we are His sheep. He watches us. He protects us and grants us not what is the source of vice, but what is necessary to live". And keep wolves away from your hearts. Wicked men are wolves: they seduce you and incite you to evil actions by Satan's order and it is Satan himself who induces you to sin so that he may tear you to pieces.

Be watchful. You shepherds know the habits of wolves. They are shrewd, as sheep are simple and innocent. They steal close to you, after watching from above the habits of the herd, they sneak closer through bushes and lie as still as stones to avoid drawing your attention. Do they not look like huge stones which have rolled down on to the meadows? Then, when they are sure that no one is watching, they spring and bite. That is how Satan behaves. He watches you to find out your weak points, he roams about you, he seems harmless and absent, concerned with something else whereas he is watching you, and then he suddenly leaps to induce you to sin, and sometimes he is successful.

But close to you there is a doctor and a compassionate spirit. God and your angel. If you are wounded, if you have been taken ill, do not go away from them, as a dog which has become rabid does. On the contrary, while weeping shout to them: "Help!". God forgives those who repent and your angel is ready to implore God with you and for you.

182.5 [5] Love one another and love this boy. Each of you must feel as if he were somehow the father of the orphan. The presence of a child amongst you should influence every action of yours through the holy restraint of respect for a child. And let your company make up for what death deprived him of. We must love our neighbour. This boy is the neighbour entrusted to you by God in a special manner. Teach him to be good, a faithful believer, honest and free from vices. He is worth much more than one of these sheep. Now, if you take care of the sheep because they belong to their owner, who would punish you if you should let them perish, how much more care you must take of this soul which God entrusts to you for Himself and for his dead father. His situation as an orphan is a sad one indeed. Do not make it more painful by taking advantage of him and vexing him because he is only a youngster. Remember that God sees the deeds and tears of every man and takes everything into account, in order to reward or punish.

And you, My boy, remember that you are never alone. God sees you and so does the spirit of your father. When something upsets you and induces you to do wrong, say: "No, I do not want to be an orphan forever and ever". You would be, if you damned your soul by sinning.

Be good. I bless you so that all goodness may be with you. If we were going the same way, I would continue to speak to you for a long time. But the sun is rising and you must go, and so must I. Your task is to protect the sheep from the heat, Mine to relieve men of another ardour, a more dreadful one, the passions of their hearts. Pray that they may consider Me as their Shepherd. Goodbye, Zacharias. Be good. Peace be with you.»

Jesus kisses the little shepherd and blesses him and while the flock moves slowly away, His eyes follow him. He then carries on along His way.

6 «You said that we are going to relieve hearts of another ardour... Where we going?» asks the Iscariot. 182.6

«For the time being as far as that shady spot, where the stream is. We will have something to eat there and then you will be told where we are going.»

Jesus says: «Insert here the vision of the second moment of Mary Magdalene's conversion, which you had last year, on the 12th of August 1944.»

183. Miracle on a Dying Man Stabbed in Mary's House in Magdala.

[12th August 1944.]

1 The entire apostolic college is around Jesus. Sitting on the grass, in the cool shade of a thicket, near a stream, they are all eating bread and cheese and drinking the cool clear water of the stream. Their dusty sandals imply that they have walked a long 183.1

way and perhaps the disciples wish but to rest on the long fresh grass.

But the Tireless Walker is not of the same mind. As soon as he deems that the hottest hour is over, He gets up, goes onto the road and looks… He then turns around and says: «Let us go.» Nothing else.

When they reach a crossroads, where four dusty roads meet, Jesus resolutely takes the one in a north-east direction.

«Are we going back to Capernaum?» asks Peter.

Jesus replies: «No.» Just: no.

«We are going to Tiberias, then» insists Peter, who is anxious to know.»

«Not there either.»

«But this road takes one to the Sea of Galilee… and Tiberias Capernaum are there…»

«And there is also Magdala» says Jesus with a half-serious expression to satisfy Peter's curiosity.

«Magdala? Oh!…» Peter is somewhat scandalised, which makes me think that the town is ill-famed.

«Yes, to Magdala. Do you consider yourself too honest to enter that town? Peter, Peter!… For My sake you will have to enter not towns of pleasure but real brothels… Christ did not come to save those who are already saved, but those who are Lost… and you shall be "Peter", or Rock, not Simon, for that purpose. Are you afraid of becoming contaminated? No! Not even this one, see (and He points at the very young John) will suffer any harm. Because he does not want, as you do not want, as your brother and John's brother do not want, as none of you, for the time being, wants. As long as one does not want, no harm is done. But one must not want resolutely and perseveringly. You will obtain will-power and perseverance from the Father, by praying with sincere intentions. Not all of you will be able to pray thus, in future… What are you saying, Judas? Do not be too self-confident. I, Who am the Christ, constantly pray to have strength against Satan. Are you better than I am? Pride is the opening through which Satan penetrates. Be vigilant and humble, Judas. Matthew, since you are familiar with this place, tell Me: is it better to go to the town this way, or is there another road?»

«It depends, Master. If You want to go to the area of Magdala where fishermen and poor people live, this is the road. But — I do not think this is the case. I am telling You to give You a complete answer — if You want to go where the rich people are, then in about one hundred yards, You have to leave this road and take another one, because their houses are approximately in this direction and it is necessary to go back...»

«We will go back because I want to go to the residential area of the wealthy people. What did you say, Judas?»

«Nothing, Master. It is the second time that You ask me in a very short time. But I have never spoken.»

«Not with your lips, no. But you have spoken, grumbling in your heart. You have grumbled with your guest: your heart. It is not necessary to have an interlocutor in order to speak. We say many words to ourselves... But we must not moan or calumniate, not even with our own ego.»

[2]The group proceeds in silence. The main road becomes a 183.2
town street, paved with one handbreath wide square stones. The houses are more and more splendid and magnificent, surrounded by luxuriant flourishing gardens and orchards. I am under the impression that the elegant Magdala was for the Palestinians a kind of place of pleasure like some towns around our lakes in Lombardy: Stresa, Gardone, Pallanza, Bellagio and so on. Among the rich Paletinians there are many Romans, who must have come from other places, such as Tiberias or Caesarea, possibly officials of the Governor or merchants who export the most beautiful products of the Palestinian colony to Rome.

Jesus proceeds, sure of Himself, as if He knew where to go. He follows the contour of the lake, which reflects the houses and gardens built on its borders.

A loud noise of crying people can be heard from a sumptuous house. It is the voices of women and children. The shrill voice of a woman shouts: «My son! My son!»

Jesus turns around and looks at His apostles. Judas steps forward. «No, not you» orders Jesus. «You, Matthew. Go and find out.»

Matthew goes and comes back: «A brawl, Master. A man is dying. A Jew. The man who wounded him, a Roman, has run away. His wife, mother and children have rushed to help him... But he is dying.»

«Let us go.»

«Master... Master... It happened in the house of a woman... who is not his wife.»

«Let us go.»

183.3 [3]Through the wide open door they enter a large hall which opens onto a lovely garden. The house seems to be divided by this kind of covered peristyle, which is full of pots with green plants, statues and inlaid articles. It is a mixture of a hall and greenhouse. In a room, the door of which opens onto the hall, there are some women weeping. Jesus goes in confidently. But He does not pronounce His usual greeting.

Among the men present there is a merchant who obviously knows Jesus, because as soon as he sees Him, he says: «The Rabbi of Nazareth!» and greets Him respectfully.

«Joseph, what is the matter?»

«Master, a stab wound in his heart... He is dying.»

«Why?»

A grey-haired unkempt woman stands up — she was kneeling near the dying man holding his limp hand — and with distracted face and voice she shouts: «Because of her, because of her... She has turned him into a devil... Mother, wife, children no longer existed for him! Hell will have you, satan!»

Jesus looks up and His eyes follow the trembling accusing hand and in a corner, against the dark red wall, He sees Mary of Magdala, more immodest than ever, wearing, I would say, nothing on half of her body, because she is half naked from the waist upwards, draped in a kind of hexagonal net decorated with little round objects which look like tiny pearls. But as she is in a half-light, I cannot see her well.

Jesus lowers His eyes once again. Mary, lashed by His indifference, stands up, whereas before she seemed somewhat depressed, and strikes a defiant pose.

«Woman» says Jesus to the mother. «Do not curse. Tell Me. Why was your son in this house?»

«I told You. Because she infatuated him. She did.»

«Silence. So, he was in sin, too, because he is an adulterer and an unworthy father of these innocent children. He therefore deserves his punishment. In this life and in the next one there is no mercy for those who do not repent. But I feel sorry for your grief and for these innocent children. [4]Is your house far?» 183.4

«About one hundred yards.»

«Lift the man and take him there.»

«It is not possible, Master» says Joseph, the merchant. «He is breathing his last breath.»

«Do as I tell you.»

They place a board under the body of the dying man and the procession slowly moves out. They cross the street and go into a shady garden. The women go on crying loudly.

As soon as they enter the garden, Jesus addresses the mother. «Can you forgive? If you forgive, God will forgive. We must be kind-hearted, to obtain grace. He has sinned and will sin again. It would be better for him to die, because, if he lives, he will fall into sin again and he will also have to answer for his ingratitude to God Who has saved him. But you and these innocent ones (and He points at the wife and children) would give yourselves up to despair. I have come to save, not to lose. Man, I tell you: stand up and be cured.»

The man begins to recover. He opens his eyes, sees his mother, wife and children and lowers his head shamefully.

«Son, son» says the mother. «You were dead, if He had not saved you. Come to your senses. Don't be infatuated for a...»

Jesus interrupts the old woman. «Be quiet, woman. Have mercy as mercy was granted to you. Your house has been sanctified by a miracle, which is always the evidence of God's presence. That is why I could not work it where there was sin. You, at least, must endeavour to keep it such, even if he will not. Take care of him now. It is fair that he should suffer a little. Be good, woman. And you. And you little ones. Goodbye.» Jesus has laid His hand on the heads of the two women and of the children.

[5]He then goes out passing in front of the Magdalene who fol- 183.5
lowed the procession as far as the entrance of the house where she remained leaning against a tree. Jesus slackens His pace as if He were waiting for His disciples, but I think He does so to give Mary a chance of making a gesture. But she does not.

The disciples reach Jesus and Peter cannot help muttering between his teeth an epithet appropriate to Mary, who, wishing to strike an attitude, bursts into a laugh of a weak triumph. But Jesus heard Peter's word and addresses him severely: «Peter. I do not insult. Do not insult. Pray for sinners. Nothing else.»

Mary stops her trilling laughter, lowers her head and runs away, like a gazelle, towards her house.

184. At Magdala, in the House of Little Benjamin's Mother. Two Parables on the Kingdom of Heaven.

10th June 1945.

184.1 [1] The miracle must have taken place only a short while ago, because the apostles are talking about it, and also some citizens are making comments, pointing at the Master, Who with a serious countenance goes straight to the outskirts of the town, where the poor people live.

He stops at a little house, from which a little boy comes bounding out followed by his mother. «Woman, will you let Me go into your kitchen garden and rest there until it cools down a little?»

«Go in, my Lord. Also into the kitchen, if You so wish. I will bring You some refreshments.»

«Do not trouble. It is quite enough for Me to stay in this peaceful garden.»

But the woman offers Him some water mixed with I do not know what and then she wanders round the kitchen garden, as if she were anxious to but dare not speak. She busies herself with her vegetables, but it is only a pretence. In actual fact she is paying attention to the Master, but the little boy annoys her because everytime he catches a butterfly or an insect, he shouts and thus prevents her from hearing what Jesus is saying. She gets angry and gives him a little slap and... he shouts louder.

Jesus — Who was replying to the Zealot who had asked Him: «Do You think Mary is upset because of it?» saying: «Much more than you would think...» — turns around and calls the child, who runs towards Him and stops crying on His knees.

The woman shouts: «Benjamin! Come here. Do not disturb the Master.»

But Jesus says: «No, leave him. He will be good and will leave you in peace.» He then says to the boy: «Do not cry. Your mummy did not hurt you. She only made you obey, or, she wanted to make you obey. Why did you shout when she wanted you to be quiet? Perhaps she is not feeling well, and your shouting was annoying her.»

The boy, with the extreme frankness of children, which is the desperation of adults, immediately exclaims: «No, she is feeling all right. She wanted to hear what You were saying... She told me. But I wanted to come to You, so I was deliberately making a lot of noise, so that You would look at me.»

Everybody laughs and the woman blushes.

«Do not blush, woman. [2]Come here. You wanted to hear Me 184.2
speak? Why?»

«Because You are the Messiah. No one but You can be the Messiah, considering the miracle You have worked... And I was anxious to hear You. I never go out of Magdala because I have... a difficult husband and five children. The youngest is four months old... and You never come here.»

«I have come, and to your house, as you can see.»

«That is why I wanted to hear You.»

«Where is your husband?»

«At sea, my Lord. If he catches no fish, there is no food for us. I have but this little kitchen garden. Can it suffice for seven people? And yet that is what Zacchaeus would like...»

«Be patient, woman. Everybody has a cross.»

«Oh! No! Shameless women have but pleasure. You have seen the deeds of the shameless ones! They enjoy themselves and make other people suffer. They do not suffer the labour of childbirth neither do they break their backs working. Their hands do not blister digging, neither do they get spoiled washing clothes. They are beautiful and fresh looking. Eve's punishment does not affect them. On the contrary, they are our punishment, because... men... You know what I mean.»

«I understand. But, believe Me, they have a terrible cross, too. The most dreadful one, which is not visible: their conscience which reproaches them, the world that sneers at them, their blood that disowns them, God that curses them. They are not happy, believe Me. They do not suffer the labour of childbirth, they do not break their backs working, they do not ulcerate their hands toiling. But they feel broken just the same, and ashamed. Their hearts are one big sore. Do not envy their fresh look, their apparent serenity. It is a veil laid over a ruin that bites and gives no peace. Do not envy their sleep, you, a mother who dreams of her innocent children... Their pillows are covered with nightmares. And in future, in their old age, in their agony, they will have nothing but remorse and terror.»

184.3 «It is true... Forgive me... [3]May I stay here?»

«Yes, stay. I will tell Benjamin a nice parable and those who are no longer children will apply it to themselves and to Mary of Magdala. Listen.

You doubt Mary's conversion to Good. There is no sign in her in that direction. Brazen and impudent, conscious of her rank and power, she dared to defy the people and come to the very threshold of the house where they are weeping because of her. She laughed at Peter's reproach. She replied to My inviting look by striking a proud attitude. Perhaps some of you, either for Lazarus' sake or for mine, would have liked Me to speak to her directly, at some length, subduing her with My power, showing My strength as Messiah and Saviour. No. All that is not needed. I already said so many months ago with regards to another sinner. Souls must react by themselves. I pass and sow the seed. The seed works in secret. A soul is to be respected in this work. If the first seed does not take root, another must be sown, and a third one... and one must give up only when there is definite proof that it is useless to sow. And one prays. Prayer is like dew on the clods of earth: it keeps them soft and nourishes them, so that the seed can sprout. Is that not what you do, woman, with your vegetables?

184.4 [4]Now listen to the parable of how God works in the hearts of men to establish His Kingdom there. Because every heart is a small kingdom of God on the earth. Later, after death, all these small kingdoms will agglomerate into one, immeasurable, holy eternal Kingdom of Heaven.

The Kingdom of God is created in men's hearts by the Divine Sower. He comes to his field — man belongs to God, because every man is initially His — and sows His seed. He then goes to other fields, to other hearts. Days follow the nights and nights the days. The days bring sunshine and rain, in our case rays of divine love and effusion of divine Wisdom speaking to the spirit. The nights bring stars and restful silence: in our case enlightening calls of God and silence for the soul so that it may collect its thoughts and meditate.

The seed, in this course of imperceptible but powerful influence, swells, splits, takes root, sprouts, grows. And all that happens without any help from man. The soil spontaneously produces grass from seeds, the herb becomes strong and supports the rising ear, the ear grows, swells, hardens, becomes golden and perfect when seeding. When it is ripe, the sower comes back and cuts it because the time of perfection has arrived for that seed. It cannot develop any further and so it is harvested.

My word does the same work in hearts. I am referring to the hearts which receive the seed. But it is a slow process. One must not spoil everything by being hasty. How troublesome it is for the little seed to split and take root! Such work is painful also for a hard wild heart. It must open itself, allow people to search it, accept new things and nourish them laboriously, appear different being covered with humble useful things, instead of the fascinating, pompous, useless, exuberant flourishing that covered it previously. It must be satisfied with working humbly for the benefit of the divine Thought, without drawing other people's admiring attention. It must exert all its talent to grow and burst into ear. It must burn with love to become corn. And after overcoming all fears of human opinion, which are so grievous, after toiling, suffering and becoming attached to its new dress, it must be deprived of it by a cruel cut. It must give everything to receive everything. It must be divested to be clad again in Heaven with the stole of sainthood. The life of a sinner who becomes a saint is the longest, most heroic and glorious fight. I tell you.

[5] You will realise from what I told you that it is fair that I should 184.5
deal with Mary as I am doing. Did I behave differently with you, Matthew?»

«No, my Lord, You did not.»

«And tell Me the truth: what convinced you more, My patience or the bitter reproaches of the Pharisees?»

«Your patience, so much so that I am here. The Pharisees, by despising and anathematizing me, made me scornful, and out of contempt I did more harm than I had done so far. That is what happens. Sinners become more obstinate when they realise that they are treated as sinners. But when we are caressed instead of being insulted, we are dumbfounded and we weep... and when one weeps, the whole framework of sin collapses... One is left naked before Goodness and one implores it wholeheartedly to be reclothed by It.»

184.6 «You are right. [6]Benjamin, did you like My story? Yes? Go Where is your mother?»

James of Alphaeus replies: «She went out at the end of the parable and ran along that road.»

«She may have gone to the seaside to see whether her husband is coming» says Thomas.

«No. She has gone to her old mother's, to get the children. Mummy takes them there so that she can work» says the little boy, who is leaning familiarly on Jesus' knees.

«And she keeps you here, my little man? You must be a handsome evil-doer if she keeps you here all by yourself!» remarks Bartholomew.

«I am the eldest, and I help her...»

«You help her to gain Paradise, poor woman! How old are you?» asks Peter.

«In three years' time I will be a son of the Law» replies the urchin proudly.

«Can you read?» asks Thaddeus.

«Yes... but very slowly... because the teacher throws me out almost every day...»

«What did I say!» exclaims Bartholomew.

«But I behave like that because the teacher is old and ugly and says the same things all the time and makes you fall asleep! If he were like *Him* (and he points to Jesus) I would pay attention. Do You hit those who sleep or play?»

«I do not hit anybody. But I say to My pupils: "Pay attention for your own good and for My sake"» replies Jesus.

«Yes, that's all right! Out of love, not out of fear.»

«But if you are good, the teacher will love you.»

«Do You love only those who are good? You just said that You were patient with this man here, who was not good...» The child's logic is cogent.

«I am good with everybody. But when one becomes good, I love that one very much and I am very good, too.»

The boy is pensive... he then looks up and asks Matthew: «And what did you do to become good?»

«I loved Him.»

[7] The boy becomes pensive again and then looking at the Twelve asks Jesus: «Are they all good?» 184.7

«Of course they are.»

«Are you sure? I sometimes behave as a good boy, but that is when... I am thinking of some big mischief.»

They all burst into laughter. Also the little fellow, who is in a confessing humour, laughs. Also Jesus laughs pressing him to His heart and kissing him.

The boy, who is now friendly with everybody, wants to play and says: «I will now tell You who is good» and he begins his selection. He looks at them all and goes straight to John and Andrew who are nearby and says: «You and you. Come here.» He then chooses the two Jameses and places them with the other two. He then takes Thaddeus. He is quite pensive in front of the Zealot and Bartholomew and says: «You are old, but good» and he joins them to the others. He examines Peter, who undergoes the examination, jokingly frowning at him, and finds him to be good. Also Matthew and Philip pass the test. He says to Thomas: «You laugh too much. I am in earnest. Don't you know that my teacher says that he who always laughs fails in the test?» After all, Thomas too passes his examination, but with low marks. The boy then goes back to Jesus.

«Hey, you urchin! I am here, too! I am not a tree. I am young and handsome. Why don't you examine me?» says the Iscariot.

«Because I don't like you. My mother says that when you don't like something, you must not touch it. You just leave it on the table, so that other people, who may like it, can take it. And she also says that if you are offered something you do not like, you must not say: "I do not like it". But you say: "Thank you, but I am not hungry". And I do not hunger for you.»

«Why not? Look, if you say that I am good, I will give you this coin.»

«What am I going to do with it? What can I buy with a lie? Mummy says that money which is the fruit of deceit, becomes straw. Once at my grandmother's, I got them to give me a didrachma by telling a lie because I wanted to buy some honey-cakes, and during the night it turned into straw. I put it in that hole over there, under the door, to take it the following morning, but I found a handful of straw in its place.»

«But how can you see that I am not good? What is wrong with me? Am I lame? Am I ugly looking?»

«No. But you frighten me.»

«Why?» asks the Iscariot going near him.

«I don't know. Leave me alone. Don't touch me or I will scratch you.»

«What a hedgehog! You are silly.» Judas gives a forced laugh.

«I am not silly. You are bad» and the boy takes shelter in the lap of Jesus, Who caresses him without speaking.

The apostles make fun of the situation which is not very pleasant to the Iscariot.

184.8 [8] In the meantime the woman comes back with half a dozen people, and behind them, many more. They must be about fifty. All poor people.

«Would You speak to them? At least a few words. This is my husband's mother, these are my children. And that man over there my husband. A word, Lord» implores the woman.

«Yes, I will speak. To thank you for your hospitality.»

The woman goes back into the house, where her suckling claims her and she sits on the threshold breastfeeding her baby.

«Listen. Here on My knees I have a little boy who has spoken very wisely. He said: "Everything that is obtained by deceit, becomes straw". His mother taught him that truth.

It is not a tale. It is an eternal truth. What is done dishonestly is never successful. Because falsehood in words, deeds, and religion is always a sign of alliance with Satan, the master of falsehood. Do not believe that the deeds worthy of achieving the Kingdom of Heaven are very noisy or showy. They are common, continuous deeds, but performed with a supernatural purpose of love. Love is the seed of the plant that sprouts in you and grows up as far as Heaven, and in its shade all the other virtues sprout. I will compare it to the tiny mustard seed. How small it is! It is one of the smallest seeds that man sows. But look how big and leafy it becomes when it has grown up and how much fruit it bears. Not one hundred per cent, but one hundred to one. The smallest. But the most diligent in working. How much profit it gives you.

Love is the same. If you enclose in your hearts a tiny seed of love for your Most Holy God and for your neighbour, and if you accomplish your deeds guided by love, you will not fail in any of the precepts of the Decalogue. You will not lie to God by means of a false religion of practices but not of the spirit. You will not lie to your neighbour, behaving as ungrateful children, as adulterers, as too exacting husbands and wives, as thieves in business, as liars in life, as violent avengers towards your enemies. Look how many birds have taken shelter, in this warm hour of the day, among the branches of the trees in the garden. Before long that mustard plant, which now is still very small, will be a real perch for birds. All the birds will come to the safe shade of those thick and comfortable trees and their little ones will learn to fly safely among those branches which are like steps and a net, which they can climb without falling. Such is love, the foundation of the Kingdom of God.

Love and you will be loved. Love and you will bear with one another. Love and you will not be cruel by wanting more than what is lawful from those who are under you. Love and sincerity to obtain the peace and glory of Heaven. Otherwise, as Benjamin said, every action of yours accomplished by lying to love and to truth will turn into straw for your beds in hell. I will not say anything else to you. I will only say: always bear in mind the great precept of love and be faithful to God the Truth, to the truth in every word, deed and sentiment, because the truth is the daughter of God. Let the work of bringing yourselves to perfection be continuous, as the seed continuously grows until it is perfect. A silent, humble, patient work. You may rest assured that God sees your efforts and He will grant you a greater reward for overcoming your selfishness, for holding back a rude word, for satisfying a necessity without being ordered to do so, than if, fighting in a battle, you killed the enemy. The Kingdom of Heaven, which you will possess if You live as just people, is built with the little things of everyday. With goodness, moderation, patience, with being satisfied with what one has, bearing with one another, and with love, love, love.

Be good. Live in peace, one with the other. Do not grumble. Do not judge. God will then be with you. I give you My peace as a blessing and thanksgiving for the faith you have in Me.»

[9] Then Jesus turns to the woman saying: «May God bless you 184.9
especially, because you are a holy wife and a holy mother. Persevere in virtue. Goodbye, Benjamin. Love the truth and obey your

mother. My blessing to you, to your little brothers and to you, mother.»

A man comes forward. He is embarrassed and stammers: «But, but... I am moved by what You say of my wife... I did not know...»

«Have you no eyes or intelligence?»

«Yes, I have.»

«Why do you not make use of them? Shall I clear them?»

«You have already done that, my Lord. But I love her, You know... The trouble is... that, that... one gets used... and... and...»

«And one thinks that it is quite all right to demand too much, because the other one is more gentle than we are... Do not do that any more. You are always in danger with your work. Be not afraid of storms if God is with you. But if there is Injustice in you, be very much afraid. Have you understood?»

«More than You have said. I will do my best to obey You... I did not know...» and he looks at his wife as if he saw her for the first time.

Jesus blesses and goes out onto the little road. He resumes walking towards the country.

185. The Calming of the Storm.

30th January 1944.

[...].

185.1 [1] Now that everybody is asleep I am telling you my joy. I «saw» today's Gospel. Mind you, this morning when I read it, I said to myself: «This is an episode of the Gospel which I will never see, because it is not very suitable for a vision.» Instead, when I was
185.2 not thinking about it, it came to fill me with joy. [2]This is what I saw.

A sailing boat, not excessively large, nor very small, a fishing boat, on which five or six people can move comfortably, is ploughing the water of the beautiful deep blue lake of Gennesaret.

Jesus is sleeping in the stern. He is dressed in white as usual. He is resting His head on His left arm and under His arm and head He has placed His blue-grey mantle, which has been folded many times. He is sitting, not lying, on the bottom of the boat and His head is resting on the board that is at the very end of the stern. I do not know how sailors call it. He is sleeping peacefully. He is tired. He is placid.

Peter is at the rudder. Andrew is busy with the sails, John and two more people — I do not know who they are — are sorting out the ropes and nets at the bottom of the boat, as if they were preparing for a catch during the night. I would say that the day is drawing to its end because the sun is already setting in the west. All the disciples have pulled their tunics up, gathering them around their waists by means of belts, in order to be free in their movements, passing from one part of the boat to another, stepping over oars, seats, baskets and nets, without being hindered by their clothes. None of them is wearing a mantle.

[3] I see that the sky is clouding over and the sun is hiding behind 185.3
huge storm clouds, which have suddenly appeared from behind the top of a hill. The wind blows them fast towards the lake. The wind, for the time being, is high up, and the lake is still quiet, it is only becoming darker and its surface is no longer perfectly smooth. There are no waves as yet, but the water is beginning to ruffle.

Peter and Andrew watch the sky and the lake and are preparing to draw close to the shore. But the wind suddenly rages over the lake that in a few minutes surges foaming. The swelling waves clash one against the other, they strike the little boat, lifting it up, lowering it down, tossing it in all directions, thus preventing all manoeuvres of the rudder as the wind prevents manoeuvring the sail, which has to be lowered.

Jesus is sleeping. Neither the steps and excited voices of the disciples, nor the howling wind, nor the waves pounding on the sides of the boat and its prow, awake Him. His hair is blowing in the wind and drops of water reach Him. But He is sleeping. John runs from stern to stern and covers Him with his mantle, which he has taken from below a board. He covers Him with delicate love.

The storm rages more and more furiously. The lake is as black as if ink had been poured into it and is streaked by the foam of the waves. The boat lets in water and is driven farther and farther to the open sea by the wind. The disciples are perspiring in their efforts to manoeuvre the boat and baling out the water which the waves pour in. But to no avail. They are paddling in the water that reaches up to their knees and the boat is becoming heavier and heavier.

185.4 [4] Peter loses his calm and patience. He hands the rudder over to his brother, staggers towards Jesus and shakes Him vigorously.

Jesus wakes up and raises His head.

«Save us, Master, we are going down!» Peter shouts to Him (he must shout to make himself heard).

Jesus stares at His disciple, looks at the others and then at the lake. «Do you believe that I can save you?»

«Quick, Master» shouts Peter, while a real mountain of water moves fast from the centre of the lake towards the poor little boat. It is so high and dreadful that it looks like a water spout. The disciples who see it coming kneel down and hang onto whatever they can, certain that it is the end.

Jesus gets up. He stands on the stern board: a white figure against the livid storm. He stretches His arms out towards the billow and says to the wind: «Stop and be quiet» and to the water: «Calm down. I want it.» And the billow dissolves into foam, which falls harmlessly with a last roar, which fades into a whisper, while the wind dies down changing into a whistle and then a sigh. And the sky becomes clear once again over the appeased lake, while hope and faith fill the hearts of the disciples.

I cannot describe Jesus' majesty. One must *see it* to understand it. And I enjoy it internally because it is still present in my mind and I think of how placid was Jesus' sleep and how imperious was His command to the winds and the waves.

185.5 [5] Jesus then says:

«I will not expound the Gospel in the same way as everybody else does. I will illustrate the circumstances preceding the Gospel passage.

Why was I sleeping? Did I perhaps not know that there was going to be a storm? Yes, I knew. Only I knew. Why was I sleeping, then?

The apostles were men, Mary. They were full of goodwill, but still very much "men". Man thinks he is always capable of everything. When he is really capable of doing something he is full of haughtiness and attachment to his "ability". Peter, Andrew, James and John were good fishermen and consequently they thought they were unexcelled in handling a boat. As far as they were concerned I was a great "Rabbi", but a mere nothing as a sailor. Thus they thought I was unable to help them, and when on the boat to cross the Sea of Galilee, they begged Me to sit down because I was not capable of doing anything else. Also their love for Me was behind their attitude, as they did not want Me to do any material work. But their attachment to their own ability was greater than their love.

I do not impose Myself, Mary, except in exceptional cases. I generally leave you free and wait. On that day, tired as I was and being requested to rest, that is to let them act, clever as they were, I went to sleep. My sleep also included the ascertainment of how man is "man" and wants to do things by himself without feeling that God asks but to help him. I saw in those "spiritual deaf men", in those "spiritual blind men", all the spiritual deaf and blind people, who throughout centuries would ruin themselves, because "they wanted to do by themselves", although I was bent over their needs awaiting to be asked to help them.

When Peter shouted: "Save us!", My bitterness dropped like a stone. I am not "man", I am the God-Man. I do not behave as you do. When someone rejects your advice or your help, and you see him in trouble, even if you are not so bad as to rejoice at it, you are uncharitable enough to look at him disdainfully and indifferently, without being moved by his shouts for help. Your attitude means: "When I wanted to help you, you did not want me? Well, help yourself now". But I am Jesus. I am the Saviour. And I save, Mary. I always save as soon as I am asked to.

[6] The poor men might object: "In that case, why do You allow 185.6
single or collective storms to break out?". If by My power I should destroy Evil, you would consider yourselves the *authors* of Good, which in actual fact is a gift of Mine, and you would not remember Me any longer, You would never remember Me. My poor children, you are in need of sorrow to remember that you have a Father. As the prodigal son remembered he had a father when he was hungry.

Misfortunes convince you of your nothingness, of your ignorance, which is the cause of so many errors, of your wickedness, the cause of so much mourning and grief, of your faults, the cause of the punishments which you inflict upon yourselves, as well as of My existence, of My power and of My goodness.

That is what today's Gospel teaches you. "Your" Gospel of the present time, my poor children. Call Me. Jesus does not sleep except when He is in anguish because He sees that He is not loved by you. Call Me and I will come.»

186. The Two Demoniacs in the Country of the Gadarenes.

11th June 1945.

186.1 [1] The vision «The calming of the storm» which you saw on 30th January 1944, is to be put here. Then the following vision.

186.2 [2] Jesus, after crossing the lake from north-west to south-east, asks Peter to land near Hippos. Peter obeys without objection and takes the boat down to the mouth of a little river, which is in flood because of the springtime rains and of the recent storm and flows into the lake through one of the wild rocky gorges common to this coastal area. The assistants — there is one in each boat — fasten the boats and are ordered to wait until evening to go back to Capernaum.

«And be as dumb as an ox» suggests Peter. «If they ask you where the Master is, reply without hesitation: "I don't know". And if anyone wants to know where He is going to, give the same reply. In any case it is the truth, for you don't know.»

They part and Jesus begins to ascend a steep path which climbs the almost upright cliff. The apostles follow Him along a very hard path up to the top of the cliff which levels over to a tableland strewn with oak-trees under which there are many pigs pasturing.

«Stinking animals!» exclaims Bartholomew. «They prevent us from passing...»

«No, they do not. There is room for everybody» replies Jesus calmly.

In any case the swineherds, when they see the Israelites, endeavour to gather the pigs under the oak-trees, leaving the path free. And the apostles pass by, making endless grimaces, among the filth left by the grouting animals, which fat as they are, seem anxious to become even fatter.

Jesus passes without any fuss, saying to the swineherds: «May God reward you for your kindness.»

The swineherds, poor people not much cleaner than their pigs but infinitely thinner, look at Him amazed and then whisper to one another. One of them says: «Is He perhaps not an Israelite?» And the others reply to him: «Don't you see that His tunic is fringed?»

The group of the apostles gather together, now that they can proceed in one group along a fairly wide path.

[3] The view is beautiful. Only a few score of feet above the lake, 186.3
it commands a view over the whole lake with the towns spread along its shores. Tiberias is splendid with its beautiful buildings on the opposite shore facing the apostles. Below this spot, at the foot the basaltic cliff, the short beach looks like a green pillow, whereas on the opposite shore, from Tiberias to the mouth of the Jordan, there is a rather widespread marshy plain due to the river having difficulty in resuming its course after delaying in the placid lake. But the plain looks like a garden, because it is so thick with marsh flora, and is densely populated with colourful variegated water fowl, which seem bedecked with jewels. The birds rise from the thick grass and from the reed-thickets, they fly over the lake, they dive into it to steal a fish from its water, and they rise even more brilliant, because the water has brightened up their plumage, and then they fly back to the plain where the wind plays swaying its many-coloured flowers.

Up here, instead, there are woods of very tall oak trees, under which the grass is soft and emerald-green, and beyond this strip of woods, on the other side of a large valley, the mountain climbs again, forming a very steep rocky summit, on which houses rise built on terraces. I think that the mountain side and the walls of the houses are all one, for its caves are used as dwellings, in a mixture of a troglodyte and ordinary village. It is a village characteristic of structures on large rising terraces, so that the roof of the house on the terrace below is at the height of the ground entrance of the terrace above it. On the sides where the mountain is very steep, so steep that no house can be built there, there are caves, deep crevices and descents dropping down to the valley. In the season of downpours the descents must become like many whimsical little torrents. All kinds of blocks, which the floods have rolled down to the valley, form a chaotic pedestal for the little mountain which is so wild and steep, hunchbacked and overbearing that it looks like a squire who wants to be respected at all costs.

«Is that not Gamala?» asks the Zealot.

«Yes, it is Gamala. Do you know the town?» says Jesus.

«I was a fugitive there, one night, a long time ago. Then I was affected by leprosy and I did not come out of the sepulchres any more.»

«Did they pursue you so far?»

«I was coming from Syria, where I had gone seeking protection. But they discovered me and only my flight to this place saved me from being captured. Afterwards slowly and continuously threatened I went down as far as the desert of Tekoa and from there, suffering already from leprosy, to the Valley of the Dead. Leprosy saved me from my enemies...»

«These people are heathens, are they not?» asks the Iscariot.

«Almost everybody. Only a few Jews are here on business, and then there is a mixture of beliefs, or no beliefs at all. But they did not treat the fugitive badly.»

«These are places for bandits. What gorges!» exclaim many.

«Yes, but believe me, there are more bandits on the other side» says John who is still impressed by the capture of the Baptist.

«On the other side there are also bandits among those who enjoy the reputation of being just» concludes his brother.

186.4 [4] Jesus begins to speak: «And yet we go near them without feeling disgusted. Whereas here you were making grimaces because you had to pass near some animals.»

«They are unclean...»

«A sinner is much more so. These animals are made like that, and it is not their fault if they are like that. Man instead is responsible for being unclean because of his sins.»

«Why, then, are they classified as unclean for us?» asks Philip. *

«I have mentioned that once. In this commandment there is

* **classified as unclean**. Specification of clean or unclean animals in: *Genesis 7:2-3*; *Leviticus 11*; *Deuteronomy 14:3-21*.

a supernatural reason and a natural one. The former reason is to teach the chosen people to live bearing in mind its election and the dignity of man, also in a common action like eating. A savage feeds on everything. It is enough for him to fill his stomach. A pagan, too, even if he is not a savage, eats everything, without considering that overeating foments vices and inclinations which degrade man. Indeed, pagans endeavour to reach this frenzy for pleasure, which is almost a religion for them. The more learned amongst you are aware of obscene celebrations in honour of their gods, which degenerate into lecherous orgies. A son of the people of God must be able to control himself, perfecting himself through obedience and prudence, bearing in mind his origin and his end: God and Heaven. The natural reason is not to stimulate the blood by means of food that causes a heat unbecoming of man, who is not forbidden also carnal love, but must always moderate it with the freshness of his soul tending to Heaven. Man must therefore make sure that the sentiment that joins him to his wife, in whom he must see a fellow creature like himself, not a female, is *love,* not sensuality. But the poor animals are neither guilty of being pigs nor of the effects that the flesh of pigs may cause in man's blood on the long run. And the swineherds are much less guilty. If they are honest, what difference will there be, in the next life, between them and the scribe who is bent over his books but does not learn to be good? I solemnly tell you that we shall see swineherds among the just and
scribes among the unjust. [5]But what are these ruins?» 186.5

They all move away from the side of the mountain because stones and earth are rolling down and bouncing on the slope and they all look around amazed.

«There, there! Over there! Two men completely naked... are coming towards us gesticulating. Mad...»

«Or demoniacs» replies Jesus to the Iscariot, who was the first to see the two demoniacs come towards Jesus.

They must have come out of some cave on the mountain side. They are howling. And one, who is running faster, rushes towards Jesus. He is running so fast and moving his arms up and down so much as if they were wings, that he looks like a strange ugly big bird stripped of its feathers. He collapses at Jesus' feet shouting: «You are here, Master of the world? What have I got to do with You, Jesus, Son of the Most High God? Has the hour of our punishment already come? Why have You come to torture us before the time?» The other demoniac, both because his tongue is tied and because he is possessed by a demon who causes him to be dullwitted, does nothing but throw himself on the ground, face down, and weep. He then sits up, remains inert, playing with little stones and his bare feet. The demon continues to speak through the lips of the other man who writhes on the ground in a paroxysm of terror. I would say that he wants to react, whereas he can but worship, attracted and rejected at the same time by Jesus' power. He howls: «I entreat You in the name of God, stop tormenting me. Let me go.»

«Yes. But out of this man. Unclean spirit, go out of them and tell Me your name.»

«Legion is my name because we are many. We have possessed these men for years and through them we break bonds and chains, and there is no strength of man capable of holding them. They are a terror, because of us, and we make use of them to have You cursed. We revenge ourselves on them for Your anathema. We degrade man below a beast to mock at You and there is no wolf, jackal, hyena, vulture or vampire like these whom we possess. But don't cast us out. Hell is too horrid!...»

«Go out! In the name of Jesus, go out!» Jesus' voice thunders and His eyes fire splendour.

«At least let us go into the herd of pigs You met.»

«Go.»

With a beastly howl the demons part from the two wretched men and in a sudden whirlwind, which causes the oak-trees to sway like reeds, they run into the large herd of pigs that with real demoniac cries begin to run, as possessed beings, through the oak trees, pushing, wounding, biting one another and hurl themselves into the lake, when, after reaching the edge of the cliff, they have but the water below as a shelter. The swineherds are overwhelmed and dumbfounded and while they shout seized by fear, hundreds of animals fall headlong into the calm water in a succession of splashes, causing the water to surge and foam; they sink, refloat, showing in turn their round bellies or their pointed
186.6 snouts with terrified eyes, and in the end drown. [6]The swineherds run towards the town howling.

The apostles go towards the place of the disaster and come back saying: «Not one of them is saved! He has done them a bad turn.»

Jesus replies calmly: «It is better if two thousand pigs perish than one man. Give them some clothes. They cannot stay like that.»

The Zealot opens his bag and gives one of his tunics. Thomas another one. The two men are still somewhat stunned as if they were just awaking from a sound sleep full of nightmares.

«Give them some food. Let them go back to the normal life of men.»

Jesus watches them while they eat the bread and olives given to them and they drink out of Peter's flask.

At last they speak: «Who are You?» asks one.

«Jesus of Nazareth.»

«We don't know You» says the other.

«Your souls know Me. Get up now and go home.»

«We have suffered very much, I think, but I cannot remember very well. Who is this man?» asks the one who spoke on behalf of the demon, and he points at his companion.

«I do not know. He was with you.»

«Who are you? Why are you here?» he asks his companion.

The one who was dumb, and is still more inert, says: «I am Demetrius. Is this Sidon?»

«Sidon is on the sea, man. Here you are beyond the lake of Galilee.»

«Why am I here?»

Nobody can reply. [7]Some people are arriving followed by the 186.7
swineberds. They look frightened and curious. When they see the two men dressed and tidy, their astonishment increases.

«That is Mark of Josiah!... And that is the son of the heathen merchant!...»

«And He is the one who cured them and caused our pigs to perish, because they became mad when the demons entered them» say the swineherds.

«Lord, You are powerful, we admit it. But You have already caused us too much harm! A damage of many talents. Go away, please, lest Your power should bring the mountain down and hurl it into the lake. Go away...»

«I will go. I do not impose Myself on anybody» and Jesus without further discussion goes back the way He came.

The demoniac who spoke follows Him, behind the apostles. Farther back, at some distance, there are many citizens watching whether He is really leaving.

186.8 [8] They go down the steep path back to the mouth of the little rent, near the boats. The citizens remain on the terrace watching. The demoniac who has been cured goes down behind Jesus.

In the boats the assistants are terrified. They saw the pigs raining into the lake and are still contemplating their bodies which surface more and more numerous, more and more swollen, with their round bellies in the air and their stiff short legs like four pegs stuck into a huge fat bladder. «What happened?» they ask.

«We will tell you later. Loosen the boats and let us go... Where, my Lord?»

«To the gulf of Tarichea.»

The man who has followed them, now that he sees them getting into the boats, implores: «Take me with You, Lord.»

«No. Go home: your relatives are entitled to have you. Speak to them of the great things the Lord has done to you and tell them how He had mercy on you. This area is in need of faith. Light the flames of faith out of gratitude to the Lord. Go. Goodbye.»

«Comfort me at least with Your blessing, that the demon may not possess me again.»

«Be not afraid. If you do not want, he will not come. But I bless you. Go in peace.»

The boats depart from the shore westwards. Only then, when the boats are ploughing through the waters strewn with the swine victims, the inhabitants of the town, *which did not want the Lord*, withdraw from the terrace and go away.

Here is a drawing of the area. *

* **drawing**, reproduced on the next page, marks the position of the towns and villages around the lake: **1.** Tarichea; **2.** Tiberias; **3.** Magdala; **4.** Capernaum; **5.** Bethsaida; **6.** Gherghesa; 7. Hippos; **8.** Landing point; **9.** Gamala (ranged on terraces); **10.** Oak-trees (as the line at the bottom says) "The dotted area represents the forest of oak-trees"; **11.** Korazim.

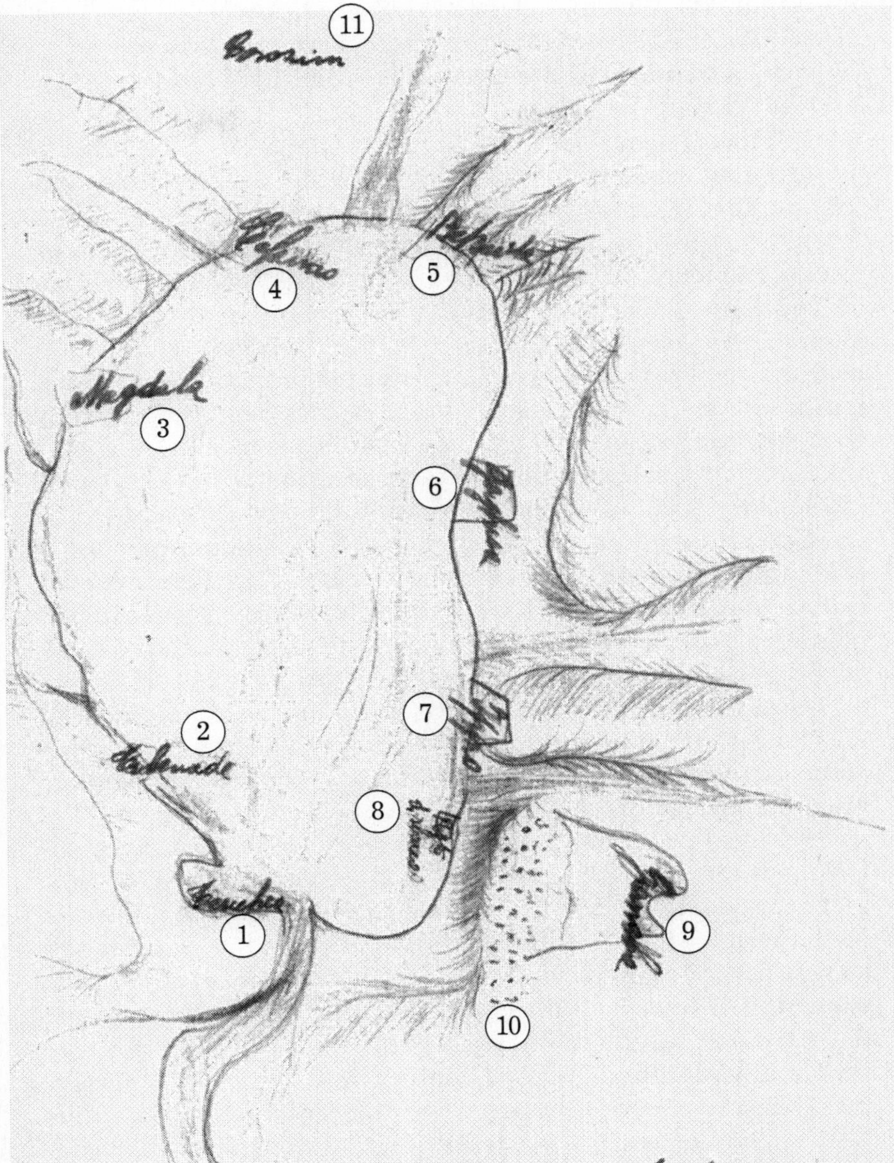
11
4
5
Magdala
3
6
2
7
8
1
9
10
Il luogo punteggiato sono i boschi di querce

187. From Tarichea Towards Jerusalem for the Second Passover. John Longs to Catch a Glimpse of the Great Sea from the Tabor.

12th June 1945.

187.1 [1] Jesus dismisses the boats saying: «I am not coming back» and followed by His apostles, and across the area which appeared to be very fertile also from the opposite shore, He turns His steps towards a mountain, which appears towards the south-west.

The apostles are walking in silence, communicating with one another only by casting glances. In fact they are not enthusiastic for the journey across this beautiful but wild area, which is full of bog grass that gets entangled with their feet; of reeds that cause drizzle of dew to fall on their heads from the edges of the leaves; of hazels that strike their faces with the hard canes of their dry fruit; of willow trees the fragile branches of which hang down everywhere tickling them; of treacherous patches of grass that seems to be growing on solid ground, whereas it conceals puddles of water into which their feet sink, they are in fact patches of foxtails and tares, growing in tiny pools and so thick as to conceal the element in which they have come up.

Jesus, instead, seems to be extremely happy in the midst of all that greenery and the thousand hues of all the flowers, which creep on the ground, or stand upright, or cling to other plants to climb up, forming thin festoons strewn with light convolvuli of a very delicate mallow pink, or forming delicate blue carpets for the thousand corollas of water myosotises, which open the perfect cups of white, pink, blue corollas among the large flat leaves of the water lilies. Jesus admires the tufts of the water reeds, as soft as silk and pearled with dew, and He bends joyfully to watch the delicate features of foxtails, which lay an emerald veil on the water. He stops ecstatically in front of the nests which the birds are building, flying happily to and fro, trilling, darting from branch to branch, working joyfully, with their beaks full of wisps of hay, of down of reeds, of flocks of wool picked on hedges, which had torn it from migrating sheep… He seems the happiest person in the world. Where is the world with its wickedness, falsehood, sorrows, snares? The world is beyond this green flowery oasis, where everything scents, shines, smiles, sings.

This is the earth created by the Father and not desecrated by man and man can be forgotten here.

[2] He wants to share His happiness with the others. But He does not find a favourable ground. The hearts of the apostles are tired and embittered by so much ill-will and they react against things and also against the Master by means of a stubborn silence, which is like the stillness of the air before a storm. Only His cousin James, the Zealot and John take an interest in what interests Jesus. All the others are… absent, if not hostile. Perhaps they are keeping quiet, not to grumble. But inside they must be speaking, and speaking too much. 187.2

It is a more lively exclamation of admiration before the living jewel of a kingfisher which flies down, taking a little silver fish to its mate, that makes them open their mouths.

Jesus says: «Can there be anything more gentle?»

Peter replies: «Perhaps not more gentle… but I can assure You that a boat is more comfortable. Here it is damp just the same, but we are not comfortable…»

«I would prefer the track for caravans to this… garden, if You wish to call it so, and I am in full agreement with Simon» says the Iscariot.

«It was you who did not want the caravan route» replies Jesus.

«Ehi! certainly… But I would not have given in to the Ghérghesenes. I would have gone away from there, but I would have continued beyond the river to Gadara, Pella and down to the south» grumbles Bartholomew.

And his great friend Philip concludes: «The roads belong to everybody, after all, and we could have passed through them well.»

«My friends! I am so anguished and disgusted… Do not increase My grief with your pettiness! Let Me seek some comfort in things which do not know how to hate…»

The reproach, kind in its sadness, moves the apostles.

«You are right, Master. We are not worthy of You. Forgive our foolishness. You can see the beautiful, because You are holy You look with the eyes of Your heart. We are coarse flesh and can only perceive coarse flesh… But never mind. Believe me, even if we were in paradise, we would be sad without You. But with You…

oh! it is always beautiful for our hearts. It is only our limbs that refuse» many of them whisper.

187.3 [3] «We will soon be going out of here and will find a more comfortable ground, even if not so cool» promises Jesus.

«Where are we going exactly?» asks Peter.

«To give Passover to those who suffer. I have been wanting to do it for a long time. But I could not. I would have done it going back to Galilee. Now that they compel us to go along roads that we have not chosen, I am going to bless Jonah's poor friends.»

«We will be wasting a lot of time! Passover is near! There are always delays for various reasons.» Another chorus of complaints rises to the sky. I do not know how Jesus can be so patient…

Without reproaching anyone He says: «Please, do not hinder Me! Endeavour to understand My need to love and to be loved. I have but this solace on the earth: to love and do the will of God.»

«And are we going from here? Was it not better to go from Nazareth?»

«If I had suggested that, you would have rebelled. No one will suspect that I am here… and I am doing it for you… because you are afraid.»

«Afraid? Ah! No! We are ready to fight for You.»

«Pray the Lord not to put you to the test. I know that you are quarrelsome, resentful, anxious to offend those who offend Me and to humble your neighbour. I know all that. But I do not know you to be brave. As far as I am concerned, I would have also gone by Myself and along the main road and nothing would have happened because it is not yet the time. But I feel sorry for you. I have to obey My Mother, yes, but I do not want to upset Simon the Pharisee. I will not disgust them. But they will disgust Me.»

«And where do we go from here? I am not familiar with this area» says Thomas.

«We will reach Tabor, we will coast part of it and will go to Nain via Endor; from there to the plain of Esdraelon. Be not afraid!… Doras, the son of Doras, and Johanan are already in Jerusalem.»

187.4 [4] «Oh! It will be beautiful! They say that from the summit, from a certain spot, one can see the Great Sea, the Sea of Rome. I like it so much! Will You take us to see it?» John begs with his kind childish face raised towards Jesus.

«Why do you like to see it so much?» asks Jesus caressing him.

«I do not know... Because it is huge and you cannot see its end... It makes me think of God... When we were up on Lebanon I saw the sea for the first time, because I had never been anywhere else, except along the Jordan or on our little sea... and I was moved so much that I wept. So much blue! So much water! And it never overflows!... What a wonderful thing! And the stars make paths of light on the sea... Oh! do not laugh at me! I looked at the golden way of the sun until I was dazzled, at the silvery way of the moon, until I could see nothing but whiteness and I saw them getting lost far far away. Those ways spoke to me. They said: "God is in that infinite distance and these are the ways of fire and purity, which a soul must follow to go to God. Come. Dive into the infinite, travelling on these two ways, and you will find the Infinite One".»

«You are a poet, John» says Thaddeus admiringly.

«I do not know whether this is poetry. I know that it inflames my heart.»

«But you have seen the sea also at Caesarea and at Ptolomais, and quite close, too. We were on the beach! I do not see the need to go all that way to see some more sea water. After all... we were born on the water...» remarks James of Zebedee.

«And we are in it now as well, unfortunately!» exclaims Peter, who diverting his mind for a moment to listen to John, has not noticed a treacherous puddle and has got soaked... They all laugh, and he laughs too.

But John replies: «That is true. But from high above it is more beautiful. You see more and farther. You think that it is deeper and vaster... You wish... you dream...» and John is already dreaming... He looks in front of himself and smiles at his dream... He looks like a flesh-coloured rose spread with minute dew drops, so downy becomes his smooth clear skin of a young fair-haired man and as it gets sprinkled with a light perspiration it looks more like the petal of a rose.

«What do you wish? What are you dreaming?» Jesus asks His favourite disciple in a low voice and He looks like a father who questions a dear son speaking in his sleep. Jesus speaks to John's soul, questioning him so gently as not to spoil the dream of His loving disciple.

«I wish to go onto the infinite sea... towards other lands beyond it. I wish to go and speak of You. I am dreaming... of going towards Rome, towards Greece, towards dark places to take the Light there... so that those living in darkness may get in touch with You and *may live* in communion with You, Light of the world... I am dreaming of a better world... to be bettered through the knowledge of You, that is, through the knowledge of the Love that makes people good, pure, heroic, of the Love that makes the world love and raise Your Name, Your Faith, Your Doctrine above hatred, sin, flesh, above the vices of the mind, above gold, above everything... and I dream of going with my brothers on the sea of God, on the road of light to take You... as Your Mother once brought You down to us from Heaven... I dream that I am a child, who knowing nothing but love, is happy also when facing trouble... and sings to comfort the adults who ponder too much, and moves forward... facing death smiling... towards glory with the humility of one who does not know what he is doing, but knows only that he is coming to You, Love...»

The apostles have not breathed during John's ecstatic confessions... They remained still where they were, looking at the youngest one speaking with his eyes covered by his eyelids, like a veil thrown over the ardour rising from his heart, and looking at Jesus Who is enraptured finding Himself so completely in His disciple...

When John stops speaking, slightly bent forward — he reminds me of the gracefulness of the humble Mary of Nazareth — Jesus kisses his forehead saying: «We shall go and contemplate the sea, to let you dream My future Kingdom in the world once again.»

187.5 [5] «Lord... You said that afterwards we shall be going to Endor. Make me happy too... that I may get over the bitterness of the boy's judgement...» says the Iscariot.

«Oh! are you still thinking about that?» asks Jesus.

«Yes, always. I feel degraded in Your eyes and in the eyes of my companions. I think of what Your thoughts...»

«Why do you fret over trifles? I was not thinking of that trifle any longer, neither were the others. You are reminding us... You are a child accustomed only to being caressed and the word of a little boy seems the sentence of a judge to you. But you must not be afraid of that word, but of your actions and of God's judgement. But to convince you that you are as dear to Me as previously, as always, I tell you that I will satisfy you. What do you wish to see at Endor? It is a poor village among the rocks...»

«Take me there... and I will tell You.»

«All right. But mind it does not cause you to suffer afterwards...»

«If it cannot be painful for him to contemplate the sea, it cannot be harmful to me to see Endor.»

«To see?... But it is the desire of what one seeks to see in looking that can be harmful. But we shall go...»

And they carry on along the road towards Mount Tabor, the huge mass of which appears to be nearer and nearer, while the marshy aspect of the ground changes, as the soil becomes solid and dry and the vegetation thinner, making room for taller plants and bushes of clematis and blackberries, the new leaves and early flowers of which are a pleasant sight.

188. Visit to the Cave of the Sorceress at Endor. The Encounter with the Miserable Felix Who Becomes the Disciple John.

13th June 1945.

[1] Jesus and the apostles have passed Mount Tabor and left it 188.1
behind them. They are now walking on a plain lying between that mountain and another one facing it, talking of the climb made by them all, although at the beginning the elder ones had not been too keen. But now they are happy they had gone up to the top. The journey is now easy because they are on a main road which is quite comfortable for walking. It is early in the morning because I am under the impression that they have spent the night on the slopes of the Tabor.

«That is Endor» says Jesus pointing to a poor village built on the first heights of the other mountain. «Do you really want to go there?»

«If You wish to make me happy...» responds the Iscariot.

«Let us go, then.»

«But is it a long way?» asks Bartholomew, who, because of his age, is not very keen on walking tours.

«Oh! no! But if you wish to stay...» says Jesus.

«Yes! You may stay. I will go with the Master» says Judas of Kerioth immediately.

«Listen, before making up my mind, I would like to know what there is to be seen... From the top of Mount Tabor we saw the sea and after the boy's speech I must admit that I saw it properly for the first time and I saw it as You see: with my heart. Here... I would like to know whether there is anything to learn, because in that case I will come even if it is tiresome...» says Peter.

«Do you hear that? You have not yet said what you intend doing. Be kind to your companions and tell us now» says Jesus invitingly.

«Did Saul not go to Endor to consult the necromancer?» *

«Yes, he did. So?»

«Well, Master, I would like to go there and hear You speak of Saul.»

«In that case I will come, too!» exclaims Peter full of enthusiasm.

«Let us go then.»

They walk fast along the last stretch of the main road, which they leave to follow a secondary road, which takes straight to Endor.

188.2 [2] It is a poor village, as Jesus said. The houses cling to the slopes which, beyond the village become steeper. Poor people live in them. Most of them must be shepherds who pasture their flocks on the sides of the mountain and in the woods of old oak-trees. There are a few small fields of barley, or similar fodder grains, in favourable sites and some apple and fig-trees. There are only a few vines around the houses, decorating the walls, which are dark because the place is obviously a damp one.

«We will now ask where the place of the necromancer was» says Jesus. And He stops a woman who is coming back from the fountain with pitchers.

She looks at Him curiously, then replies impolitely: «I don't know. I have much more important things to worry about than

* **Saul... to Endor**, in *1Samuel 28:3-25*; *1Chronicles 10:13-14*; *Sirach 46:20.*

such nonsense!» and she goes away.

Jesus turns to an old man who is carving a bit of wood.

«The necromancer?... Saul?... Who bothers about them now? But, wait... There is one here who has studied and perhaps he knows... Come with me.»

And the old man climbs laboriously up a stony lane to a very poor and shabby looking house. «He lives here. I will go in and call him.»

Peter, pointing at some poultry scratching about in a dirty yard, says: «This fellow is not an Israelite.» But he says no more because the old man comes back followed by a man blind in one eye, who is as dirty and untidy as everything around his house.

The old man says: «See? This man says that it is over there beyond that dilapidated house. There is a path, a stream, a wood and some caves, the one at the top, where there are still traces of ruined walls on one side, is the one you are looking for. Is that right?»

«No. You have muddled everything. I will go with these strangers.» The man's voice is harsh and guttural, which increases everybody's feeling of uneasiness.

[3] He starts walking. Peter, Philip and Thomas make repeated 188.3
signs to Jesus to advise Him not to go. But Jesus does not pay attention. He walks with Judas behind the man, and the others follow Him... unwillingly.

«Are You an Israelite?» asks the man.

«Yes, I am.»

«I, too, or almost, although I do not look like one. But I lived a long time abroad and I got into many habits, of which these fools here disapprove. I am better than the others. But they say that I am a demon, because I read a great deal, I breed poultry which I sell to the Romans and I can cure people by means of herbs. When young, because of a woman, I quarrelled with a Roman — I was at Cintium then — and I stabbed him. He died, I lost one eye and all my wealth and I was sentenced to life imprisonment. But I knew how to cure people, and I cured the daughter of one of the guards. I thus won his friendship and some freedom... I used it to escape. I acted badly, because the man certainly paid for my flight with his life. But freedom seems so beautiful when one is a prisoner...»

«Is it not really beautiful afterwards?»

«No. Jail, where one is alone, is better than being in contact with men who do not allow you to be alone and come around us to hate us...»

«Did you study philosophy?»

«I was a teacher at Cintium... I was a proselyte...»

«And now?»

«Now I am nothing. I live according to the reality of facts. *And I hate,* as I was and am still hated.»

«Who hates you?»

«Everybody. And God is the first. She was my wife... and God allowed her to be unfaithful to me and ruin me. I was free and respected, and God allowed me to become a convict serving a life sentence. God abandoned me, men were unfair. Both He and they destroyed me. There is nothing left here...» and he strikes his forehead and his chest. «Rather, here, in my head, there are my thoughts, my knowledge. It is in here that there is nothing» and he spits contemptuously.

«You are wrong. You still have two things there.»

«Which?»

188.4 «Remembrance and hatred. Remove them. [4]Become really empty... and I will give you something new to put in there.»

«What?»

«Love.»

«Ah! Ah! You make me laugh. I have not laughed for thirty-five years, man. Since I had the proof that the woman was unfaithful to me with the Roman wine merchant. Love! Love to me! It is like me throwing jewels to my chickens! They would die of indigestion, unless they passed them out with their excrement. The same would happen to me. Your love would be a burden to me, if I could not digest it...»

«No, man! Do not say that!» Jesus lays His hand on the man's shoulder, He is deeply and openly distressed.

The man looks at Him with his only eye and what he sees on that most sweet and beautiful face causes him to be struck dumb and to change his expression. From being sarcastic he becomes very serious and then really sad. He lowers his head and with a different voice he asks: «Who are You?»

«Jesus of Nazareth. The Messiah.»

«You!!!»

«I. Did you not know about Me, since you read so much?»

«I knew... But I did not know that You were alive and... above all, I did not know this. I did not know that You are good to everybody... thus... to murderers too... Forgive me for what I said... about God and love... Now I understand why You want to give me love... Because without love the world is hell, and You the Messiah want to make a paradise of it.»

«A paradise in every heart. Give Me the remembrance and the hatred that make you ill and let Me put love into your heart!»

«Oh! I wish I had known You before!... then... But when I killed, You were certainly not born yet... But later... when I was free, as free as a snake in a forest, I lived to poison people with my hatred.»

«But you did some good as well. Did you not say that you cured people by means of herbs?»

«Yes. To be tolerated. But how many times I had to struggle against my desire to poison people by means of potions!... See? I took refuge here because... it is a place where the world is ignored and which the world ignores. A cursed place. In other places I hated and was hated and I was afraid of being recognised... But I am wicked.»

«You regret having harmed the prison guard. Do you not see that there is still some goodness in you? You are not wicked... Your only trouble is that you have a large open wound, which nobody is curing... Your goodness runs out of it as blood from a wound. But if someone would cure your wound and heal it, My dear brother, goodness would increase in you, because it would no longer vanish as it forms...»

The man weeps with a bent head trying to conceal his tears. Only Jesus Who is walking beside him notices them. He notices but does not say anything else.

5 They arrive at a cavern made of rubble and mountain caves. 188.5
The man endeavours to steady his voice and says: «Here it is. You may go in.»

«Thank you, My friend. Be good.»

The man does not say anything and remains where he was, while Jesus with His apostles, passing over large stones which must have been part of very strong walls, upsetting green lizards and other ugly looking insects, enters a large smoky grotto, on the walls of which there are still graffiti signs of the zodiac and similar things. In a corner blackened by smoke there is a niche and under it a hole which looks like a gully-hole for water. Bats hanging in disgusting bunches decorate the ceiling and an owl, upset by the light of a branch which James has lit to ensure they do not tread on scorpions or asps, complains by flapping its wadded wings and closing its ugly eyes which cannot bear the light. It is perched in the niche, and the foul smell of dead mice, of weasels and birds in decomposition at its feet is mixed with the stench of dung and of the damp soil.

«It is really a lovely place!» says Peter. «Your Tabor and your sea were much better, my boy!» And then addressing Jesus: «Master, satisfy Judas at once because this is not... Antipa's royal hall!»

«Certainly. What is it that you want to know?» He asks Judas of Kerioth.

«Well... I would like to know whether and why Saul sinned coming here... I would like to know whether it is possible for a woman to evoke the dead. I would like to know whether... Oh! It is better if You speak. I will ask You questions.»

«It's a long story. At least let us go out there, in the sunshine, on the stones... We will get away from the dampness and the stench» begs Peter.

And Jesus agrees. They sit as best they can on the ruins of the walls.

«Saul's sin was only *one* of his sins. It was preceded and followed by many more. All of them serious. Double ingratitude towards Samuel who had annointed him king and who subsequently disappeared so as not to share with the king the admiration of the people. He was several times ungrateful to David who saved him from Goliath and spared him in the caves at Engedi and Hachilah. He was guilty of many acts of disobedience and of scandalising his people. He was guilty of grieving his benefactor Samuel by lacking in charity. He was guilty of jealousy, of making attempts on David's life, David being another benefactor of his, and finally, of the crime he committed here.»

«Against whom? He did not kill anyone here.»

188.6 «He killed his soul in here, he finished killing it. [6]Why are you lowering your head?»

«I am thinking, Master.»

«You are thinking. I can see that. What are you thinking about? Why did you want to come? You must admit it was not out of mere curiosity of a scholar.»

«We always hear someone talk of magicians, necromancers, evoked spirits... I wanted to see whether I could discover anything... I would like to know how it is done... I think that since we are destined to amaze people in order to attract them, we should be, somehow, necromancers too. You are You and You do things by means of Your power. But we must ask for power, for help in order to perform exceptional deeds, which are necessary...»

«Are you mad? What are you saying?» shout many.

«Be quiet. Let him speak. He is not mad.»

«Yes, I thought that by coming here a little of the magic of gone by days would assume possession of me and make me greater. In Your interest, believe me.»

«I know that your present desire is a sincere one. But I will reply to you with eternal words, because they are words of the Book, and the Book will exist as long as man exists. Believed or mocked at, employed to defend the truth or scorned at, it will always exist. It states: "And Eve, seeing that the fruit of the tree was good to eat and pleasing to the eye, took it and ate it and gave some to her husband... Then their eyes were opened and they realised that they were naked and they made themselves loin-cloths... And God said: 'How did you realise that you were naked? Only because you ate the forbidden fruit'. And He expelled them from the garden of delights". And in the book of Saul, it states: "Samuel appearing said: 'Why have you disturbed me, conjuring me up? Why do you consult me when the Lord has abandoned you? The Lord will deal with you as I told you... *because you did not obey the voice of the Lord'* ". Son, do not stretch your hand towards the forbidden fruit. It is imprudent even to go near it. Do not be curious to know ultramundane things, lest its satanic poison should conquer you. Avoid the occult and what cannot be explained. One thing only is to be accepted with holy faith: God. But avoid what is not God and what cannot be explained by man's reason or cannot be done by man's power, so that the sources of wickedness may not be opened for you and you may realise that you are "naked". *Naked: repel-*

lent in your humanity mixed with satanism. Why do you wish to amaze people by means of obscure prodigies? Amaze them through your holiness, which should be as bright as things coming from God. Do not be anxious to tear the veils which separate the living from the dead. Do not disturb the deceased. Listen to them, if they are wise, while they are on the earth, venerate them by obeying them also after their death. But do not upset their second life. *He who does not obey the voice of the Lord, loses the Lord. And the Lord has forbidden occultism, necromancy, satanism in all its forms.* What more do you wish to know than the Word already tells you? What more do you wish to perform than your goodness and My power enable you to perform? Do not crave for sin, but for holiness, son. Do not feel mortified. I am glad that you disclose your humanity. Many people, *too many,* like what you like. But the purpose of your desire: "to be power to attract people to Me" removes a heavy weight from that humanity and puts wings on it. But they are the wings of a night bird. No, My dear Judas. Put wings as bright as the sun, wings of an angel on your spirit. By the simple breeze caused by flapping them you will attract hearts and will lead them in your wake to God. Can we go?»

«Yes, Master! I was wrong...»

«No. You have been an inquirer... The world will always be full of them. Come. Let us get away from the stench of this place. Let us go towards the sun! In a few days it will be Passover, and afterwards we will go to your mother's. I conjure her up for you: your honest home, your holy mother. How peaceful it is!»

As usual, the recollection of his mother and the Master's praise for her, cheer Judas.

188.7 [7] They come out of the ruins and they begin to descend the path they had walked up previously. The man blind in one eye is still there.

«Are you still here?» asks Jesus pretending that He does not notice that his face is flushed because of the many tears he has shed.

«Yes, I am still here. I will follow You if You allow me. I have something to tell you...»

«Come with Me, then. What do you want to tell Me?»

«Jesus... I find that to have the strength to speak and to work the holy magic of changing myself, of conjuring up my dead soul as the necromancer evoked Samuel for Saul, I must pronounce Your Name, which is as sweet as Your eyes, and as holy as Your voice. You have given me a new life, but it lacks form and energy, like the life of a new-born baby after a difficult birth. It still struggles in the grip of wicked old habits. Help me to come out of my death.»

«Yes, My friend.»

«I... I have realised that there is still a little humanity in my heart. I am not entirely a beast, and I can still love and be loved, forgive and be forgiven. Your love, which is forgiveness, has taught me. Is it not so?»

«Yes, My friend.»

«Then... take me with You. I was Felix! What irony! But give me a new name. That my past may be really dead. I will follow You like a stray dog, which finally finds a master. I will be Your slave, if You wish so. But do not leave me alone...»

«Yes, My friend.»

«What name will You give me?»

«A name dear to Me: John. Because you are grace granted by God.»

«Will You take me with You?»

«Yes, for the time being. Later you will follow Me with My disciples. But what about your house?»

«I have no house any longer. I will leave what I have to the poor. Just give me love and bread.»

«Come.» Jesus turns around and calls His apostles. «I thank you, My friends, and you in particular, Judas. Through you, Judas, through you all, a soul is coming to God. Here is a new disciple. He is coming with us until we can entrust him to our brother disciples. Be happy because you have found a heart and bless God with Me.»

But the Twelve do not really look very happy. But out of obedience and kindness they welcome him.

«If You do not mind I will go ahead. You will find me at the door of my house.»

«Yes, go.»

The man runs away. He seems another man.

«And now that we are by ourselves I order you, *and this is an order*, to be kind to him and not to mention his past *to anybody*. I will immediately reject anyone who should speak or be uncharitable to our redeemed brother. Is that clear? And see how good the Lord is! We came here for a human purpose and He allowed us to go away after achieving a supernatural deed. Oh! I rejoice because of the joy now in Heaven for the new convert.»

188.8 [8] They reach the house. The man is there, on the threshold, wearing a clean dark tunic and a mantle to match, a pair of new sandals and carrying a large haversack over his shoulder. He closes the door and then, what is strange in a man who might be considered hard-hearted, he takes a white hen, perhaps his pet, which squats tamely in his hands, he kisses it weeping and lays it down.

«Let us go... and forgive me. But my chicken always loved me... I used to speak to them and... they understood me...»

«I understand you, too... and I love you. So much. I will give you all the love that the world denied you in thirty-five years...»

«Oh! I know! I can feel it! That is why I am coming. But be indulgent to a man who... loves an animal which has been more faithful to him than men...»

«Yes... Forget your past. You will have so much to do! And, experienced as you are, you will do it very well. Simon, come here and you, too, Matthew. See? This man was more than a prisoner, he was a leper. And this one... a sinner. And they are very dear to Me, because *they know* how to understand poor hearts... Is that right?»

«Thanks to Your goodness, my Lord. But you may rest assured, my friend, that everything is cancelled by serving Him. Only peace remains» says the Zealot.

«Yes. Peace and a new youth taken over from old vices and hatred. I was a tax collector. Now I am an apostle. The world is in front of us. And we know all about it. We are not absentminded children who pass near the harmful fruit and the bending plant and do not see facts. We know. We can avoid evil and teach other people how to avoid it. And we can straighten up those who bend.

Because we know what a relief it is to be supported. And we know Who supports: *Him*» says Matthew.

«That's true! Quite true! You will help me. Thank you. I feel as if I were passing from a dark foul smelling place to the open

in a flowery meadow... I felt something similar when I came out, at long last free, after twenty years of imprisonment and brutal work in the mines in Anatolia and I found myself — I escaped one stormy evening — on the top of a wild mountain, but in the open, in a place full of sunshine at dawn, and covered with scented woods... Freedom! But now it is better! Everything is more sublime! I had not been in chains for fifteen years. But hatred, fear and solitude were still like chains to me... But now they have
been shaken off!... [9]Here we are at the house of the old man who 188.9
brought You to me. Ehi! Man!»

The old man rushes towards them and is dumbfounded seeing the fellow blind in one eye clean, wearing new clothes and smiling.

«Here, take this. It's the key of my house. I am going away, *for good.* I am grateful to you because you are my benefactor. You have given me a family. Do *what you like with* my property... and look after my chicken. Treat them well. A Roman comes every Sabbath and buys eggs... You will make a profit... Take care of my little hens... and may God reward you for it.»

The old man is astonished... He takes the key and stands open-mouthed.

Jesus says: «Yes, do as he told you and I will be grateful to you, too. I bless you in the name of Jesus.»

«The Nazarene! You! Mercy! I have spoken to the Lord! Women! Men! The Messiah is here!»

He screams like an eagle and people rush from everywhere.

«Bless us! Bless us!» they shout. Some shout: «Stay here!» and others: «Where are You going? At least tell us where You are going.»

«To Nain. I cannot stay.»

«We will follow You. Do You mind?»

«Come. Peace and blessing to those who remain here.»

They go towards the main road and take it.

[10]The man, who is walking near Jesus and can hardly carry his 188.10
haversack, attracts Peter's curiosity. «What have you got in there that is so heavy?» he asks.

«My clothes... and some books... My friends after and at the same time as the chicken. I could not part with them. But they are heavy.»

«Eh! Science is heavy! Of course! And who likes it, eh?»

«They prevented me from becoming mad.»

«Eh! You must be fond of them! What books are they?»

«Philosophy, history, Greek and Roman poetry...»

«Lovely, certainly lovely. But... do you think you will be able to carry them with you?»

«Perhaps I will be able to part with them. But you cannot do everything at once, can you, Messiah?»

«Call Me Master. No, you cannot. But I will let you have a place where you will be able to keep your friends, your books. They may help you to talk about God with the heathens.»

«Oh! How free Your thought is from all restrictions!»

Jesus smiles and Peter exclaims: «No wonder! He is Wisdom!»

«And Goodness, believe me. And are you learned?»

«Me? Oh! Most learned. I can tell an allice from a carp and my erudition ends there. I am a fisherman, my friend!» and Peter smiles humbly and frankly.

«You are an honest man. It is a science you learn by yourself. And a very difficult one to learn. I like you.»

«And I like you, too. Because you are sincere. Even when you accuse yourself. I forgive everything, I help everybody. But I am a ruthless enemy of false people. They make me sick.»

«You are right. A false man is a delinquent.»

«A delinquent. You are right. Say, would you mind giving me your sack for a little while? In any case, you may be sure that I will not run away with books... I think you are finding it difficult.

«Twenty years in a mine breaks your back... But why do you want to toil?»

«Because the Master has taught us to love one another like brothers. Give them to me. And take my rags. My bag is not heavy... There is no history, no poetry in it. My history, my poetry and the other thing you mentioned, is He, my Jesus, our Jesus.»

189. The Son of the Widow of Nain.

14th June 1945.

[1]Nain must have been a town of some importance in the days 189.1
of Jesus. It is not a large town, but is well built, surrounded by its walls, lying on a low pleasant hill, an off shoot of the Little Hermon, commanding a very fertile plain which stretches towards
* the north-east.

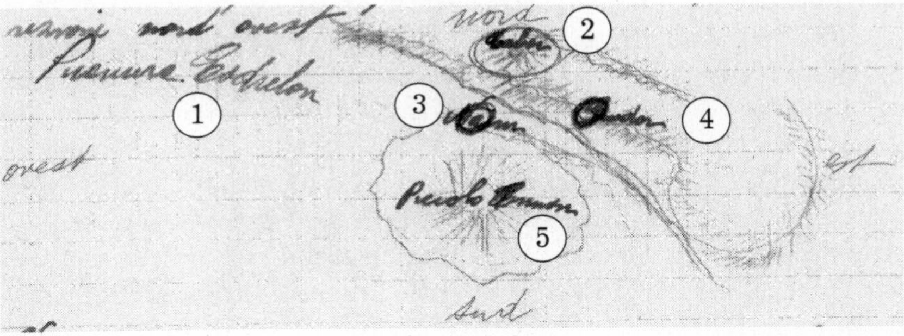

One arrives here coming from Endor, after crossing a little river, which flows into the Jordan. But neither the Jordan nor its valley can be seen any longer, because they are concealed by hills which form an arch shaped like a question mark in the east.

Jesus follows a main road which links the lake region to the Hermon and its villages. Many inhabitants of Endor walk behind Him talking to one another animatedly.

Only a short distance separates the group of the apostles from the walls: about two hundred yards, at the most. And as the main road runs straight to one of the town gates, which is wide open because it is broad daylight, it is possible to see what is happening in the inner side of the walls. Thus Jesus, Who is speaking to the apostles and the new convert, sees a funeral coming towards them, with a great noise of weepers and similar eastern displays.

«Shall we go and see, Master?» ask many. And many of the inhabitants of Endor are already rushing to see.

«Yes, let us go» says Jesus condescendingly.

«Oh! It must be a boy. See how many flowers and ribbons there are on the stretcher» says Judas of Kerioth to John.

---

* **towards the north-east.** M.V.'s drawing indicates — besides the four cardinal points — **1.** Esdrelon Plain; **2.** Tabor; **3.** Nain; **4.** Endor; **5.** Little Hermon.

«Or it is probably a virgin» replies John.

«No, it is certainly a young man, because of the shades they have used. And there is no myrtle either...» says Bartholomew.

The funeral comes out from the other side of the walls. It is not possible to see what there is on the stretcher, which is carried shoulder high by the bearers. One understands that there is a corpse, wrapped in bandages and covered by a sheet, only because of its outline and that it is the body of a fully grown person, because it is as long as the stretcher.

A veiled woman is walking beside it, weeping, supported by relatives or friends. The only sincere tears in all that farce of mourners. And when a bearer trips on a stone or heap in the ground or stumbles and causes the stretcher to shake, the mother moans: «Oh! No! Be careful! My boy has suffered so much!» and she raises her trembling hand to caress the edge of the stretcher. And as she is unable to do anything else, she kisses the veils and the ribbons, which blown by a gentle breeze lightly touch the immobile corpse.

Peter, sympathetic, his good keen eyes welling up with tears whispers: «She is the mother.» But he is not the only one whose eyes are shining with tears at the sight. Also the Zealot, Andrew, John, and even the ever merry Thomas have tears in their eyes. They are all deeply moved. Judas Iscariot whispers: «If it were I! Oh! Poor mother of mine...»

189.2 [2] Jesus, the kindness of Whose eyes is so deep as to be unbearable, makes His way towards the stretcher.

The mother, who is now sobbing louder because the funeral is about to turn towards the open sepulchre, pushes Him aside resolutely, when she sees that Jesus wants to touch the stretcher. I wonder what she is afraid of in her grief. She shouts: «He is mine!» and looks at Jesus with staring eyes.

«I know, mother. He is yours.»

«He is my only son! Why should he die, he was so good and dear, he was my joy, and I am a widow. Why?» The crowd of the hired mourners mourn more loudly, forming a chorus with the mother who continues: «Why he, and not I? It is not just that she who has borne a child, should see her offspring perish. The offspring must live, otherwise why was my womb torn to give birth to a man?» and she strikes her abdomen wildly and desperately.

«Do not do that! Do not weep, mother.» Jesus takes her hands clenching them firmly in His left hand, while with His right one He touches the stretcher saying to the bearers: «Stop and put the stretcher down.»

The bearers obey and lower the little bed that rests on its four legs.

Jesus takes the sheet covering the dead boy and pulls it back uncovering the corpse.

The mother shouts her grief and the name of her son, I think: «Daniel!»

Jesus, still clenching the mother's hands in His, stands up, His eyes imposingly bright, the power of miracle shining majestically on His face, lowering His right hand, orders in the full strength of His voice: «Young man! I tell you: get up!»

[3] The dead boy, wrapped in bandages as he is, sits up on the little bed and calls: «Mother!» He calls her with the stammering frightened voice of a terrified child. 189.3

«He is yours, woman. I give him to you in the name of God. Help him to get rid of the sudarium. And be happy.»

And Jesus makes the gesture of withdrawing. Impossible! The crowds rivet Him to the stretcher, on which the mother has thrown herself groping for the bandages, endeavouring to be quick, while the imploring childish moaning repeats: «Mother! Mother!»

The sudarium and bandages are undone and mother and son can embrace each other, and they do so without bothering about the sticky balms, which the mother removes from his dear face and hands, making use of the same bandages. As she has not clothes to put on him, she takes off her mantle and wraps him in it, caressing him all the time...

[4] Jesus looks at her... he looks at the loving group, close together on the edge of the little bed, no longer a stretcher, and He weeps. 189.4

Judas Iscariot sees His tears and asks: «Why are You weeping, my Lord?»

Jesus turns His face towards him and says: «I am thinking of My Mother...»

The brief conversation draws the woman's attention to her Benefactor. She takes her son by the hand, she supports him because his limbs are still somewhat numb, and kneeling down she says: «You, too, my son. Bless this Holy man Who has restored you to life and to your mother» and she bends to kiss Jesus' tunic while the crowd sing hosannas to God and to His Messiah, Who by now is well known for what He is, because the apostles and the people of Endor have taken it upon themselves to tell Who is He Who worked the miracle.

And the crowds exclaim: «Blessed be the God of Israel. Blessed be the Messiah, His Messenger! Blessed be Jesus, Son of David! A great Prophet is risen among us! God has really visited His people! Hallelujah! Hallelujah!»

189.5 [5] At last Jesus can steal away and enter the town. The crowd follow and pursue Him, exulting in their love.

A man rushes towards Jesus and bows deeply to Him. «Please come and stay under my roof.»

«I cannot. Passover prevents Me from making any stop except those programmed.»

«In a few hours it will be sunset and this is Friday...»

«Exactly, that is why I must reach My resting place before sunset. I thank you just the same. But do not keep Me back.»

«I am the head of the synagogue.»

«So you mean that you are entitled to have Me. Man, if I had arrived here only one hour later, that woman would not have had her son restored to her. I am going where other unhappy people are waiting for Me. Do not be so selfish as to delay their joy. I will certainly come again and I will be with you in Nain for several days. Now let Me go.»

The man does not insist any more. He only says: «As You said. I will wait for You.»

«Yes. Peace to you and to the citizens of Nain. Also to you, people of Endor, peace and blessings. Go back to your homes. God has spoken to you through the miracle. Endeavour, through the power of love, to have all your hearts restored to Goodness.»

A last chorus of hosannas. Then the crowds let Jesus go and He crosses the town diagonally and goes out into the country, towards Esdraelon.

190. The Arrival in the Plain of Esdraelon at Sunset.

15th June 1945.

1 The sun is setting in a red sky when Jesus comes in view of Johanan's fields. 190.1

«Let us quicken our pace, My friends, before the sun sets. And you, Peter, go with your brother to inform our friends, Doras' men.»

«I will go indeed, to see also whether the *son* has really gone away.» Peter stresses the word «son». And he goes away.

In the meantime Jesus proceeds at a slower pace, looking around to see whether any of Johanan's men are about. But He can only see the fertile fields, in which the ears of grain are already well formed.

At last, a face, wet with perspiration, appears among the vine-leaves and an exclamation is heard: «Oh! Blessed Lord!» and the peasant runs out of the vineyard and prostrates himself at Jesus' feet.

«Peace to you, Isaiah!»

«Oh! You remember my name too?»

«It is written in My heart. Stand up. Where are your companions?»

«Over there. In the apple-orchards. But I will tell them at once. You will be our guest, will You not? The master is not here and we can welcome You. In any case... what with the fear, what with the joy... it is better. Just imagine, he gave us a lamb this year and will allow us to go to the Temple! He has only given us six days.... but we will run all the way... We will be in Jerusalem, too... Imagine!... And thanks to You.» The man is in his seventh heaven of delight because he has been treated as a man and as an Israelite.

«I have done nothing, as far as I know...» says Jesus smiling.

«Eh! no! You have done a great deal. Doras, and the fields of Doras, and these ones here, which are instead so beautiful this year... Johanan was informed of your visit, *and he is not a fool.* He is afraid and... and he is afraid.»

«Of what?»

«He is afraid that what happened to Doras may happen to him. Both with regards to his life and to his property. Have You seen Doras' fields?»

«I have come from Nain...»

«In that case You have not seen them. They are a complete ruin. (The man whispers that in a low but clear voice, like someone imparting a secret concerning something dreadful.) They are all ruined! There is no hay, no fodder, no fruit. Vines and orchards withered... Dead... everything is dead... like Sodom and Gomorrah... Come, I will show You.»

«It is not necessary. I am going to see those peasants...»

«But they are no longer here! Did You not know? Doras, the son of Doras, has scattered them or dismissed them, and the ones he sent to the other country places which belong to him, must not speak of You, or they will be lashed... Not to speak of You! That will be difficult! Also Johanan said so to us.»

«What did he say?»

«He said: "I am not so foolish as Doras and I will not say to you: 'I do not want you to speak of the Nazarene'. It would be useless, because you would do it just the same and I do not want to lose you by lashing you to death like untameable animals. On the contrary I say to you: 'Be good as the Nazarene certainly teaches you and tell Him that I treat you well'. I do not want to be cursed, too". Of course, he can see what these fields are like after You
190.2 blessed them, and what the ones You cursed are like. [2]Oh! Here are the ones who ploughed the field for me...» and the man runs to meet Peter and Andrew.

But Peter greets him briefly and proceeds on his way and begins to shout: «Oh! Master! There is no one left! They are all new faces. And everything is laid waste! He could very well do without any peasants here. It is worse than the Salt Sea!...»

«I know. Isaiah told Me.»

«But come and see! What a sight...»

Jesus pleases him after saying to Isaiah: «I will stay with you. Tell your companions. But do not go to any trouble. I have enough food. All we need is a barn to sleep in and your love. I will come back soon.»

The sight of Doras' fields is really distressing. Fields and meadows are dry and barren, vineyards are withered, the foliage and fruit of trees are completely destroyed by millions of insects of all kinds. Also the garden-orchard near the house looks like a desolate dying wood. The peasants wander to and fro uprooting weeds, crushing caterpillars, snails, earthworms and the like, shaking branches under which they place basins full of water to drown little butterflies, aphides and other parasites which cover the leaves and eat away the plant until it dies. They endeavour to find a sign of life in the vine-shoots, which break like dry wood as soon as they are touched and sometimes fall off the main branch, as if the roots had been cut by a saw. The contrast with Johanan's fields, vineyards and orchards is most striking and the ruin of the cursed fields seems more impressive when compared to the fruitfulness of the others.

«The hand of the God of Sinai is a heavy one» whispers Simon the Zealot.

Jesus makes a gesture as if to say: «How right you are!» but He does not say anything. He only asks: «How did it happen?»

A peasant replies between his teeth: «Moles, locusts, worms... but go away! The steward is faithful to Doras... Don't cause us trouble...»

Jesus sighs and goes away.

Another peasant, who is bent under an apple-tree earthing it up, in the hope he may save it, says: «We will reach You tomorrow... when the steward goes to Jezreel for the prayer... we will come to Micah's house.»

Jesus makes the gesture of blessing and goes away.

[3] When He goes back to the cross-road, all the peasants of Johanan are there and joyful and happy they surround their Messiah and take Him to their poor dwellings. 190.3

«Did You see, over there?»

«Yes, I did. Doras' peasants are coming tomorrow.»

«Of course, when the hyenas go to pray... We do that every Sabbath... and we speak of You, we tell what we heard from Jonah, from Isaac, who often comes to see us, and what we learned from You in Tishri. We speak as best we can. Because it is impossible not to speak of You. And the more we suffer, the more we are forbidden, the more we speak of You. Those poor people... they drink the essence of life every Sabbath... But how many there are in this plain who are in need of knowing, of knowing You at least, and yet they cannot come here...»

«I will see to them as well. And may you be blessed for what you do.»

The sun is setting while Jesus enters a kitchen blackened by smoke. The Sabbath rest begins.

191. The Sabbath in Esdrelon. Little Jabez. The Parable of Rich Dives.

16th June 1945.

191.1 [1] «Give Micah enough money so that tomorrow he may pay for what he borrowed today from the peasants of this area» says Jesus to the Iscariot, who usually handles the... common possessions. Then Jesus calls Andrew and John and sends them to two spots from which it is possible to see the road or the roads coming from Jezreel. He calls also Peter and Simon and sends them to meet the men of Doras with instructions to stop them at the boundary between the two estates. He then says to James and Judas: «Take the foodstuffs and come with Me.»

The peasants of Johanan, women, men and children follow them. The men are carrying two small amphoras, which, however, are not very small, and which must be full of wine. They are jars rather than amphoras and contain about ten litres each. (Please do not take my estimate literally). They go towards a thick vineyard, which is already all covered with new leaves, at the end of Johanan's property. Beyond it there is a large ditch which is kept full of water with, I wonder, how much work.

«See? Johanan quarrelled with Doras over this ditch. Johanan said: "It is your father's fault if everything is ruined. If he did not want to adore Him, he should have been afraid of Him instead of provoking Him". And Doras shouted like a demon: "It was this ditch that saved you. The insects did not cross it...". And Johanan replied: "Why is all your property ruined, then, when previously your fields were the nicest ones in Esdraelon? It's God's punishment, believe me. You went beyond the limit. This water?... It has been here all the time and that is not what saved me". And Doras shouted again: "Which proves that Jesus is a demon". "He is a just man" Johanan shouted back. And they continued for some time, while they had breath. Later Johanan spent a lot of money to divert the torrent, to find other underground water sources, and to dig more ditches on the boundary line between him and his relative, and he made them deeper and told us what we told You yesterday... After all, he is happy that it happened. He was so envious of Doras... He now hopes that he will be able to buy everything, because Doras will end up by selling everything at a very low price.»

[2]Jesus benignly listens to all the confidential information, 191.2
while waiting for Doras' poor peasants, who arrive without any delay and prostrate themselves on the ground as soon as they see Jesus in the shade of a tree.

«Peace to you, My friends. Come here. The synagogue is here today and I am your head of it. But first I wish to be the father of your family. Sit around Me, that I may give you some food. The Groom is with you today, and we will have a wedding banquet.»

And Jesus uncovers a basket, from which He takes some loaves of bread handing them to the amazed peasants of Doras. From another basket He takes the foodstuffs He has been able to find: cheese, cooked vegetables, and a little kid or lamb, cooked whole, which He divides among the unhappy men. He then pours out some wine and hands around a coarse chalice so that everybody may drink.

«Why all this? And what about them?» ask Doras' men pointing to Johanan's men.

«They have already had their share.»

«All this expense! How could You do that?»

«There are still some good people in Israel» replies Jesus smiling.

«But this is Sabbath...»

«Thank this man» says Jesus pointing at the man from Endor. «He got the lamb. It was easy to get the rest.»

The poor men devoured — it is the right word — the food, the like of which they had not tasted for a long time.

[3]One of them, a rather elderly man, is pressing to his side a 191.3
boy about ten years old; he eats and weeps.

«What is the matter, father?...» asks Jesus.

«It's because Your goodness is too great...»

The man from Endor says in his guttural voice: «That is true... and it makes you weep. But the tears are not bitter ones...»

«They are not bitter. That's true. And then... There is something I would like. My tears express also a desire.»

«What do you want, father?»

«See this child. He is my grandson. He was left to me after the landslide of last winter. Doras does not even know that he has come to me, because I have to let him live like a wild animal in the wood and I see him only on the Sabbath. If he finds out he will either drive him away or compel him to work... and this tender offspring of mine will be treated worse than a pack animal. At Passover I am sending him to Jerusalem with Micah, to become a son of the Law... and after?... He is my daughter's son...»

«Would you give him to Me, instead? Do not weep. I have many friends who are honest, holy and without any children. They will bring him up in a holy manner, in My Way...»

«Oh! Lord! That is what I have been wishing for since I heard of You. And I prayed that holy man Jonah to save my grandchild from this death, because he knows what it means to belong to this master...»

«Child, would you come with Me?»

«Yes, my Lord. And I will cause You no grief.»

«That is settled.»

191.4 4 «But... to whom do You wish to give him?» asks Peter pulling Jesus by the sleeve. «Also this one to Lazarus?»

«No, Simon. But there are so many without any children...»

«And I am one of them...» Peter's desire seems to make his face grow thinner.

«Simon. I have already told you. You are to be the "father" of all the children I will bequeath to you. But you are not to be bound by any child of your own. Do not be upset. You are too important to your Master, Who cannot detach you from Himself because of an affection. I am exacting, Simon. I am more exacting than a very jealous husband. I love you most partially and I want you to be entirely Mine.»

«All right, my Lord... all right... Let it be done as You wish.» Poor Peter is really heroic in adhering to Jesus' will.

«He will be the son of My dawning Church. All right? He will belong to everybody and to nobody. He will be "our" child. He will follow us when distances will allow him to, or he will come to us and the shepherds will be his guardians, as in every child they love "their" Child Jesus. Come here, My child, what is your name?»

«Jabez of John and I am from Judah» says the boy without hesitating.

«Yes. We are Judaeans» confirms the old man. «I used to work in Doras' lands in Judaea, and my daughter got married to a man from that area. He worked in the woods near Arimathea and last winter...»

«I saw the disaster.»

«The boy was spared because that night he was far away with a relative... In actual fact the boy was appropriately named Jabez. I said to my daughter at once: "Why? Do you not remember the ancient tradition?". But her husband insisted in giving him that name, so he is Jabez.» *

«"The child will call on the Lord and the Lord will bless him and will extend his lands, and the hand of the Lord will be with him and will keep harm away from him". That is what the Lord will grant him to comfort you, father, and the souls of the dead, and to console the orphan.

5 And now that we have separated the needs of the body from 191.5
those of the soul, by an act of love for the boy, listen to the parable that I have thought out for you.

There was once a very rich man. He wore the most beautiful garments, and in his purple and byssus clothes he used to strut about in squares and at home, respected by his citizens as the most powerful man in the country, and by his friends, who gratified his pride to gain benefits thereby. They feasted every day in his halls, where the multitude of his guests, all rich and none therefore needy crowded flattering Dives. His banquets were famous for the copiousness of food and of choice wines.

In the same town there lived a beggar, a great beggar. He was great in his misery as the other was great in his wealth. But under the crust of the human misery of Lazarus, the beggar, there was a treasure, which was even greater than Lazarus' misery and Dives' wealth. And it was Lazarus' true holiness. He had never infringed the Law, not even when urged by need, and above all he had complied with the precept of love for God and

* **Jabez** was not considered a lucky name. See *1Chronicles 4:9-10*.

for his neighbour. He, as is wont with poor people, used to go near the doors of rich people to ask for alms, so that he would not starve to death. And every evening he would go to Dives' house, hoping to receive at least the crumbs of the pompous banquets which took place in the magnificent halls. He would lie in the street, near the door, and wait patiently.

But if Dives noticed him, he would have him driven away because that underfed body, covered with sores and ragged clothes, was too sad a sight for his guests. That is what Dives used to say. In actual fact, it was because the sight of so much misery and goodness was a continuous reproach to him. His well fed dogs, adorned with precious collars, were more pitiful than he was and they used to go near poor Lazarus and lick his sores, showing their great joy at being caressed by him. They even took the remains of the bountiful tables to him, so that Lazarus survived malnutrition thanks to animals. If he had relied on man he would have died, because man did not even allow him to enter the halls, after the banquet, to pick up the crumbs which had fallen from the tables.

191.6 [6] One day Lazarus died. No one on earth noticed it, no one mourned him. On the contrary, Dives rejoiced not seeing on that day or afterwards that misery which he called a "disgrace" near his door. But the angels noticed it in Heaven. And when he was about to breathe his last breath in his cold barren cave, the celestial cohorts were present and in a bright dazzling light they picked up his soul and singing hosannas they took it to the bosom of Abraham.

Some time went by and Dives died. Oh! What a grand funeral! The whole town, already aware of his agony, crowded in the square where his abode was, some to be noticed as friends of the great man, some out of curiosity, some to gain favour with the heirs, and they all joined in the mourning, and their cries rose to the sky and with their cries also the false praises of the "great, just benefactor" who had died.

Can the word of man change God's judgement? Can human apology cancel what is written in the book of Life? No, it cannot. What has been judged is judged and what has been written is written. And notwithstanding the grand funeral, the soul of Dives was buried in hell.

Then, in that horrible jail, eating and drinking fire and darkness, finding hatred and torture everywhere and in every moment of eternity, he raised his eyes to heaven. He raised his eyes to heaven which he saw in the brightness of lightning, in the fraction of a second, and the indescribable beauty of heaven remained present in his mind and tormented him in the midst of atrocious tortures. And he saw Abraham up there. Far, but bright, happy... and in his lap, bright and happy there was also Lazarus, poor Lazarus, once miserable, despised, revolting... and now? He was handsome in the light of God and of his holiness, full of God's love, admired not by men but by the angels of God.

Dives weeping cried: "Father Abraham, have mercy on me! Send Lazarus, as I cannot possibly hope that you will do it yourself, send Lazarus to dip the tip of his finger in water and touch my tongue with it, to cool it, for I am in agony in these flames which pierce me continuously and burn me!".

Abraham replied: "Remember, son, that you had all good things during your life, whereas Lazarus had all bad things. But he turned evil into good, whereas you did nothing but evil of all the good things. It is therefore just that now he should be comforted here and that you should suffer. In any case it is not possible to do it. Holy people are spread over the earth so that men may take advantage of them. But, if notwithstanding all the opportunities, he remains what he was — in your case, a demon — it is useless to make recourse to saints. We are now separated. Herbs are mixed when they are in the field. But when they are cut, the good ones are separated from the evil ones. That is what happens to you and to us. We were together on the earth and you rejected and tortured us in every possible way, you forgot us, acting against the law of charity. We are now divided. There is an abyss between you and us, and those who wish to cross it and come to you, cannot do it. Neither can you, where you are, cross the dreadful abyss and come to us".

[7] Dives, crying more loudly shouted: "Holy father, at least 191.7
please send Lazarus to my father's house. I have five brothers. I have never understood what love is, not even among relatives. But now I understand what a terrible thing it is not to be loved. And since where I am there is hatred, in the fraction of a second,

when my soul saw God, I understood what Love is. I do not want my brothers to suffer the pains that I am suffering. I am terrified because they are leading the same life as I did. Oh! send Lazarus to tell them where I am, and why I am here, and let them know that hell does exist, and it is dreadful, and that those who do not love God and their neighbour come to hell. Send him! So that they may provide in good time, and may not come here, to this place of eternal torture" .

But Abraham replied: "Your brothers have Moses and the Prophets. They should listen to them".

And with a deep groan of a tormented soul Dives replied: "Oh! Father Abraham! They will be more impressed by a dead person... Listen to me! Have mercy!".

But Abraham said: "If they have not listened to Moses and the Prophets, they will not believe either one who has risen from the dead for one hour to speak words of Truth to them. In any case it is not fair that a blessed soul should leave my bosom to go and be insulted by the sons of the Enemy. The time of insults is over for such souls. They are now in peace by the order of God Who sees that it is useless to endeavour to convert those who do not even believe in the word of God and do not practice it".

That is the parable and its meaning is so clear that no clarification is required.

191.8 [8] My Jonah lived here and really achieved the holiness of Lazarus, whose glorious position near God is made clear by the protection He grants to those who hope in Him. Jonah can come to you, as a friend and protector, and he will come if you are always good.

I would like, and I tell you now what I told him last spring, I * would like to be able to help you all, also materially, but I cannot, and I am sorry for that. I can but point Heaven to you. I can only teach you the great wisdom of resignation and promise the future Kingdom to you. Do not hate, never, for any reason whatsoever. Hatred is strong in the world. But it always has a limit. Love has no limit of power or time. Love therefore, to possess love, as a defense and comfort on the earth, and as a reward in

* **last spring**, in 89.1.

Heaven. It is better to be Lazarus than Dives, believe Me. Believe it and you will be blessed.

In the desolation of these fields you cannot hear one word of hatred, even if facts could have justified it. Do not misunderstand the miracle. I am Love and I would not have struck. But seeing that Love could not bend cruel Doras, I abandoned him to Justice which avenged the martyr Jonah and his brothers. This is what the miracle teaches you. That Justice is always vigilant, even when it seems to be absent and that since God is the Master of creation, in pursuance of Justice, He can also make use of the lesser beings, such as caterpillars and ants, to punish the hearts of cruel and greedy people letting them die choked by a regurgitation of their own poison.

[9] I bless you, now. And I will pray for you at every dawn. And 191.9
you, father, do not worry about the little lamb you are entrusting to Me. I will bring him back now and again, that you may rejoice seeing him grow in wisdom and goodness in the way of the Lord. He will be your lamb of this poor Passover of yours, the most pleasing of all the lambs offered at the altar of Jehovah. Jabez, say goodbye to the old father and then come to your Saviour, to your Good Shepherd. Peace be with you!»

«Oh! Master! Good Master! How painful it is to leave you!»

«Yes, it is painful. But it is better if the steward does not find you here. I came here deliberately to avoid punishment for you. Please obey for the sake of the Love Who advises you.»

The unhappy men rise with tears in their eyes and go back to their cross. Jesus blesses them once again and then, holding the boy by the hand and with the man from Endor on the other side, He goes back to Micah's house along the same way He came.

Andrew and John join Him and the disciples after their watch.

192. A Prediction to James of Alphaeus. The Arrival at Engannim After a Stop in Mageddo.

17th June 1945.

[1] «Is that the top of Mount Carmel, my Lord?» asks His cousin 192.1
James.

«Yes, it is, brother. That is the chain of the Carmel and the highest peak is the one that gives the name to the chain.»

«The world must be beautiful also from there. Have You ever been up there?»

«Yes, once, by Myself, at the beginning of My mission. And at the foot of it I cured the first leper. But we will go there together, to commemorate Elijah...»

«Thank You, Jesus. You have understood me as usual.»

«And as usual I perfect you, James.»

«Why?»

«The reason is written in Heaven.»

«Would You not tell me, brother, since You can read what is written in Heaven?»

Jesus and James are walking one beside the other and only little Jabez, who is held by the hand by Jesus, can hear the confidential conversation of the two cousins who smile looking at each other's eyes.

Jesus embraces James' shoulders with His arm to draw him closer to Himself and asks: «Do you really want to know? Well, I will tell you by means of a riddle, and when you find the answer you will be wise. Listen: "After assembling the false prophets on Mount Carmel, Elijah stepped out in front of all the people: 'How long' he said 'do you mean to hobble first on one leg then on the other? If the Lord is God, follow Him; if Baal, follow him'. The people did not reply. Elijah then said to the people: 'I, I alone am left as a prophet of the Lord' and the only strength of the lonely prophet was his cry: 'Answer me, Lord, answer me, so that this people may know that You are the Lord God, and are winning back their hearts'. Then the fire of the Lord fell and consumed the holocaust". Guess, My brother.» *

James is pensive with his head lowered and Jesus looks at him smiling. They walk for a few yards thus, then James asks: «Is it in connection with Elijah or with my future?»

«With your future, of course...»

James becomes thoughtful again and then whispers: «Am I perhaps destined to invite Israel to follow a way with sincerity? Am I destined to be the only one left in Israel? If so, do You mean

---

* **Listen**, quotation from *1Kings 18:20-22.36-38*.

that all the others will be persecuted and scattered and that... I will pray You for the conversion of this people... as if I were a priest... as if I were... a victim... But if it is so, Jesus, inflame me as from now...»

«You already are inflamed. But you will be carried away by * Fire, like Elijah. That is why you and I will go, all alone on Mount Carmel to speak...»

«When? After Passover?»

«Yes, after *a* Passover. And then I will tell you many things...»

[2] A lovely little river which flows towards the sea and is in flood 192.2
because of the springtime rains and the thawing snow, prevents them from proceeding.

Peter runs towards them and says: «The bridge is further up, where the road from Ptolomais to Engannim passes.»

Jesus goes back submissively and crosses the little river by a strong stone bridge. Immediately afterwards they meet some little mountains and hills, but they are of little importance.

«Shall we be at Engannim by evening?» asks Philip.

«Certainly... But... we have the boy now. Are you tired, Jabez?» Jesus fondly. «Be as frank as an angel.»

«A little, Lord. But I will do my best to walk.»

«This boy is very weak» says the man from Endor in his guttural voice.

«No wonder!» exclaims Peter. «Considering the life he has been leading for months! Come here, I will carry you in my arms.»

«Oh! No, sir. Don't tire yourself. I am still able to walk.»

«Come, come here. You are certainly not heavy. You look like an underfed little bird» and Peter puts him astride his square shoulder's, holding him by the legs.

They walk fast because the sun is now strong and urges them to reach the shady hills.

[3] They stop in a village, the name of which I hear is Mageddo, to 192.3
take some food and rest near a very cool fountain, which is also noisy because of the abundance of water that gushes out into a dark stone basin. But no one in the village takes an interest in the travellers, anonymous among many other more or less rich

* **like Elijah**, in *2Kings 2:11.*

pilgrims, who on foot or riding donkeys or mules are going towards Jerusalem for Passover. There is already a holiday atmosphere and there are many boys among the travellers, exhilarated at the idea of the ceremony for their coming of age.

Two boys, of well-to-do families, who have come to play near the fountain while Jabez is there with Peter — who takes the boy with him everywhere attracting him with a thousand little things — ask the boy: «Are you going also, to become a son of the Law?»

Jabez replies shyly: «Yes» almost hiding himself behind Peter.

«Is this man your father? Are you poor?»

«Yes, I am poor.»

The two boys, probably the sons of Pharisees, look him over ironically and curiously and then say: «One can see it.»

It can be seen, indeed... His tunic is really shabby! Perhaps the boy has grown, and although the hem of the tunic has been let down, the garment, a brown one faded by inclement weather, hardly reaches half way down his thin legs. His little feet are badly shod in two shapeless sandals held together by strings which must torture his feet.

The boys, with the ruthless selfishness typical of many children and with the cruelty of ill-mannered urchins, say: «Oh! In that case you will not have a new suit of clothes for your feast! We instead!... Is that right Joachim? Mine is all red with a mantle to match. His, instead, is sky blue and we will have sandals with silver buckles, a precious belt and a talet held by a pale gold leaf and...»

«...and a heart of stone, I would say!» bursts out Peter, who has finished cooling his feet and drawing water to fill all the flasks. «You are bad boys. The ceremony and your clothes are not worth a fig if your hearts are not good. I prefer my boy. Go away, you proud urchins! Go amongst the rich but respect the poor and
192.4 the honest. [4]Come, Jabez! This water is good for your tired feet. Come here that I may wash them. You will walk better afterwards. Look how these strings have hurt you! You must not walk anymore. I will carry you in my arms until we reach Engannim. I will find a shoemaker there and I will buy you a new pair of sandals.» And Peter washes and dries the little feet which had not received so many caresses for a long time.

The boy looks at him, hesitates, then bends over the man who is tying his sandals and embraces him with his emaciated arms saying: «How good you are!» and kisses his grey hair.

Peter is moved. He sits on the damp ground, as he is, takes the boy in his lap and says to him: «Call me "father" then.»

They form a tender group. Jesus and the others approach them.

But before the two parties meet, the two proud little fellows already mentioned, who had remained there inquisitively, ask:«But is he not your father?»

«He is father and mother to me» replies Jabez without hesitation.

«Yes, dear! You are right: father and mother. And, my dear little gentlemen, I can assure that he will be properly dressed for the ceremony. He, too, will have a dress fit for a king, as red as fire and a belt as green as grass, and his talet will be as white as snow.»

And alhough the match is not a very harmonising one, it shocks the two conceited boys and drives them away.

«What are you doing, Simon, sitting on the wet ground?» asks Jesus smiling.

«Wet? Ah! yes. I have just noticed. What am I doing? I am becoming a lamb again having innocence on my heart. Ah! Master. Well, let us go. But you must leave this boy in my hands. Afterwards I will surrender him. But he is mine until he becomes a true Israelite.»

«All right! And you will be his guardian, like an old father. Is that all right? Let us go, so that we shall be at Engannim before evening, without making the boy run too much.»

«I will carry him. My fishing net is heavier. He cannot walk with these broken soles. Come here.» And with his godson astride his shoulders Peter takes happily to the road again. The road is now more shady, through woods of various kinds of trees, gently ascending hills, from which one's eyes rove over the fertile plain of Esdraelon.

[5] They are already near Engannim — which must be a beau- 192.5
tiful little town supplied with water brought from the hills by means of an elevated aqueduct, probably a Roman work — when the noise of an oncoming military squad makes them take refuge

on the edge of the road. The hooves of the horses resound on the road, which here, near the town, shows signs of a paving that appears through the dust gathered on it with rubble. The road has obviously never been swept with a besom.

«Hail, Master! How do You happen to be here?» shouts Publius Quintilianus dismounting from his horse, and going towards Jesus with a broad smile, holding the horse by the reins. His soldiers slow down to keep pace with their superior.

«I am going to Jerusalem for Passover.»

«I am going, too. We are reinforcing the guard for the festivity, also because Pontius Pilate is coming to town, too, and Claudia is there. We are her runners. The roads are so insecure! The eagles drive jackals away» says the soldier laughing and looks at Jesus. He then continues in a low voice: «Double watch this year, to protect the back of filthy Antipas. There is a lot of ill-feeling because of the capture of the Prophet. Ill-feeling in Israel... and consequently dissatisfaction among us. But... we have already ensured that the High Priest and his stooges have been... benignly lectured...» and he ends in a low voice: «Go without any fear. All the claws have been retracted into the paws. Oh! They are afraid of us. If we only clear our throats, they take it for a roar. Will you speak at Jerusalem? Come near the Praetorium. Claudia speaks of You as of a great philosopher. That is a good
192.6 thing because Claudia is the proconsul.» [6]He looks around and sees Peter flushed, perspiring with his load. «And that boy?»

«An orphan I brought with Me.»

«But that man of Yours is working too hard! Boy, are you afraid to come on the horse with me for a few yards? I will keep you under my chlamys and I will go slow. I will hand you back to him when we are at the gate.»

The boy does not object, he is as mild as a lamb, and Publius lifts him up onto the saddle.

And while he is ordering his soldiers to go slow he also sees the man from Endor. He stares at him and says: «What! You here?»

«I am here. I have stopped selling eggs to the Romans. But the chicken are still there. I am now with the Master...»

«Good for you! You will have greater comfort. Goodbye. Hail, Master. I will wait for You at that group of trees.» And he spurs his horse.

«Do you know him? And does he know you?» many ask John of Endor.

«Yes, as his supplier of chicken. He did not know me before, but once I was summoned to the headquarters at Nain to fix the prices, and he was there. Since then he always spoke to me when I went to Caesarea to buy books or tools. He calls me Cyclops or Diogenes. He is not a bad fellow, and although I cannot bear Romans I have never offended him because he might be useful to me.»

«Did you hear that, Master? My speech to the centurion at Capernaum was a good thing. I feel more relaxed now» says Peter.

They reach the thicket in the shade of which the patrol has dismounted.

«I am handing the boy back to You. Have You orders, Master?»

«No, Publius. May God show Himself to you.»

«Hail», he mounts his horse and spurs it, followed by his men with a loud rattle of hooves and body-armour.

[7] They enter the town and Peter with his little friend goes to 192.7
buy sandals.

«That man is dying for a son» says the Zealot, and he concludes: «He is right.»

«I will give you thousands. Now let us go and look for a place to rest, so that tomorrow we can start at dawn.»

193. From Engannim to Shechem in Two Days.

18th June 1945.

[1] Jesus goes on His way towards Jerusalem along roads which 193.1
are more and more crowded with pilgrims. A heavy shower during the night has made the road somewhat muddy, but, on the other hand, it has removed dust and made the air clearer. The fields look like gardens diligently tended by skilled men.

They all walk fast because they are well rested after a night's sleep, and because the boy, with his new sandals, no longer suffers when walking: on the contrary, as he becomes more and more familiar, he chatters with this one and that one, and confidentially informs John that his father's name was also John and his mother's Mary, and that he therefore is very fond of John as well. «But» he concludes, «I love you all, and in the Temple I will pray so much for you and for the Lord Jesus.»

It is moving to see how this group of men, most of whom have no children, are so paternal and full of attention for the youngest of Jesus' disciples. Even the countenance of the man from Endor softens when he forces the little one to swallow a beaten egg, or when he climbs up among the woods, which make the hills as well as the higher mountains green, to pick acidulous branches of shrubs or scented stems of wild fennel, which he takes to the boy to quench his thirst, without overburdening his stomach with water. He also draws his attention to the different aspects and sights of the country, which is split here by large valleys at the bottom of which run main roads, to take his mind off the length of the journey.

The old teacher of Cintium, ruined by human wickedness, revives because of this boy, a wretch like himself, and the wrinkles of misfortune and bitterness smooth into a gentle smile. Jabez is already less shabby looking, because of his new sandals, and his face is not so sad, because I do not know which hand of an apostle has erased every trace of the wild life the boy led for so many months, sorting his hair so far ruffled and dusty and now made soft and tidy by a good wash. The man from Endor is quite different too. He is still somewhat puzzled when he hears anyone call him John, but then he shakes his head and smiles pitying his bad memory. Day by day his countenance loses its habitual hardness and gains a gravity, which is quite serene. Of course these two wretched people, who are reviving through Jesus' kindness, gravitate towards the Master in their love. Their companions are dear, but Jesus... When He looks at them or speaks just to them, the expression on their faces is a most happy one.

193.2 [2] After crossing the large valley and then a beautiful green hill, one can still dimly see the plain of Esdraelon. This causes the child to sigh: «What will my old father be doing?» and with a very sad sigh and tears in his brown eyes he exclaims: «Oh! he is not so happy as I am... and he is so good!» and the lament of the child casts a sad veil over everybody. They begin to descend a very fertile valley, completely covered with cultivated fields and olive-groves. A light breeze causes the tiny flowers of vines and of the earlier olive-trees to fall like snow. The plain of Esdraelon is out of sight for good.

They stop for a meal and then resume the journey towards Jerusalem. But it must have rained heavily or the area is rich in underground water, because the meadows look like a marsh owing to the water that glitters among the thick grass and rises lapping on the banked road, which, however, is still very muddy. The adults pull their tunics up to prevent them from becoming soiled with mud, and Judas Thaddeus puts the boy on his shoulders to let him rest and to cross more quickly the flooded and perhaps unhealthy area.

Daylight is beginning to fade when, after walking along the edge of other hills and crossing a dry rocky valley, they enter a village situated on a raised rocky embankment. They push their way through the crowd of pilgrims and look for accommodation in a very rural type hotel: a large shed under which is spread much straw and nothing else. Small lamps lit here and there shed a glow on the supper of the pilgrim families, poor families, like the apostolic one, because most of the rich people have put up tents outside the village, disdaining contact with either the local people or the poor pilgrims.

Night and silence fall... The first to fall asleep is the boy, who, tired as he is, lays his head on the lap of Peter, who lays him on the straw and covers him carefully.

Jesus gathers the adults in prayer and then each throws himself on the straw to rest after the long journey.

[3]The day after: the apostolic group that left in the morning is 193.3
about to enter Shechem in the evening, having passed through Samaria, a beautiful town, surrounded by walls, adorned with splendid imposing buildings, around which are grouped some lovely tidy houses. I am under the impression that the town, like Tiberias, has been recently rebuilt with systems borrowed from Rome. Outside the walls, around the town, the land is very fruitful and well cultivated.

The road from Samaria to Shechem winds down from terrace to terrace, in a series of walls supporting the earth, which reminds me of the Fresoli hills. There is a splendid view of green mountains to the south and of a most beautiful plain westwards. *

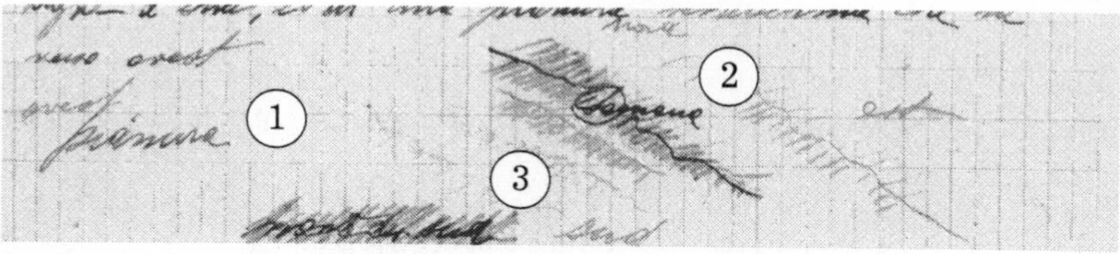

The road tends to descend to the valley, but it climbs now and again to cross other hills from the top of which one commands the land of Samaria with its lovely olive-groves, corn fields, vineyards, watched over from the hill crests by woods of oak and other forest trees, which must be protective against the winds that blowing through the gorges are inclined to create whirlwinds damaging cultivations. This area reminds me very much of certain spots in our Apennines, around Mount Amiata, where one can contemplate at the same time the flat cultivations of cereals in the Maremma and the bright hills and majestic mountains that rise higher inland. I do not know what Samaria is like now. It was very beautiful in those days.

Now, between two high mountains, the highest in the area, one can see straight through a valley, in the middle of which there is the very fertile well-watered land of Shechem. It is here that Jesus and His disciples are caught up with by the joyful caravan of the Consul's court, on its way to Jerusalem for the festivity. There are slaves on foot and slaves on the wagons guarding the luggage... My God, how many items they carried with them in those days!!! And with the slaves there are wagons that are packed with all sorts of goods, even complete litters and travelling coaches: the four wheel wagons are very wide, well sprung, with tilt, under which the ladies are sheltered. And then many other carts and slaves...

A curtain is drawn, by the bejewelled hand of a lady and the severe profile of Plautina appears: she nods smiling but does not say anything. Valeria, whose little girl on her knees trills and smiles, greets people in the same fashion. The other wagon,

---

* **westwards.** In the following drawing MV has written, besides the four cardinal points: **1.** *plain*, **2.** *Samaria*; **3.** *mounts of the south.*

which is even more stately, passes by but no curtain is drawn. But when it has gone by, the pinkish face of Lydia looks out from the rear, through the closed curtains and she nods, too. The caravan goes away...

[4] «They travel in comfort!» says Peter who is tired and wet with perspiration. «But, if God helps us, the day after tomorrow evening we shall be in Jerusalem.» 193.4

«No, Simon. I must make a detour and go towards the Jordan.»

«But why, my Lord?»

«Because of the boy. He is very sad, and it would be too sad for him to see the mountain of the disaster.»

«But we shall not see it! Or rather, we shall see the other side... and I take it upon myself to divert his attention. John and I... His attention is easily distracted, poor little dove without a nest. To go towards the Jordan! Well! It is better this way. A straight road. Shorter. Safer. No. No. This one, this one. See? Also the Roman ladies are taking it. Along the sea and the river there is the risk of fever during the first summer rains. It is healthy here. In any case... When are we going to arrive if we increase the distance? Consider how agitated Your Mother must be after that unpleasant business of the Baptist!...» Peter wins and Jesus agrees.

«In that case we will stop early and have a good rest and tomorrow we will leave at dawn to be at Gethsemane in the evening of the day after tomorrow. The day after Friday we will go to Bethany to see My Mother and we will leave John's books there, as they have been quite a burden for you, and we will find Isaac there and will entrust him with this poor brother of ours...»

«And the boy? Are You handing him over at once?»

Jesus smiles. «No. I am giving him to My Mother, Who will prepare him for "his" feast. And then we will keep him with us for Passover. But after we will have to leave him... Do not become too attached to him! Or rather: love him as if he were your own son, but with a supernatural spirit. As you can see he is weak and gets tired. I, too, would have liked to teach him Myself and bring him up nourished in Wisdom by Me. But I am the Untiring One and Jabez is too young and too weak to do the work we do. We will go through Judaea and will come back to Jerusalem for Pentecost, and then we will go... evangelizing... We shall

193.5 find him again in our fatherland in summer. [5]Here we are at the gate of Shechem. Go ahead with your brother and with Judas of Simon and look for accommodation. I will go to the market square and wait for you there.»

They part and Peter goes away looking for a shelter, while the others walk with difficulty in the streets crowded with people shouting and gesticulating, with donkeys, wagons, all going to Jerusalem for the oncoming Passover. The shouting, calling cursing of people, added to the braying of donkeys cause a noise that resounds very loudly under the vaults, which link one house to another, a noise that resembles the rumble of certain shells when placed near one's ear. The echo travels from vault to vault where the shades become darker and the crowds, like an impetuous torrent, rush into the streets, insinuating themselves everywhere, looking for a roof, a square, a meadow in which to pass the night...

Jesus, holding the child by the hand, leaning against a tree, is waiting for Peter in the square, which, for the occasion, is always full of vendors.

«Let us hope that no one sees us and recognises us!» says the Iscariot.

«How can you recognise a grain of sand among the sands?» replies Thomas. «Don't you see the crowds?»

Peter comes back: «Outside the town there is a shed with some hay. I could not find anything else.»

«Neither shall we look for anything else. It is even too much for the Son of man.»

194. Revelations to Little Jabez While Going from Schechem to Beeroth.

19th June 1945.

194.1 [1] As a river grows larger when new tributary streams flow into it, so the road from Shechem to Jerusalem is becoming gradually more and more crowded, as believers heading for the Holy City pour onto it along secondary roads from villages. A situation which is of great help to Peter in distracting the attention of the boy who is now passing near the hills where he was born and where his parents are buried under a landslide. The child is not aware of it.

After Shiloh on its steep hill, had been left behind to the left, the long march is interrupted by a pause to rest and take some food in a green valley resounding with pure crystal-clear waters. The pilgrims set forth again and cross a little calcareous mountain, which is rather barren, and on which the sun is blazing down mercilessly. They then begin to descend through a range of most beautiful vineyards, which with their festoons adorn the crags of the calcareous mountains. The area is most sunny.

Peter smiles significantly and makes a sign to Jesus, Who in turn smiles. The boy does not notice anything, engrossed as he is in listening to John of Endor who is speaking to him of other lands he has visited where the most sweet grapes grow that, however, are not so much used to make wine, as to make cakes, which are more delicious than honey cakes.

[2] They are now climbing a very steep hill, because they have 194.2
left the dusty crowded main road and have taken this short cut through woods. And when they reach the summit, they can distinctly see in the distance a huge bright light shining above an agglomeration, perhaps whitewashed houses.

«Jabez» calls Jesus «come here. Can you see that golden spot? It is the House of the Lord. There you will swear to obey the Law. But do you know it well?»

«My mother used to speak to me about it and my father taught me the precepts. I can read... and... and I think I know what "they" told me before they died...» The boy, who had come smiling when Jesus called him, is now weeping with his head lowered and his trembling hand in Jesus' hand.

«Do not weep. Listen. Do you know where we are? This is Bethel. Holy Jacob dreamt of the angels here. Do you know? Do you remember?»

«Yes, Lord. He saw a ladder that from the earth reached up to Heaven and the angels went up and down, and my mother used to say that when one dies, if one has always been good, one sees the same thing and goes up that ladder to the House of God. My mother used to tell me many things... But now she does not tell me anymore... I have them all in here and that is all I have of hers...» Tears stream down his little sad face.

«Do not weep like that! Listen, Jabez. I also have a Mother and Her name is Mary and She is holy and good and can tell many things. She is wiser than a teacher and more gentle and beautiful than an angel. We are going to see Her now. She will love you so much. And She will tell you many things. And then John's mother is with her and she is very good, too, and her name is Mary. And there is the mother of my brother Judas, and she is as sweet as a honey cake and her name is Mary, too. They will love you so much. Because you are a clever boy and for My sake, because I love you so much. And you will grow up with them and when you are big, you will be a holy man of God, like a doctor you will preach Jesus Who has given you a new mother here and Who will open the gates of Heaven to your dead mother and to your father, and will open them also to you when your hour comes. You will not even need to climb the long ladder of Heaven when you die. You will have climbed it during your lifetime, being a good disciple, and you will find yourself up there, at the gate of Paradise, and I will be there and I will say to you: "Come, My friend and son of Mary" and we shall be together.» Jesus' bright smile, while walking slightly bent to be closer to the raised face of the child who is walking beside Him with his hand held by Jesus, and the wonderful story wipe his tears and make him smile.

194.3 [3] The boy, who is far from being dim of wit but is only stunned by grief and the hardships he has suffered, is interested in the story and asks: «You said that You will open the gates of Heaven. Are they not closed because of the great Sin? My mother used to say that no one could enter until forgiveness had come and the just were waiting for it in Limbo.»

«It is so. But preaching the word of God I will go to the Father and... having obtained forgiveness for you, I will say to Him: "Father, I have fulfilled Your will. Now I want My reward for My sacrifice. Let the just, who are waiting, come to Your Kingdom". And the Father will say to Me: "Let it be done as You wish". I will then come down and I will call all the just, and at the sound of My voice Limbo will open its gates and the holy Patriarchs, the bright Prophets, the blessed women of Israel will come out rejoicing. And do you know how many children? There will be children of all ages, as many as the flowers in a flowery meadow!

And they will follow Me singing and will ascend to the beautiful Paradise.»

«And will my mother be there?»

«Most certainly.»

«You did not say to me that she will be with You at the gate of Heaven when I am dead, too...»

«There is no need for her and for your father to be at that gate. Like bright angels they will fly continuously from Heaven down to the earth, from Jesus to their little Jabez, and when you are about to die, they will do what those two little birds over there, in that hedge, are doing. Can you see them?» And Jesus takes the boy in His arms to let him see better. «See how they are sitting on their little eggs. They are waiting for them to hatch, then they will spread their wings over the brood to protect them from all evils, and then, when they are grown and ready to fly, they will support them with their strong wings and will take them up, up, up... towards the sun. Your parents will do the same with you.»

«Will it be just like that?»

«Exactly like that.»

«But will You tell them to remember to come?»

«That is not necessary, because they love you, but I will tell them.»

«Oh! How I love You!» The child, who is still in Jesus' arms, presses against His neck and kisses Him with such joyful effusion that is really moving.

Jesus kisses him, too, and puts him down.

[4] «Well! Let us go on. Towards the Holy City. We must arrive 194.4
there tomorrow, towards evening. Why such a hurry? Can you tell me? Is it not the same if we arrive the day after tomorrow?»

«No. It would not be the same. Because tomorrow is Parasceve and after sunset one can walk only for six stadia. You are not allowed to go farther because the Sabbath and its rest have begun.»

«So one idles about on the Sabbath.»

«No. You pray to the Most High Lord.»

«What is His name?»

«Adonai. But saints can pronounce His name.»

«Also good children. Tell Me if you know.»

«Jaave» (the boy pronounces it thus: a very soft G, which is almost a J, and a very long 'a').

«And why does one pray to the Most High Lord on the Sabbath?»

«Because He told Moses, when He gave him the tables of the Law.»

«Oh! Did He? And what did He say?»

«He said that we must keep it holy. "For six days you shall labour, but on the seventh day you shall rest and make others rest, because that is what I did, too, after the creation".»

«What? Did the Lord rest? Did He become tired creating? And was it He Who created? How do you know? I know that God never tires.»

«He was not tired, because God does not walk and does not move His arms. But He did it, to teach Adam and us, and to have a day on which we think of Him. And He created everything, most certainly. The Book of the Lord tells us.»

«But was the Book written by Him?»

«No. But it is the Truth. And one must believe it unless one wants to go to Lucifer.»

«You said that God does not walk and does not move His arms. How did He create then? What is He like? A statue?»

«He is not an idol: He is God. And God is... God is... let me think and remember what my mother said, and even better than she did, that man who, in Your name goes to visit the poor people at Esdraelon... My mother used to say, to make me understand God: "God is like my love for you. It has no body, but it exists". And that little man, but with such a gentle smile, would say: "God is an Eternal Spirit, One and Triune, and the Second Person became flesh for the sake of us, poor people, and His name is... " Oh! My Lord! Now that I think of it... it's You!» The child, dumbfounded, prostrates himself on the ground adoring.

They all run thinking that he has fallen, but Jesus with His finger on His lips beckons them to be silent and then says: «Stand up, Jabez. Children must not be afraid of Me!»

The boy looks up reverently and looks at Jesus with a changed expression, almost of fear.

But Jesus smiles and stretches out His hand saying: «You are
194.5 a wise little Israelite. [5]Let us continue the examination. Now that

you have recognised Me, do you know whether the Book mentions Me?»

«Oh! Yes, Lord. From the beginning to now. Everything speaks of You. You are the promised Saviour. Now I understand why You will open the gates of Limbo. Oh! Lord! Lord! And do You love me so much?»

«Yes, Jabez.»

«No, no longer Jabez. Give me a new name that means that You loved me and saved me...»

«I will choose a name together with My Mother. All right?»

«But a name that means just that. And I will have it as from the day I become a son of the Law.»

«You will have it as from that day.»

They pass Bethel and rest in a little cool valley, rich in water, to take some food. Jabez is half stunned by the revelation and eats in silence, accepting with veneration every mouthful that Jesus hands to him. But he slowly takes heart again, and after playing happily on the green grass with John while the others are resting, he goes back to Jesus together with his smiling friend John, and the three chat together.

«You did not tell Me who speaks of Me in the Book.»

«The Prophets, Lord. And even before, the Book speaks of You when Adam was expelled, and... then to Jacob, Abraham and Moses... Oh!... My father told me that he went to John — not this one other John, the one of the Jordan — and he, the great Prophet, called You the Lamb... Oh! Now I understand the lamb of Moses... You are Passover!»

John teases him: «But which Prophet spoke best of Him?»

«Isaiah and Daniel. But I...I like Daniel more, now that I love You as my father. Can I say that? That I love You as I loved my father? Yes? Well, now I prefer Daniel.»

«Why? Who speaks most of the Christ is Isaiah.»

«Yes, but he speaks of the sorrows of the Christ. Daniel instead speaks of the beautiful angel and of Your coming. It is true... he also says that Christ will be sacrificed. But I think that the Lamb will be sacrificed with one single blow. Not as Isaiah and David say. I always wept when my mother read them and she did not read them anymore.» He is almost weeping even now while caressing Jesus' hand.

«Forget about it for the time being. Listen. Do you know the precepts?»

«Yes, my Lord. I think I know them. I used to repeat them when I was in the wood, so that I would not forget them, also because I wanted to hear the words of my mother and my father. But now I will not weep anymore (tears, however, are shining in his eyes) because I have You.»

John smiles and embraces Jesus saying: «The same words as mine! All those who are children in their hearts speak the same language.»

194.6 «Yes. Because their words come from one wisdom only. [6]But now we ought to go, so that we can be in Beeroth very early. The number of the people is increasing and the weather looks threatening. There will be a rush for shelters. And I do not want you to be taken ill.»

John calls his companions and they set forth again towards Beeroth, across a plain which is not very well cultivated, but is not so barren as the little mountain they climbed after Shiloh.

195. John of Endor Endeavours to Teach the Iscariot. The Entrance in Jerusalem.

20th June 1945.

195.1 [1]It is raining and Peter seems to me the opposite of Aeneas, because instead of carrying his father, he has little Jabez on his shoulders, completely covered by Peter's large mantle. The boy's little head emerges above the grey-haired head of Peter, who, with the boy's arms around his neck, dabbles in the puddles, laughing wholeheartedly.

«We might have been spared all this» grumbles the Iscariot, who is irritable because of the water pouring from the sky and splashing his clothes with mud.

«Eh! Many things could be spared!» replies John of Endor, staring at handsome Judas with his one good eye, which I think can see as well as two.

«What do you mean?»

«I mean that it is useless to expect the elements to have consideration for us, when we have none for our neighbour, and concerning matters that are by far more important than a few drops of water or a splash of mud.»

«That is true. But I like to be tidy and clean when I go to town. I have many friends there, and high up.»

«Then watch that you do not fall.»

«Are you teasing me?»

«Nooooh! But I am an old teacher and... an old pupil. I have been learning since I was born. First I learned to vegetate, then I observed life, then I became acquainted with the bitterness of life, I practised a useless justice, the justice of "man alone" against God and society. God punished me with remorse, society with fetters, so, after all, I was the victim of justice. At last, now, I have learned, *I am learning* how "to live". Now, since I am a teacher and a pupil, you will realise that it is natural for me to repeat the lessons.»

«But I am an apostle...»

«And I am a poor wretch, I know, and I should never take the liberty of teaching you. But, see, you never know what one may become. I thought I was going to die an honest and respected teacher in Cyprus and I became a murderer and a convict serving a life sentence. But when I raised a knife to take vengeance, and when I was dragging the fetters hating the universe, if anyone told me that I was to become a disciple of the Holy One, I would have doubted whether his mind was sound. And yet... Here I am! So, I may be able to give a good lesson also to you, an apostle. Because of my experience. Not because of my holiness, I would not dream of it.»

«That Roman was right in calling you Diogenes.»

«Of course. But Diogenes was looking for a man and could not find one. I, luckier than he, found a snake where I thought there was a woman, and an adulterer where I thought I saw a friendly man, but after wandering about for many years, as I became insane through such experience, I have found the Man, the Holy One.»

«I know no other wisdom but Israel's.»

«If that is so, you already have the means for salvation. But now you have also the science, or rather the wisdom of God.»

«It is the same thing.»

«Oh! no! It is like a foggy day compared to a sunny day.»

«Well! Are you anxious to teach me? I don't feel like it.»

«Let me speak! Once, I used to speak to children: they were absent-minded. Then I spoke to shadows, they cursed me. Then to chickens: they were better, far better than the first two groups. Now I speak to myself, as I am not yet able to speak to God. Why do you want to stop me? I have but one eye, the mines ruined my life, I have suffered from heart trouble for years. At least let my mind be fruitful.»

«Jesus is God.»

«I know, and I believe it. More than you do. Because I have revived through His work, you have not. No matter how good He is, He is still God, and I, a poor wretch dare not treat Him with familiarity as you do. My soul speaks to Him... my lips dare not. My soul does, and I think that He perceives it weeping out of gratitude and repentant love.»

195.2 [2] «That is true, John. I do perceive your soul.» Jesus comes into the conversation of the two. Judas blushes with shame, the man of Endor with joy. «I perceive your soul, that is true. And I perceive also the work of your mind. What you said is correct. When you have been formed in Me, your experience as a teacher and a diligent pupil will be of great help to you. Speak, do speak, also to yourself.»

«Once, Master, not long ago, you told me that it is wrong to speak to one's ego» remarks Judas insolently.

«That is true, I did. But that was because you were grumbling * with your *ego.* This man is not grumbling, he is meditating, and for a good purpose. He is not doing anything wrong.»

«In brief, I am wrong!» Judas is aggressive.

«No, your heart is impatient. But the weather cannot be always good. Farmers want rain. It is charity to pray that it may rain. *And this is also* charity. But look, there is a beautiful rainbow forming an arch from Ataroth to Ramah. We are already beyond Ataroth, we have passed the large sad valley, and here the country is cultivated and pleasant under the sun, which is breaking through the clouds. When we are in Ramah we shall be thirty-six stadia from Jerusalem. We shall see the Holy City again after that hill, which is the place of the horrid lewd crime

---

* **I did**, in 183.1.

* committed by the men of Gibeah. What a terrible thing is the concupiscence of the flesh, Judas...»

Judas does not reply, instead he delays splashing angrily in the puddles.

[3] «What's the matter with him, today?» asks Bartholomew. 195.3

«Be quiet, lest Simon of Jonah should hear you. Let us avoid all arguments... and do not let us upset Simon. He is so happy with his boy!»

«Yes, Master. But it is not right. I will tell him.»

«He is young, Nathanael. You were young, too...»

«Yes... but... he should not be lacking in respect towards You!» He raises his voice without wishing to do so.

Peter rushes towards them: «What's the matter? Who is lacking in respect? The new disciple?» and he looks at John of Endor, who has discreetly withdrawn when he understood that Jesus was correcting the apostle and is now speaking to James of Alphaeus and Simon Zealot.

«Not in the least. He is as respectful as a young girl.»

«Oh! Good! Otherwise... his only eye was in danger. Well... it must be Judas!...»

«Listen, Simon, could you not busy yourself with your little friend? You took him away from Me, and now you want to become engaged in a friendly conversation I am having with Nathanael. Do you not think that you want to do too many things?»

Jesus smiles so gently that Peter becomes uncertain about his own thoughts. He looks at Bartholomew... who, however, has raised his aquiline face and is scanning the sky... Peter's suspicion fades away.

Peter's attention is completely diverted by the apparition of the Holy City, which is now near and is visible in all the beauty of hills, olive-groves, houses, and above all of the Temple, a sight which must always have been a source of emotion and pride for Israelites. The warm April sun of Judaea has soon dried up the slabstones of the consular road. Puddles of water have disappeared completely. The apostles are tidying themselves on the side of the road, they let down the tunics which they had pulled up, they wash their muddy feet in a clear stream, they tidy their

* **the men in Gibeah**, in *Judges 19:22-28.*

hair and drape their mantles. Also Jesus does that. I see them all doing it.

195.4 [4]The entrance into Jerusalem must have been an important matter. To present oneself at the walls on these feast-days was like presenting oneself to a sovereign. The Holy City was the «*real*» queen of Israelites. I realise that this year, because I can notice the crowds and their behaviour on the consular road. The processions of the various families form here, the women in one group, the men in another, the children in either, but all very serious and serene at the same time. Some fold up their old mantles and pull out a new one from their travelling bags, or change sandals. Their gait then becomes solemn, it is already hieratic. In each group there is a soloist who gives the tone, and the hymns, the glorious old hymns of David, are intoned. And people look at one another more lovingly, as if they had been pacified by the sight of the House of the Lord and they look at the Holy House, a huge cube of marble surmounted by golden domes, placed like a pearl in the centre of the imposing enclosure of the Temple.

The apostolic procession is formed as follows: Jesus and Peter in front, with the boy between them; behind them Simon, the Iscariot and John; then Andrew, who has forced John of Endor to stay between him and James of Zebedee; in the fourth row the two cousins of the Lord and Matthew; last Thomas, Philip and Bartholomew. It is Jesus Who intones in His beautiful powerful voice of a light baritone, a mellow voice with refined tenor vibrations, and Judas Iscariot, a pure tenor, answers together with John, with his limpid voice typical of young people, the two baritone voices of Jesus' cousins and the almost bass voice of Thomas, whose baritone voice is so deep that it can hardly be classifed as such. The others, who are not gifted with such beautiful voices, follow the chorus of the virtuosi singing in low voices. (The psalms are the known ones, called gradual psalms). Little *
Jabez, the voice of an angel among the strong voices of men, sings very well, probably because he knows Psalm 121 better than the others: «How I rejoiced when they said to me: "We shall go to the house of the Lord".» His little face, which only a few days ago

* **gradual Psalms** (or Song of Ascent) are called the *Psalms 120-134* (119-122 in the Vulgate). They were sung by pilgrims as they ascended the road to Jerusalem.

was so sad, is now bright with joy.

The walls are now close at hand. Here is the Gate of the Fish. And the overcrowded streets.

They go straight to the Temple to say the first prayer. And then peace in the peace of Gethsemane, then supper and rest.

The journey towards Jerusalem is over.

196. The Sabbath at Gethsemane. The Virgin Mary Archetype of Maternity. The Different Degrees of the Power of Love.

21st June 1945.

[1]The group has spent most of the Sabbath morning resting their tired bodies and cleaning their clothes which had become dusty and creased during the journey. There is so much inviting water in the spacious cisterns of Gethsemane, full of rain water, and in the foamy Kidron, now in flood, because of the recent downpours, where the water resounds against the stones like a symphony. And the apostles, one after the other, defying the low temperature of the water, plunge into it and then, clad from head to foot in fresh clothes, their hair rather sleeked by the spray of the torrent, they draw water from the cisterns pouring it into large vats in which they have sorted out their clothes according to the colours. 196.1

«Well! Once they are soaked in there, it will be less troublesome for Mary to wash them.» (I suppose that Mary is the woman who stays at Gethsemane). «Only you, my dear little friend, cannot change. But tomorrow...» In fact the boy is wearing a clean robe, which has been taken from his little sack: so small that it would be quite sufficient for the garments of a doll! But the boy's little tunic is even more discoloured and torn than the other one and Peter looks at it with apprehension, whispering: «How can I possibly take him to town? I think I will cut one of my mantles in two, because a mantle... would cover him completely.»

Jesus, Who has heard this paternal soliloquy says: «It is better to let him rest now. This evening we are going to Bethany...»

«But I want to buy him a robe. I promised it.»

«You certainly will. But it is better to seek My Mother's advice. You know... women... have more experience in such purchase... and She will be happy to take care of the child... You will go together.»

Peter is enraptured to the seventh heaven of delight at the idea of going shopping with Mary. I do not know whether Jesus has expressed all His thoughts or whether He has held back some, those implying that His Mother's taste is more refined than Peter's and would thus avoid the clashing of atrocious hues. The fact is that He achieves His aim without mortifying Peter.

196.2 [2] They scatter in the olive-grove, which is so beautiful on this serene April day. The rain of the past days seems to have silvered the olive-trees and sown flowers, so bright are the leaves in the sun and so numerous the little flowers at the foot of each tree. Birds are singing and flying everywhere. The town is lying over there, to the west of an onlooker. *

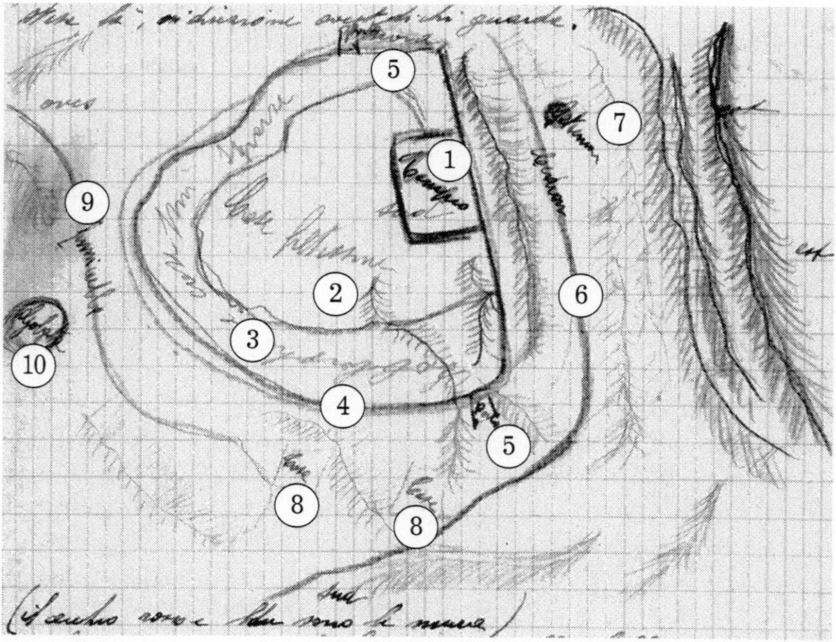

* M.V.'s sketch shows Jerusalem and its outskirts: **1.** *Temple*; **2.** *crammed houses*; **3.** *suburbs with houses more detached*; **4.** *town walls* (outlined in red and blu pencil, as explained in the line of the text at the bottom of the drawing); **5.** *gate* (twice); **6.** *Kidron*; **7.** *Gethsemane*; **8.** *houses* (twice); **9.** *brook*; **10.** *Golgotha*.

It is not possible to see the crowds thronging inside, but one can see the caravans going towards the Gate of the Fish and to others, with names unknown to me, on this eastern side, and the travellers are swallowed by the town as it if were a hungry mouth.

Jesus is walking up and down watching Jabez who is playing with John and the younger ones. Also the Iscariot, who has got out of yesterday's huff is cheerful and plays. The elder ones watch and smile.

«What will Your Mother say of this child?» asks Bartholomew.

«I think She will say: "He is very thin"» says Thomas.

«Oh! no! She will say: "Poor child!"» replies Peter.

«Instead She will say to You: "I am glad that You love him"» objects Philip.

«His Mother would never have doubted it. But I don't think She will say anything. She will press him to Her heart» says the Zealot.

«And You, Master, what do You think She will say?»

«She will do what you said. She will think many things, or rather, all of them, and will say them in Her heart, and when kissing him She will only say: "May you be blessed" and She will take care of him as if he were a little bird fallen from its nest. [3]One 196.3
day, listen, She told Me of when She was a little girl. She was not yet three years old because She was not yet in the Temple, and Her heart was full of love, emanating, like flowers and olives pressed and crushed in a mill, all Her oils and perfumes. And in a rapture of love She said to Her mother that She wanted to be a virgin to please the Saviour more, but that She would have liked to be a sinner in order to be saved, and She almost wept, because Her mother could not understand Her and could not tell Her how it is possible to be "pure" and a "sinner" at the same time. Her father satisfied Her by bringing her a little sparrow, which he had saved when it was about to be drowned on the edge of a fountain. He explained the parable of the little bird, * saying that God had saved her in advance and therefore She was to bless Him twice. And the little Virgin of God, the Most Great

* **the parable of the little bird**, in 7.5.

Virgin Mary, practised Her first spiritual maternity on behalf of the little bird, which She let free when it was strong enough. But the bird never left the kitchen garden in Nazareth where, flying and twittering, it comforted the sad house and the broken hearts of Anne and Joachim, when Mary was in the Temple. It died shortly before Anne breathed her last breath... It had ful-
196.4 filled its duty... [4]My Mother had dedicated Herself to virginity for love. But, since She was a perfect creature, maternity was in Her blood and spirit. Because woman is created to be a mother and it is an aberration, if she is deaf to such sentiment, which is love of second power...»

Also the others have come near slowly.

«What do You mean, Master, by love of second power?» asks Judas Thaddeus.

«My brother, there are many loves and various powers. There is the love of first power: the one given to God. Then there is the love of second power: the love of a mother or of a father, because if the previous one is entirely spiritual, this one is spiritual by two parts and carnal by one. It is true that human affection is mixed in it, but the superior sentiment prevails, because a father and mother, who are such in a wholesome and holy way, do not only feed and caress the body of their child, but they also give nourishment and love to the mind and the spirit of their creature. And what I am saying is so true, that those who devote themselves to children, even if only to educate them, end up by loving their pupils as if they were of their own flesh.»

«In fact I was very fond of my pupils» says John of Endor.

«I understood that you must have been a good teacher by the way you deal with Jabez.»

The man of Endor bows and kisses Jesus' hand without speaking.

«Please go on with Your classification of loves» begs the Zealot.

«There is the love for one's wife: love of third power because it is made — I am always talking of wholesome and holy love — half of spirit and half of flesh. A man, besides being the husband of his wife, is a teacher and a father to her; and a woman is an angel and a mother to her husband, besides being his wife. These are the three highest loves.»

196.5

[5] «And the love for our neighbour? Are You not wrong? Or have You forgotten it?» asks the Iscariot. The others look at him dumbfounded and... furious because of his remarks.

But Jesus replies placidly: «No, Judas. Watch. God is to be loved because He is God, so no explanation is required to convince one to have such love. He is He Who is, that is Everything; and man: Nothing, who participates of Everything, because of the soul infused in him by Eternal God — without which soul man would be one of the many animals that live on the earth, or in water or in the air — he must adore Him out of a sense of duty and to deserve to survive in Everything, that is to deserve to be part of the holy People of God in Heaven, a citizen of the Jerusalem that will know neither profanation nor destruction forever.

The love of man, and particularly of woman, for their offspring, is indicated as an order in the words of God to Adam and Eve, after He had blessed them, seeing that He had made a *"good thing"*, on a remote sixth day, the first sixth day of creation. God said to them: "Be fruitful and multiply and fill the earth..." I can see your tacit objection, and this is My reply to you: Since before sin everything in creation was regulated by and based on love, that multiplication of children would have been a holy, pure, powerful, perfect love. And God gave it as His first commandment to man: "Be fruitful and multiply". Therefore, love your children after Me. Love, as it is now, the present procreator of children, did not exist then. There was no malice nor the detestable thirst for sensuality. Man loved woman and woman loved man, naturally, not naturally according to nature as we understand it, or rather, as you men understand it, but *according to the nature of children of God: supernaturally*. Sweet were the days of love of the Two who were brothers, because born of one Father, and yet were husband and wife, who loved and looked at each other with the innocent eyes of twins in a cradle; and man felt the love of a father for his wife "bone from his bones and flesh from his flesh", what a son is for his father; and the woman experienced the joy of being a daughter, protected by a very high love, because she felt that she had in herself something of the wonderful man who loved her, with innocence and angelical ardour, in the beautiful meadows in Eden!

Later, in the sequence of commands that God, smiling, gave

to His beloved children, there comes what Adam himself, gifted by Grace with an intelligence inferior only to God's, decreed speaking of his wife and of every woman through Eve, a decree of the thought of God, which was clearly reflected by the spotless mirror of Adam's spirit, a flower in thought and in word: "Man will leave his father and his mother and will join himself to his wife and they will become one body".

If there had not been the three pillars of the three above mentioned loves, could there have been love for one's neighbour? No. It could not have existed. The love of God makes God a friend and teaches love. He who does not love God, Who is good, cannot certainly love his neighbour who in most cases is faulty. If there had been no conjugal love and paternity in the world, there could have been no neighbours, because a neighbour is the son of man. Are you convinced?»

«Yes, Master. I had not thought of that.»

«It is difficult indeed to go back to the sources. Man has been stuck in mud for thousands of years, and those sources are so high up on the summits! The first one, above all, is a source that comes immense from an immense height: God... But I will take you by the hand and lead you to the sources. I know where they are...»

196.6 [6] «And the other loves?» ask together Simon Zealot and the man from Endor.

«The first one of the second series is the love for our neighbour. In actual fact it is the fourth in power. Then comes the love for science. Finally the love for work.»

«Is that all?»

«That is all.»

«But there are many more loves!» exclaims Judas of Kerioth.

«There are other hungers. But it is not love. They are the negation of love. They deny God, they deny man. It cannot be love because it is negation and Negation is Hatred.»

«If I deny consent to evil, is that Hatred?» asks Judas Iscariot once again.

«Poor me! You are more captious than a scribe! Can you tell me what is the matter with you? Is the rarified air of Judaea affecting your nerves like a cramp?» exclaims Peter.

«No. I like to learn and to have many clear ideas. It is quite possible we may have to speak to scribes and I do not want to be short of arguments...»

«And do you think that in the moment of need you will be able to pull out the colour required from the sack where you stock all the rags?» asks Peter.

«Rags the words of the Master? You are swearing?»

«Don't pretend you are scandalized. They are not rags in His mouth; but once they have been mishandled by us they become rags. Try and give a piece of precious byssus to a boy... It will soon become a dirty torn rag. And that is what happens to us. Now if you expect to fish at the right moment the little rag you need, what with the rag, and what with its dirt... uhm! I do not know what you will be up to.»

«Don't worry. That is my business.»

«Oh! You may be sure that I will not worry! I have enough problems of my own. And then... ! I am happy providing you cause no harm to the Master. Because, in that case, I would also mind your business...»

«You can do that when I do something wrong. But that will never happen, because I know how to behave... I am not ignorant...»

«Instead I am, I know. And because I am, I do not stock any ballast, to flaunt it later, at the right moment. But I implore God and God will help me for the sake of His Messiah, of Whom I am the least and most faithful servant.»

«We are all faithful» replies Judas haughtily.

«Oh! You are bad! Why do you offend my father? He is old and he is good. You must not do that. You are bad and you frighten me» says Jabez with stern countenance, after being silent and listening carefully.

«And that makes two!» whispers James of Zebedee in a low voice, touching Andrew with his elbow.

Although he has spoken in a low voice, the Iscariot hears him.

«You can see, Master, whether the words of the silly boy of Magdala have left a trace» says Judas raging with anger.

[7] «Would it not be more pleasant to continue listening to the lesson of the Master, instead of behaving like angry kids?» asks peaceful Thomas. 196.7

«Of course, Master. Tell us more about Your Mother. Her childhood is so bright! The very reflection of that brilliance makes our souls pure, and I, a poor sinner, need that light so badly!» exclaims Matthew.

«What shall I tell you? There are so many episodes, one more touching than the other...»

«Did She tell You about them?»

«Yes, some. But Joseph told Me many more, as the most beautiful stories he could tell a child, and also Alphaeus of Sarah, who was a few years older than My Mother, and was Her friend during the short period She was at Nazareth...»

«Oh! Please, tell us...» begs John.

They are all sitting in a circle in the shade of the olive-trees, with Jabez in the centre staring at Jesus as if he were listening to a heavenly tale.

«I will tell you about the lesson on chastity that My Mother gave Her little friend and many more people a few days before entering the Temple. A girl in Nazareth, a relative of Sarah's, got married on that day and also Joachim and Anne had been invited to the wedding. Little Mary went with them and with other children She was to spread loose flower petals on the bride's way. They say that She was most beautiful, as a child, and everybody contended for Her after the joyful arrival of the bride. It was not easy to see Mary every day, as She lived mostly at home, where She loved a little grotto more than any other place, and even nowadays She calls it "the grotto of Her nuptials". So when She appeared outside, fair-haired, rosy and kind, She was overwhelmed by caresses. They used to call Her "the Flower of Nazareth" or "the Pearl of Galilee" or also "the Peace of God" in remembrance of a huge rainbow, which suddenly appeared as soon as She was born. She was in fact all that, and much more. She is the Flower of Heaven and of creation, the Pearl of Paradise and the Peace of God... Yes, the Peace of God. I am the Peaceful One because I am the Son of the Father and the Son of Mary: the Infinite Peace and the sweet Peace. On that day everybody wanted to kiss Her and take Her on their laps. And as She was averse to being kissed and touched, She said with kind seriousness: "Please, do not rumple Me". They thought She was talking of Her linen dress, held tight to Her waist, to Her wrists and neck by a blue band, or of Her little wreath of blue flowers, with which Anne had adorned Her head to keep Her light curls in place, and they assured Her that they would not crease Her dress or the wreath. But, sure of Herself, a little three year old woman standing in the middle of a circle of adults, She said seriously: “I am not thinking of what can be mended. I am speaking of My soul. It belongs to God. And it does not wish to be touched but by God”. They objected: “But we are kissing You, not Your soul”. She replied: “My body is the temple of My soul and the Spirit is its priest. People are not allowed to enter the enclosure of priests. Please, do not enter the enclosure of God”. Alphaeus, who was then about eight years old and was very fond of Her, was greatly impressed by that reply and the following day, seeing Her near Her little grotto, he asked Her: “Mary, when You are grown up, would You marry me?”. He was still under the excitement of the nuptial feast at which he had been present. And She answered: “I am very fond of you. But I do not see you as a man. I will tell you a secret. I see only the soul of a living being. And I love it so much, with all My heart. But I see only God as the ‘True Living Being’ to Whom I will be able to give Myself”. That is one of the episodes.»

«The True Living Being”!!! That is a very deep word!» exclaims Bartholomew.

And Jesus, humbly and smiling replies: «She was the Mother of Wisdom.»

«Was She?... But was She not three years old?»

«She was. I already lived in Her, as God was in Her, in His most perfect Unity and Trinity, since She was conceived.»

[8] «Excuse me if I, a sinner, dare speak, but did Joachim and Anne know that She was the chosen Virgin?» asks Judas Iscariot. 196.8

«No, they did not know.»

«In that case, how could Joachim say that God had saved Her in advance? Does that not refer to Her privilege over sin?»

«Yes, it does. But Joachim spoke inspired by God, like all the prophets. He himself did not understand the sublime supernatural truth that the Spirit spoke through his lips. Because Joachim was just. So just as to deserve that paternity. And he was humble. There is no justice where there is pride. He was just and humble. He comforted his Daughter out of fatherly love. He taught her through his wisdom of a priest, as he was such as a guardian of the Ark of God. As a Pontiff he consecrated Her with the sweetest title: "The Immaculate One". And the day will come when another grey haired Pontiff will say to the world: "She is the Immaculate Conception" and will give this truth to the world of believers, as a dogma which cannot be rejected, so that the Most Beautiful Virgin of God, crowned with stars, clad with the rays of the moon, which are not so pure as She is, brighter than all stars, the Queen of Creation and of God, may shine, fully revealed, in the world which in those days will be sinking deeper and deeper in the grey fog of heresies and vices. Because God-King has as His Queen, in His Kingdom, Mary.»

«So Joachim was a prophet?»

«He was a just man. His soul repeated like an echo what God said to his soul which was loved by God.»

196.9 [9] «When are we going to this Mother, my Lord?» asks Jabez with eager eyes.

«This evening. What will you say to Her when you see Her?»

«"I greet You, Mother of the Saviour". Is that all right?»

«Very good» confirms Jesus caressing him.

«But are we going to the Temple today?» asks Philip.

«We shall go there before leaving for Bethany. And you will stay here and be a good boy. Will you not?»

«Yes, my Lord.»

The wife of Jonah, the caretaker of the olive-grove, who has come near very quietly says: «Why don't you take him. The boy is anxious to come...»

Jesus stares at her without saying anything.

The woman understands and says: «I see! I should still have a little mantle belonging to Mark. I will look for it» and she runs away.

Jabez pulls John's sleeve: «Will the teachers be severe?»

«Oh! no. Don't be afraid. In any case it is not today. In a few days' time, with His Mother, you will be more learned than a doctor» John comforts him.

The others hear and smile at Jabez' concern.

«But who will present him as if he were his father?» asks Matthew.

«Of course I will! Unless... the Master wishes to present him» says Peter.

«No, Simon. I will not present him. I leave that honour to you.»

«Thank You, Master. But... You will be there, too?»

«Certainly. We shall all be there. He is "our" boy...»

Mary of Jonah comes back with a dark violet mantle, which is still good. But what a colour! She says so herself: «Mark never wanted to wear it because he did not like the colour.»

No wonder! It is vile! And poor Jabez with his olive complexion looks ghastly in the violent violet colour. But he cannot see himself... and he is therefore happy to have the mantle in which he can drape himself like an adult.

«The meal is ready, Master. The woman has taken the lamb off the spit just now.»

«Let us go, then.»

And going down from the place where they were, they go into the large kitchen for their meal.

197. In the Temple with Joseph of Arimathea at the Hour of Incense.

22nd June 1945.

1 Peter is really stately while entering the enclosure of the Temple, acting as the father of Jabez, whom he is holding by the hand. He is walking so erect that he looks even taller than he really is. 197.1

All the others are behind him, in a group. Jesus is last and is engaged in close conversation with John of Endor, who seems to be ashamed to enter the Temple.

Peter asks his protege: «Have you ever been here before?» and the boy replies: «When I was born, father. But I do not remember» which makes Peter laugh heartily. Also the others, when they are told by Peter, laugh and say gently and wittily: «Perhaps you were sleeping and so...» or «We are all like you. We do not remember when we came here when we were born.»

2 Also Jesus asks John of Endor the same question and gets a similar reply. In fact John says to Him: «We were proselytes and my mother carried me here in her arms, just at Passover, because I was born early in Adar and my mother, who came from Judaea, set out as soon as she was able to, to offer her son to the Lord in good time. Perhaps too early, because she was taken ill 197.2

and never recovered. I was under two years of age when I lost my mother. The first misfortune in my life. I was her first-born, I became her only child because of her disease, and she was very proud to die having complied with the Law. My father used to say to me: "She died a happy death because she had offered you to the Temple"... Poor mother! What did you offer? A future murderer...»

«John, do not say that. You were Felix then, now you are John. Bear in mind the great grace that God granted you, always remember that. Forget your past debasement... Did you not come back to the Temple again?»

«Oh! Yes. When I was twelve years old and always after that, as long as... I was able to... Later, when I could have come, I did not, because I told You that I worshipped only one thing: Hatred... And that is why I dare not proceed further here. I feel like a stranger in the House of the Father... I have abandoned it for too long...»

«You are coming back to it led by the hand by Me Who am the Son of the Father. If I am taking you up to the altar, it means that I know that everything has been forgiven.»

John of Endor sobs deeply and says: «Thank You, my God.»

«Yes, thank the Most High. Can you not see that your mother, a true Israelite, had a prophetic spirit? You are the son sacred to the Lord and never ransomed. You are Mine, you belong to God, you are a disciple and thus a future priest of your Lord in the new era and in the new religion, which will be called after Me. I absolve you of *everything*, John. Proceed confidently towards the Holy. I solemny tell you that among those who live in this enclosure there are many more guilty and less worthy than you to go near the altar...»

197.3 [3] Peter in the meantime is busy showing the boy the most noteworthy things in the Temple, but he asks the more learned ones, particularly Bartholomew and Simon, to help him, because in the fulfilment of his duty as a father he feels more at ease with the elder ones.

They are near the treasury to make their offering when Joseph of Arimathea calls them. «You are here? When did you arrive?» he asks after greeting them.

«Yesterday evening.»

«And the Master?»

«He is over there, with a new disciple. He is coming.»

Joseph looks at the boy and asks Peter: «One of your grandsons?»

«No... yes... well: nothing by blood, a great deal by faith, everything by love.»

«I do not understand...»

«He is a little orphan... so nothing by blood. A disciple, therefore a great deal by faith. A son... so everything by love. The Master took him... and I caress him. He will be coming of age in the next few days...»

«Already twelve years old? And so small?»

«Eh!... The Master will tell you... Joseph, you are good... one of the few good people in here... Tell me... would you help me in this matter? You know... I am presenting him as if he were my son. But I am a Galilean and I am a nasty leper...»

«A leper?!» exclaims Joseph inquisitively moving away in fright.

«Don't be afraid! I am a leper because I belong to Jesus! The most loathesome form of leprosy for those of the Temple, with a few exceptions.»

«No! Don't say that!»

«It's the truth and we must admit it... So I am afraid they will be cruel to the boy because of me and because of Jesus. In any case I do not know how much he knows of the Law, of the Halascia, the Haggadha and of the Midrasciots. Jesus says that he knows quite a lot...»

«Well, if Jesus says so! Don't be afraid!»

«Only to cause me trouble they would...»

«You are very fond of this little fellow! Do you keep him with you all the time?»

«I cannot!... I am always about... The boy is too young and delicate...»

«But I would willingly come with you...» says Jabez who has been reassured by Joseph's caresses.

Peter is bright with joy... But he says: «The Master says that we must not do that and we will not do it... But we shall meet now and again just the same... Joseph... will you help me?»

«Of course, I will! I will come with you. They will not do him

197.4 an injustice in front of me. When? [4]Oh! Master! Give me Your blessing!»

«Peace to you, Joseph. I am happy to see you and I am glad that you are in good health.»

«I am happy, too, Master, and also Your friends will be pleased to see You. Are You staying at Gethsemane?»

«I was there, but after the prayer I am going to Bethany.»

«To Lazarus'?»

«No, to Simon's. My Mother, the mother of My brothers and the mother of John and James are also there. Will you come and see Me?»

«Are You asking me? I will come with great joy and it is a great honour, for which I thank You. I will come with some friends...»

«Be careful, Joseph, with friends!...» suggests Simon Zealot.

«Oh! You already know them. Prudence teaches: "Do not let the air know". But when you see them you will understand that *they are friends.*»

«Well...»

«Master, Simon of Jonah was telling me about the ceremony for the little one. You arrived when I was asking when you intend having it. I want to be there, too.»

«On the Wednesday before Passover. I want him to keep Passover as a son of the Law.»

«Very good. That is settled. I will come and join you at Bethany. But I will come with my friends on Monday.»

«Agreed.»

«Master, I must leave You. Peace be with You. It is the hour of incense.» *

197.5 «Goodbye, Joseph. Peace be with you. [5]Come, Jabez. This is the most solemn hour of the day. There is another one in the morning. It is right that man should bless the Lord to be blessed during the day, in all his deeds. But in the evening it is more solemn. Light fades, work ends, night falls. The fading light reminds us of the fall into sin and in fact sinful deeds are generally accomplished during the night. Why? Because man, no longer engrossed in his work, can be more easily entrapped by the Evil One who avails himself of his allurements and nightmares.

---

* **the hour of incense** as prescribed in *Exodus 30:7-8.*

It is therefore right, after thanking God for protecting us during the day, that we should implore Him to deliver us from night phantasms and temptations. Night, sleep... the symbols of death. Blessed be those who after living with the blessing of the Lord go to sleep in a bright dawn and not in darkness. The priest who offers incense does so on behalf of us all. He prays for all the people, in communion with God, and God entrusts him with the blessing for the whole people of His children. See how great the ministry of a priest is?»

«I would like... I would feel as if I were closer to my mummy...»

«If you are always a good disciple and a good son to Peter, you will become one. Come now. The trumpets are announcing that the time has come. Let us go and praise Yahweh with veneration.»

198. Jesus Meets His Mother at Bethany. Little Jabez Becomes Marjiam.

23rd June 1945.

[1] Jesus is walking fast with His disciples towards Lazarus' town, along a shady road which links the Mount of Olives to Bethany. One could say that the green ramifications of the mountain stretch as far as the countryside of Bethany. Jesus is recognised even before entering the town and voluntary messengers run in all directions to inform people of His arrival. Thus Lazarus and Maximinus arrive running from one side, Isaac with Timoneus and Joseph from another, and the third group to arrive is Martha with Marcella, who lifts her veil to bend down and kiss Jesus' tunic. Immediately after Mary of Alphaeus and Mary Salome reach the spot, they greet the Master and then embrace their sons. Little Jabez, still held by the hand by Jesus, is tossed about by so much rushing and watches everything dumbfounded. John of Endor, feeling like a stranger, withdraws to the end of the group and stands aside. Suddenly, in the lane leading to Simon's house, Jesus' Mother comes forward. 198.1

Jesus drops Jabez' hand and gently pushes His friends to one side to hasten towards Her. The well-known words resound in the air, like a solo of love above the whispering of the crowd:

«Son!»; «Mother.» They kiss each other and in Mary's kiss there is the anguish of a mother who has been afraid for a long time and now that the terror, which had seized her, is dissolving, she feels the tiredness of the effort she made and evaluates the risks He has run…

Jesus, Who understands, caresses Her saying: «Beside My angel I had Yours, Mother, watching over Me. No harm could have befallen Me.»

«May the Lord be praised for that. But I suffered so much!»

«I wanted to come sooner, but in order to obey You, I had to come a different way. But it was a good thing, because Your order, Mother, bore good fruit, as usual.»

«It was Your obedience, Son!»

«It was Your wise order, Mother… » They smile at each other like two lovers.

Is it possible that this Woman is the Mother of this Man? Where are the sixteen years of difference in age? The freshness and grace of Mary's face and of Her virginal body make Her a sister of Her Son, Who is in the fullness of a handsome manliness.

«Are You not asking Me why it bore good fruit?» asks Jesus smiling all the time.

«I know that My Jesus conceals nothing from Me.»

«My dear Mother!» He kisses Her again…

People have kept away a few yards pretending not to be watching the scene. But I bet that there is not one of all the eyes that seem to be looking elsewhere that does not cast sidelong glances at the loving scene.

198.2 [2] The one who is most keen in watching is Jabez, whom Jesus left when He ran to embrace His Mother, and who has been left all alone, because owing to the quick succession of questions and answers, everybody's attention was diverted from the poor boy… He looks, then bends his head, endeavours to restrain his tears… but he cannot and bursts out weeping, moaning: «Mummy! Mummy!»

Everybody turns around, Jesus and Mary are the first, and everybody endeavours to help or find out who the boy is. Mary of Alphaeus rushes towards him with Peter — they were together — and they both ask: «Why are you crying?»

But before Jabez can catch his breath and speak while shedding so many tears, Mary has run towards him and taken him in Her arms saying: «Yes, my little child, your Mother! Do not cry anymore... and excuse Me if I did not see you before. My friends, here is My little son...» It is obvious that Jesus, in the few seconds approaching the boy, must have said to Her: «He is a little orphan brought with Me.» Mary realised the rest.

The boy is still weeping, but not so disconsolately, and as Mary is holding him in Her arms and kissing him, he ends up by smiling while his face is still wet with tears.

«Let me dry those tears of yours. You must not cry any more! Give Me a kiss...» Jabez was expecting nothing but that and after being caressed by bearded men, he is overjoyed in kissing Mary's smooth cheek.

[3] Jesus has been looking for John of Endor and when He sees 198.3
him, He goes to get him in his remote corner. And while all the apostles are greeting Mary, Jesus comes towards Her, holding John of Endor by the hand and He says: «This is the other disciple, Mother. Your command gained these two sons for You.»

«It was Your obedience, Son» repeats Mary and She greets the man saying: «Peace to you.»

The man, the coarse restless man of Endor, who has changed so much since that morning when Judas' whim took Jesus to Endor, completely divests himself of his past while bowing to Mary. I think it is so, because his face, after bowing, looks really serene and truly «at peace».

[4] They all set out towards Simon's house: Mary with Jabez in 198.4
Her arms, Jesus holding John of Endor by the hand, and then, around them and behind them, Lazarus and Martha, the apostles with Maximinus, Isaac, Joseph, and Timoneus.

They enter the house on the threshold of which Simon's old servant greets Jesus and his master with deep respect.

«Peace to you, Joseph, and to this house» says Jesus, lifting His hand to bless after laying it on the old servant's white head.

Lazarus and Martha, after their first expression of joy, are somewhat sad and Jesus asks them: «Why, My friends?»

«Because You are not staying with us and because everybody comes to You except the soul that we would like to be Yours.»

«Fortify your patience, your hope and your prayers. After

all, I am with you. This house!... This house is but the nest from which the Son of man will fly every day to His dear friends, so close in space, but if we consider the situation in a supernatural way, infinitely closer in love. You are in My heart and I am in yours. Can we be closer than that? But we will be together this evening. Please sit at My table.»

«Oh! Poor me! And I am idling about! Come, Salome, there is a lot to be done!» The exclamation of Mary of Alphaeus makes everybody laugh while Jesus' good relative gets up immediately to her work.

Martha joins her: «Don't worry about the food, Mary. I will go and give the necessary instructions. Just lay the table. I will send you enough chairs and what is necessary. Come, Marcella. I will be back at once, Master.»

198.5 [5] «I saw Joseph of Arimathea, Lazarus. He is coming here on Monday with some friends.»

«Oh! Well, You are my guest on that day!»

«Yes. He is coming to spend the day with us, but also to arrange a ceremony concerning Jabez. John: take the boy up to the terrace. He will enjoy himself there.»

John of Zebedee, who is always obedient, gets up at once and shortly afterwards the boy can be heard chattering and running about on the terrace that surrounds the house.

«The child» Jesus explains to His Mother, His friends, the women among whom there is also Martha, who has rushed back so that she would not miss one moment of joy near the Master, «is the grandson of one of Doras' peasants. I passed through Esdraelon...»

«Is it true that the fields are a complete ruin and that he wants to sell them?»

«They are a ruin. Whether he wants to sell them, I do not know. One of Johanan's men mentioned it to me. But I do not know whether it is certain.»

«If he should sell them... I would willingly buy them to have a refuge for You also in the middle of that nest of snakes.»

«I do not think that you will be successful. Johanan is ready to buy them.»

«We shall see... But go on. Who are the peasants? He scattered all the former servants.»

«Yes, he did. The present ones come from his land in Judaea, at least the old man, the boy's relative, does. The boy was kept in a wood, like a wild animal, so that Doras could not see him... and he had been there since last winter...»

«Oh! poor boy! But why?» The women are all moved.

«Because his father and mother were buried under the landslide near Emmaus. The whole family: father, mother and his little brothers. He survived because he was not at home. They took him to the old father. But what could a peasant of Doras do? Isaac, *also* in this case, you spoke of Me as a saviour.»

«Was that wrong?» asks Isaac humbly.

«You did the right thing. God wanted it. The old man gave me the boy, who is to come of age in the next few days.»

«Oh! poor little thing! So tiny at twelve years of age?! My Judas was twice his size at that age... And Jesus? What a beautiful flower!» says Mary of Alphaeus.

And Salome: «Also my children were much stronger!»

Martha whispers: «He is really tiny! I thought he was not ten yet.»

«Eh! Hunger is a nasty thing. And he must have suffered from starvation since he was born. And now... What could the old man give him, if they are all dying of starvation there?» says Peter.

«Yes, he suffered a great deal. But he is good and intelligent. I took him to comfort both the old man and the boy.»

[6] «Are you going to adopt him?» asks Lazarus. 198.6

«No. I cannot.»

«Well, I will take him.»

Peter sees his hopes vanish and he utters a really deep groan: «Lord! Everything to him?»

Jesus smiles: «Lazarus, you have already done so much and I am grateful to you. But I cannot entrust this child to you. He is "Our" boy. He belongs to *all* of us. He is the joy of the apostles and of the Master. Besides, he would be brought up in luxury here. I want to make him a present of My royal mantle: "honest poverty". The poverty that the Son of man wanted for Himself, to be able to go near the greatest miseries without mortifying anybody. You have had a gift from Me also recently...»

«Ah! Yes! The old patriarch and his daughter. The woman is

very active, the old man very good.»

«Where are they now? I mean: in which place?»

«They are here, in Bethany. Do You think I was going to send away the blessing You had sent me? The woman weaves linen. Light skilful hands are required for that job. Since the old man insists on working, I put him at the beehives. Yesterday he had a long golden beard, didn't he, sister? The bees swarmed and clung to his long beard and he was speaking to them as if they were daughters. He is happy.»

«I am sure he is! May you be blessed!» says Jesus.

198.7 «Thank You, Master. [7]But that boy will cost You a lot. You will allow me at least to...»

«I will see to his clothes for the ceremony» shouts Peter. They all laugh at his impulsive reaction.

«All right. But he will need other clothes. Simon, be good. I have no children either. Allow Martha and me to find some solace seeing to some little garments to be made for him.»

Peter, who has been thus besought, is moved at once and he says: «His clothes... yes... But his dress for Wednesday... I am going to get it. The Master promised me and He told me that I would be going with His Mother to buy it tomorrow.» Peter explains everything in detail lest there should be some unexpected change to his disadvantage.

Jesus smiles and says: «Yes, Mother. Please go with Simon tomorrow. Otherwise he will die of heart-failure. You will give him some advice as to what he should choose.»

«I said: a red dress and a green sash. He will look lovely. Much better than the shade he has on now.»

«Red will be all right. Also Jesus was dressed in red. But I would say that a red sash would be better on a red dress, or at least it should be embroidered in red» says Mary gently.

«I was saying green because I see that Judas, who is swarthy, looks very smart with those green stripes on his red tunic.»

«But these are not green, my friend!» laughs Judas.

«No? What shade are they then?»

«This hue is called "agate vein".»

«How do you expect me to know that?! They look green to me. I saw that hue also on leaves...»

The Most Holy Virgin interrupts benignly: «Simon is right.

It is the exact shade of leaves at the first rain in the month of Tishri...»

«That's it! And since leaves are green I was saying that it was green» concludes Peter happily. The Sweet Mother has also settled this small matter peacefully.

[8] «Will you call the boy, please?» begs Mary. And the child arrives at once with John. 198.8

«What is your name?» asks Mary caressing him.

«It is... it was Jabez. But I am expecting a new one ..»

«Are you?»

«Yes, Jabez wants a name meaning that I have saved him. You will find one for him, Mother. A name of love and of salvation.»

Mary is pensive... She then says: «Marjiam (Maarhgziam). You are the little star in the sea of those saved by Jesus. Do you like it? Thus it will remind you also of Me besides Salvation.»

«It is beautiful» says the boy joyfully.

«But isn't it a woman's name?» asks Bartholomew.

«With "I" at the end instead of "m", when this tiny drop of Mankind is grown up, you can change his name into the name of a man. For the time being he has the name which the Mother has given him. Is that right?»

The boy says «yes» and Mary caresses him.

Her sister-in-law says to Her: «This wool is good» and she feels Jabez' mantle. «But its colour! What do You think? I would dye it very dark red. It will come out lovely.»

«We will do it tomorrow evening. Because he will have his new mantle. We cannot take it off him now.»

Martha says: «Would you come with me, my little boy? I will take you to a place near here, to see many things, then we will come back here...»

Jabez does not object. He never refuses... but he seems somewhat afraid to go with the woman who is almost unknown to him. He says shyly and gently: «Could John come with me?»

«Of course...»

They go away. [9]And during their absence the various groups 198.9
continue their conversations. They narrate, comment and sigh on human harshness. Isaac tells what he has been able to find out about the Baptist. Some say he is at Machaerus, some at Tiberias. His disciples have not yet come back...

«But did they not follow him?»

«Yes. But near Doco those who had captured him crossed the river with their prisoner and no one knows whether they went up to the lake or down to Machaerus. John, Matthias and Simeon are moving around to find out and they will certainly not abandon him.»

«And you, Isaac, will certainly not abandon this new disciple. He will stay with Me for the time being. I want him to celebrate Passover with Me.»

«I will celebrate it in Jerusalem, in Johanna's house. She saw me and offered a room for me and my companions. They are all coming this year. And we shall be there with Jonathan.»

«Those from Lebanon too?»

«Yes. Perhaps John's disciples will not be able to come.»

«Johanan's men are coming, did you know?»

«Are they? I will be at the door, near the priests offering sacrifices. I will see them and take them with me.»

«They will be arriving at the last moment. Their time is very limited. But they have a lamb.»

«I have one, too. A marvellous one. Lazarus gave me it. We will sacrifice this one and they can keep theirs for their journey back home.»

198.10 [10]Martha comes back with John and the boy who is wearing a little white linen dress and a red overall. On his arm he is carrying a mantle which is also red.

«Do you remember them, Lazarus? See, things are always useful.»

They smile at each other.

Jesus says: «Thank you, Martha.»

«Oh! My Lord! I have a passion for keeping things. I inherited it from my mother. I still have many of my brother's robes. They are dear to me because they were handled by my mother. Now and again I take one to give it to a child. I will now give them to Marjiam. They are a little long for him, but they can be shortened. When Lazarus came of age, he did not want them any more... The typical passing fancy of a child... and he got his own way because my mother adored her Lazarus.»

She caresses her brother fondly and Lazarus takes her beautiful hand, kisses it and says: «And do you not?» They smile at each other.

«That is a gift of Providence» remark many.

«Yes, my whim has done a good turn. Perhaps I shall be forgiven because of that.»

Dinner is ready and everyone sits at his place...

11 ... It is late in the night when Jesus can speak to His Mother 198.11
in peace. They have gone up to the terrace, and sitting one beside the other, hand in hand, they speak and listen to each other.

Jesus is the first to tell the story of the things that happened. Then Mary says: «Son, after Your departure, immediately after, a woman came to Me... She was looking for You. A *great* misery. And a *great* redemption. But the poor creature needs to be forgiven by You so that she may persevere in her decision. I entrusted her to Susanna saying that she had been cured by You. That is true. I could have kept her with Me if our house were not like a sea-port, where all the boats come in... and many with evil intentions. And the woman is disgusted with the world by now. Do You want to know who she is?»

«She is a soul. But tell Me her name that I may receive her without any mistake.»

«She is Aglae. The Roman mime and sinner whom You began to save at Hebron, who looked for You and found You at the Clear Water and she has already suffered because of her revived honesty. How much she has suffered!... She told Me everything... How horrible!...»

«Her sin?»

«That... and I would say how much more: how horrible the world is. Oh! My Son! Do not trust the Pharisees in Capernaum! They wanted to use the unhappy creature to harm You. They would have used *even* her...»

«I know, Mother... Where is Aglae?»

«She will be coming with Susanna before Passover.»

«Very well. I will speak to her. I will be here every evening and with the exception of Passover evening, which I am reserving for the family, I will wait for her. All You need do is tell her to wait, if she comes. It is a great redemption, as You said. And such a spontaneous one! I solemnly tell You that in few hearts My seed took root with the same strength as it did in this unhappy soil. And later Andrew helped it to grow until it was fully formed.»

«She told Me.»

«Mother, what did You feel when that ruin approached You?»

«Disgust and joy. I seemed to be on the brink of a hellish abyss, and at the same time I felt as if I were being carried into the blue sky. You are God indeed, My Son, when You work such miracles!»

They remain silent, under the very bright stars and the pale light of the first quarter of the moon, which is tending to become full. Silent, loving each other and resting in each other's love.

199. A Visit to the Lepers of Siloam and Ben Hinnom. The Power of Mary's Intercession.

24th June 1945.

199.1 [1]The beautiful morning invites people to leave their homes and beds and go for a walk, and the people living in the Zealot's house get up very early, and like bees at sunrise they go out to breathe the pure air in Lazarus' orchard around the hospitable house. They are soon joined by Lazarus' guests, that is, Philip, Bartholomew, Matthew, Thomas, Andrew and James of Zebedee. The sun shines in joyfully through all the windows and wide open doors and illuminates the simple tidy rooms with a golden hue, which brightens the shades of clothes and enlivens the hues of hair and eyes.

Mary of Alphaeus and Salome are busy serving the men who enjoy a hearty appetite. Mary instead is watching one of Lazarus' servants who is sorting Marjiam's hair, cutting it with greater skill than his first barber ever did. «That will do for the time being» says the servant. «Later, when you have offered God the curls of your childhood, I will cut it shorter. The warm season is coming and you will feel better without any hair on your neck. And your hair will grow stronger. It is dry, weak and has been neglected. See, Mary? It needs some attention. I will now put some oil on it to keep it in place. Can you smell the lovely scent, my boy? It is oil that Martha uses. It is very good. Almond, palm and medulla of the finest quality with a rare essence. My mistress told me to keep this little jar for the boy. Oh! Here you are! You now look like the son of a king» and the servant, who is probably the barber of Lazarus' house, pats Marjiam on the cheek, greets Mary and goes away looking quite satisfied.

«Come and let Me dress you» says Mary to the boy who has only a short tunic with short sleeves; I think it is a shirt or what was used in those days as a shirt. By its fine linen I gather that it must have belonged to Lazarus when a boy. Mary takes off the towel in which Marjiam was wrapped and puts on him a linen vest puckered round the neck and cuffs, and a red woollen robe with wide neck and sleeves. The shining snow-white linen protrudes from the neck-opening and the sleeves of the dull red cloth. Mary's skilful hands must have adjusted the length of the robe and of the sleeves during the night, and it now fits the boy, particularly when Mary girds his waist with a soft sash adorned with a woollen white and red tassel. The child no longer looks like the poor little creature of a few days earlier.

«Now go and play, but do not get dirty, while I get ready» says Mary, caressing him. And the boy bounds out happily, looking for his big friends.

[2] Thomas is the first one to see him: «How lovely you are! Fit for 199.2
a wedding! You make me cut a poor figure» says plump Thomas who is always merry and genial. And he takes him by the hand saying: «Let us go and see the women. They were looking for you to feed you.»

They go into the kitchen and Thomas causes the two Maries, who are bent over the kitchen-stove, to start, when he shouts in his loud voice: «There is a young man here looking for you» and laughing he introduces the boy who was hiding behind his robust back.

«Oh! dear! Come here that I may give you a kiss! Look, Salome, how lovely he is!» exclaims Mary of Alphaeus.

«He is, indeed! All he needs now is to become more robust. But I'll see to that. Come here, that I may kiss you, too» replies Salome.

«But Jesus is going to entrust him to the shepherds...» objects Thomas.

«Not on your life! My Jesus is mistaken here. What can you men do or pretend you can do? You are only good at quarrelling — because, incidentally, you are rather quarrelsome... like little goats which are fond of one another and gore one another with their horns — at eating, speaking and you have a thousand needs and you claim the Master to pay all His attention to you… otherwise you become sulky… Children need mothers. Is that right? What is your name?»

«Marjiam.»

«Of course! But blessed be my Mary! She could have given you an easier name!»

«It's almost like Hers!» exclaims Salome.

«Yes, but Hers is more simple. There aren't those letters in the middle of it… They are too many…»

The Iscariot, who has just come in, says: «She gave a name which is precise in its meaning, according to the genuine old language.»

«All right. But it is difficult, and I will take one letter away and say Marziam. It is easier and the world will not collapse because of that. Is that right, Simon?»

Peter, who is passing by the window speaking to John of Endor, looks in and asks: «What do you want?»

«I was saying that I shall call the boy Marziam. It is easier.»

«You are right, woman. If the Mother allows me, I will call him thus, too. But how wonderful you look! So do I, eh? Look!»

In fact he is perfectly tidy, his cheeks have been shaved, his hair cut, his beard trimmed and scented with oil, his clothes show no creases and his sandals are so clean that they look like new ones. I do not know what he has polished them with. The women admire him and he laughs happily.

The boy has finished eating and goes out to meet his great friend, whom he always calls: «Father».

199.3 [3] And there is Jesus coming from Lazarus' house together with the latter. The boy runs towards Him and Jesus says: «Peace be with us, Marjiam. Let us exchange the kiss of peace.»

Lazarus, greeted by the boy, caresses him and gives him a sweet.

They all gather around Jesus. Also Mary, wearing a turquoise woolen dress on top of which a darker mantle is draped, comes towards Her Son smiling.

«We can go, then» says Jesus. «You, Simon, with My Mother and the boy, if you still wish to buy his robe, now that Lazarus has seen to it.»

«Of course I do! And then... I will be able to say that once I walked beside Your Mother. A great honour.»

«Go, then. Simon, you will take Me to your leper friends...»

«Really, Master? Then, if You do not mind, I will run ahead, to gather them... You will reach me. You know where they are...»

«All right, go. The others can do what they like. You are all free until Wednesday morning. At the third hour everybody is to be at the Golden Gate.»

«I am coming with You, Master» says John.

«And I» says his brother James.

«And us, too» say the two cousins.

«I will come, too» says Matthew, and Andrew after him.

«And I? I would like to come, too... but if I go to do the shopping, I cannot come...» says Peter, pressed by two desires.

«It can be done. We shall go to the lepers first, while My Mother with the boy goes to the house of a friend in Ophel. We will reach Her later and you will go with Her, while the others and I go to Johanna's. We will meet at Gethsemane for our meal and towards sunset we will come back here.»

«If You allow me, I will go to see some friends...» says Judas Iscariot.

«I have already told you. Do what you like.»

«In that case, I will go to my relatives. Perhaps my father has already come. If he is there, I will bring him to see You» says Thomas.

«What about us two? What do you say, Philip? We could go and see Samuel.»

«Very good» Philip replies to Bartholomew.

«And what about you, John?» Jesus asks the man of Endor. «Do you prefer to remain here and sort out your books, or do you wish to come with Me?»

«Really, I would prefer to come with You... My books... I am already less fond of them. I prefer to read You, the Living Book.»

«Come, then. Goodbye, Lazarus...»

«I will come, too. My legs are a little better, and after we have seen the lepers, I will leave You and go to Gethsemane and wait for You there.»

«Let us go, Peace to you, women.»

They remain all together until they are near Jerusalem. Then they part, the Iscariot goes on his own and enters the town probably through the Gate near the Antonia Tower; Thomas, Philip and Nathanael walk for about ten more yards with Jesus and their companions and then enter the town through the suburb of Ophel, together with Mary and the boy.

199.4 [4] «And now, let us go and see those unhappy people!» says Jesus, and turning His back to the town He goes towards a desolate place on the slope of a rocky hill which lies between the two roads from Jericho to Jerusalem, A strange place, similar to a flight of steps after the first slope, up which climbs a path, so that there is a drop of at least three yards from the first terrace to the path, and the same from the second one. It is an arid, dead... extremely sad place.

«Master» shouts Simon the Zealot «I am here. Stop where You are, that I may show You the way...» and the Zealot, who was leaning against a rock to be in the shade, comes forward and leads Jesus up the steps of a path leading towards Gethsemane, but separated from it by the road that from the Mount of Olives goes to Bethany. *

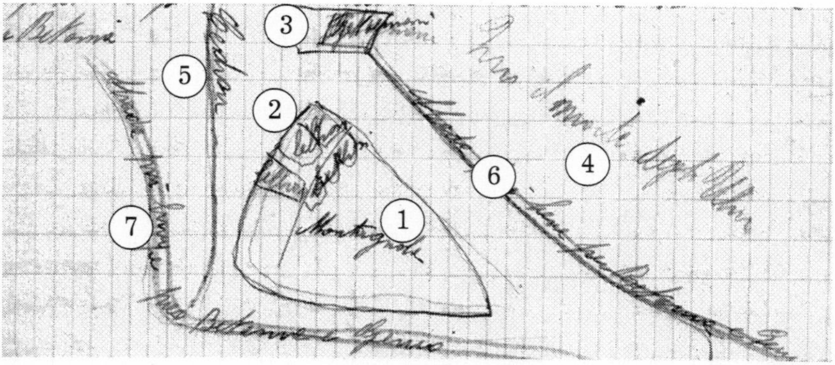

«Here we are. I lived among the tombs of Siloam and my friends are here. Some of them. The others are at Ben Hinnom, but cannot come... They would have to cross the road and would be seen.»

«We shall go to them also.»

* The drawing made by MV shows the desolate place where lepers live: **1.** *Hillock*; **2.** *lepers* (three times); **3.** *Gethsemane*; **4.** *"Here is the Mount of Olives"*; **5.** *Kidron*; **6.** *"The shorteat road to Bethany and Jericho"*; **7.** *"the longest road to Bethany and Jericho"*.

«Thank You! On their part and mine.»

«Are they many?»

«Winter has killed most of them. But here there are still five of those to whom I had spoken. They are waiting for You. There they are, on the edge of their prison...»

There are probably ten monsters. I say «probably», because if five, who are standing up, are clearly visible, the others, because of the greyish hue of their skin, the deformity of their faces and the fact that they hardly protrude from the stone barrier, cannot be counted accurately and they may be more than five or less. Among those standing up there is only one woman. One can tell only by her white dishevelled hair hanging coarse and dirty over her shoulders down to her waist. There is no other sign by which one could tell her sex, because the disease, which is in an advanced stage, has reduced her to a skeleton, destroying all feminine forms. Likewise among the men, only one still has traces of moustache and beard. All the others have been made hairless by the destructive disease.

They shout: «Jesus, our Saviour, have mercy on us!» and they stretch out their deformed or ulcerated hands. «Jesus, Son of David, have mercy on us!»

«What do you want Me to do for you?» asks Jesus looking towards their misery.

«We want You to save us from sin and from this disease.»

«Your will and repentance will save you from sin...»

«But if You wish, You can cancel our sins. At least those, if You do not want to cure our bodies.»

«If I say to You: "Choose either one or the other", which one would you prefer?»

«God's forgiveness, Lord. To be less desolate.»

Jesus has a gesture of approval. He smiles brightly, raises His arms and shouts: «Let it be granted. I want it.»

Granted! The grace might be granted for their sins, or for their disease, or for both, and the five unhappy people remain uncertain. But the apostles have no uncertainty and they can but shout their hosannas when they see the leprosy disappear as fast as a flake of snow that falls on a fire. The five then understand that the full grace has been granted to them. Their shouting resounds like a cry of victory. They embrace one another and throw kisses at Jesus, as they cannot prostrate themselves at His feet. They then turn to their companions saying: «And you still refuse to believe? What miserable wretches are you?»

«Good! Be good! Your poor brothers need time to think. Say nothing to them. *Faith is not imposed, it is preached with peace, kindness, patience and perseverance.* That is what you will do after your purification, exactly as Simon did with you. After all, the miracle preaches by itself. You who have been cured, will go to the priest as soon as possible. You, who are still ill, wait for us this evening. We will bring you some food. Peace be with you.»

Jesus descends again on to the road followed by the blessings of everybody.

199.5 [5] «And now let us go to Ben Hinnom» says Jesus.

«Master... I would like to come. But I realise that I cannot. I will go to Gethsemane» says Lazarus.

«Go, Lazarus. Peace be with you.»

While Lazarus is slowly walking away, the apostle John says: «Master, I will go with him. He walks with difficulty and the road is not very good. I will join You later at Ben Hinnom.»

«Yes, you may go. Let us go.»

They cross the Kidron, walk along the southern side of Mount Tophet and enter the little valley completely strewn with tombs and filth. There is not one tree or any shade from the sun, which blazes down on this southern side heating the stones of these new hellish terraces where the stinking smell of burning rubbish increases the heat. And inside the sepulchres, similar to crematoria, there are poor bodies, which are wasting away... Siloam may be unpleasant in winter, damp as it is and facing north, but this place must be dreadful in summer...

Simon Zealot lets out a shout calling them, and first three lepers, then two, then one, and another one come, as best they can, to the prescribed limit. There are two women here, and one of them is holding by the hand a horrible looking boy whose face is particularly affected by leprosy. He is already blind... And there is a noble looking man, notwithstanding his miserable state. He speaks on behalf of everybody: «Blessed be the Messiah of the Lord, Who has come down to our Gehenna, to free from it those who hope in Him. Save us, o Lord, because we are perishing! Save us, Saviour! King of the House of David, King of Israel, have mercy on Your subjects. Oh! Shoot of the stock of Jesse, of Whom it is said that in Your time there will be no evil, stretch out Your hand and pick up the remains of Your people. Cast away this death from us, wipe our tears, because that is what is said of You. Call us, Lord, to Your delicious pastures, to Your fresh waters, for we are thirsty. Lead us to the eternal hills where there is no sin or sorrow. Have mercy, Lord...»

«Who are you?»

«John, one of the Temple. I was probably infected by a leper. As You can see, I caught the disease only recently. But these!... Some of them have been awaiting death for years, and this little girl came here even before she could walk. She does not know what is the creation of God. What she knows or what she remembers of the wonders of God are these tombs, this merciless sun and the stars at night. Have mercy on the guilty and the innocent ones, o Lord, our Saviour.» They have all knelt down stretching out their hands.

Jesus weeps at so much misery. He then opens His arms shouting: «Father, I want it: health, life, sight and salvation for them.» He remains with His arms stretched out praying intensely with all His spirit. He seems to become thinner and to rise in prayer, a flame of love, white and powerful in the powerful gold of the sun.

«Mummy, I can see!» is the first cry, which is answered by the shout of the mother who clasps her cured little girl to her heart; then the shouts of the others and of the apostles... The miracle has been worked.

«John, as you are a priest, you will lead your companions in the rite. Peace be with you. Towards evening we shall bring some food also to you.» He blesses and is about to go away.

But John, the leper, shouts: «I want to follow Your steps. Tell me what I must do, where I must go to preach You!»

«In this desolate barren land, which must turn to the Lord. Let the town of Jerusalem be your field. Goodbye.»

[6] «And now let us go to My Mother» He says to the apostles. 199.6

«But where is She?» ask many of them.

* «In a house known to John. In the house of the girl who was cured last year.»

---

* **who was cured**: Annaleh, healed in 86.4/5; she made a vow of virginity in 156.3/5.

They enter the town, covering a good deal of the thickly populated suburb of Ophel until they reach a little white house.

With His usual kind greeting He enters the house, the door of which is half open and one can hear the sweet voice of Mary, the silvery voice of Annaleah and the thick voice of her mother. The girl prostrates herself adoring and her mother kneels down. Mary stands up.

They would like to keep the Master with His Mother. But Jesus promises to go back some other day, He blesses them and says goodbye. Peter goes away with Mary and is very happy. They are both holding the boy by his hands and they look like a happy family. Many people turn around to look at them. Jesus watches them go away smiling.

«Simon is happy!» exclaims the Zealot.

«Why are You smiling, Master?» asks James of Zebedee.

«Because I see a great promise in that group.»

«Which promise, Brother? What do You see?» asks Thaddeus.

«This is what I see: that I shall be able to go away with a peaceful mind, when the time comes. I need not be afraid for My Church. Then it will be small and slender like Marjiam. But My Mother will be there to hold it by the hand and to be its Mother; and there will be Peter as its father. In his honest rough hands I can place the hand of My dawning Church without any worry. He will give it the strength of his protection. My Mother the strength of Her love. And the Church will grow... like Marjiam... He is really the symbol-child! May God bless My Mother, My Peter and their child and ours! Now let us go to Johanna's.»

199.7 [7]... And once again, in the evening, we are in the little house in Bethany. Many have already withdrawn, because they were tired. Peter is walking up and down the path, often looking up to the terrace where Jesus and Mary are sitting talking. John of Endor, instead, is speaking to the Zealot sitting under a pomegranate-tree in full blossom.

Mary has already spoken a great deal because I can hear Jesus say: «Everything You told Me is just and I will bear in mind its justice. And I say that Your advice concerning Annaleah is also right. It is a good sign that the man has accepted it so readily. It is true that the people high up in Jerusalem are dull-minded and envious, I could also say that they are filthy. But in the humble people there are pearls of unknown value. I am glad that Annaleah is happy. She belongs more to Heaven than to the earth, and perhaps the man, who has now understood the concept of the spirit, realises that and he respects her almost religiously. His intention to go elsewhere, so that no human sentiment may upset the pure vow of his girl, proves it.»

«Yes, My Son, Man perceives the perfume of virgins... I remember Joseph, I did not know which words to use. He was not aware of My secret... And yet he helped Me to disclose it with the intuition of a saint. He had perceived the scent of My soul... Also John, see?... How peaceful he is! And everybody seeks him. Even Judas of Kerioth, although... No, Son. Judas has not changed. I know and You know. We do not speak because we do not want to start a war. But even if we do not speak, we know... and even if we do not speak, the others realise... Oh! My Jesus! The younger apostles told Me today, at Gethsemane, the episode at Magdala and the other one of Sabbath morning... Innocent children speak... because they see through the eyes of their angels. But also old people have an idea... They are not wrong. He is an elusive being... Everything is elusive in him... and I am afraid of him and I have on My lips the same words of Benjamin at Magdala and of Marjiam at Gethsemane, because I feel the same disgust for Judas as children do.»

«Not everybody can be John!...»

«I do not demand that! In that case, it would be paradise on the earth. But, see, You told Me about the other John... A man who killed... but I only feel sorry for him. Judas frightens Me.»

«Love him, Mother! Love him, for My sake!»

«Yes, Son, I will. But not even My love will serve. It will only make Me suffer and make him guilty, Oh! Why did he come to You? He upsets everybody, he offends Peter who deserves all respect.»

8 «Yes. Peter is very good. I would do anything for him, because 199.8
he deserves it.»

«If he heard You, he would say with his good frank smile: "Ah! My Lord, that is not true!" And he would be right.»

«Why, Mother?» But Jesus smiles, because He has already understood.

«Because You are not satisfying him by giving him a son. He

told Me all his hopes, his desires... and Your refusals.»

«And did he not tell You the reasons justifying them?»

«Yes, he did and he added: "It is true... but I am a man, a poor man. Jesus persists in seeing a great man in me. But I know that I am a poor fellow, and so... he could give me a child. I got married to have them... and I will die without any". And he said — pointing at the boy who, delighted because of the lovely dress bought by Peter, had kissed him, saying: "Beloved father" — he said: "See, when this little creature, whom only ten days ago I did not know, says that to me, I feel that I become softer than butter and sweeter than honey and I weep, because... every day that goes by, takes this child away from me".»

Mary becomes silent, watching Jesus, studying His face, waiting for a word... But Jesus has placed His elbow on His knee, resting His head in His hand and is silent, looking at the green expanse of the orchard.

Mary takes His hand and caressing it She says: «Simon has this *great* desire... When I went with him, he did nothing but speak to Me about it, and his reasons are so good that... I could say nothing to keep him quiet. They are the same reasons that all women and mothers think of. The boy is not strong. If he were as strong as You were... oh! he could have faced the life of a disciple without any fear. But he is so thin!... He is very intelligent, very good... but nothing more. When a little dove is so delicate, you cannot throw it in the air to let it fly very early, as you do with strong ones. The shepherds are good... but they are still men. Children need women. Why do You not leave him with Simon? While You refuse him a son of his own, born of him, I understand the reason. A son is like an anchor. And Simon, who is destined to such a great task, cannot be hindered by anchors. But You must agree that he is to be the "father" of all the sons You will be leaving him. How can he be a father if he has had no training with a child? A father must be sweet. Simon is good, but not sweet. He is impulsive and intolerant. Only a little creature can teach him the fine art of being indulgent to whoever is weak... Consider Simon's destiny... He is Your successor after all! Oh! I must say that cruel word! But for all the sorrow it causes Me saying it, listen to Me. I would never advise You anything unless it were good. Marjiam... You want to make a perfect disciple of him... But he is only a boy. You... You will be going before he is a man. To whom then can You give him, to complete his formation, better than Simon? Finally, poor Simon, You know how much trouble he has had, with his mother-in-law, also because of You. And yet he has not picked up a tiny part of his past, of his freedom of a year ago, to be left in peace by his mother-in-law, whom not even You have been able to change. And his poor wife? She is longing so much to love and be loved. Her mother... oh! Her husband? A dear domineering man... No affection is ever given to her without exacting too much... Poor woman!... Leave her the boy. Listen, Son. For the time being we will take him with us. I will come to Judaea, too. You will take Me to one of My companions of the Temple, who is almost a relative, because she is of the House of David. She lives at Bethzur. I will be pleased to see her, if she is still alive. Then, when we go back to Galilee, we will give him to Porphirea. When we are near Bethsaida, Peter will take him. When we come here, so far, the boy will stay with her. Ah! You are smiling now! So You are going to please Your Mother. Thank You, My Jesus.»

«Yes, let it be done, as You wish.» [9]Jesus stands up and calls 199.9
out loud: «Simon of Jonas: come here.»

Peter starts and rushes up the steps. «What do You want, Master?»

«Come here, you usurper and corrupter!»

«Me? Why? What have I done, Lord?»

«You have corrupted My Mother. That is why you wanted to be alone. What shall I do with you?»

But Jesus smiles and Peter recovers confidence. «Oh!» he says. «You really frightened me! But now You are laughing... What do You want from me, Master? My life? I have but that, because You have taken everything... But if You want, I will give it to You.»

«I do not want to take anything from you. I want to give you something. But do not take advantage of your victory and do not disclose the secret to the others, you most artful fellow who defeats the Master by means of the weapon of His Mother's word. You will have the boy, but...»

Jesus can say no more, because Peter, who had knelt down, bounces to his feet and kisses the Master with such delight that he makes the words die on His lips.

«Thank Her, not Me. But remember that this must be of assistance to you, and not an impediment...»

«My Lord, You will not have to repent of the gift... Oh! Mary! May You be always blessed, You are holy and good...» And Peter, who has fallen on his knees again, weeps, kissing Mary's hand...

200. Aglae Meets the Master. Her Joy for Feeling Forgiven and Saved.

25th June 1945.

200.1 [1] Jesus goes back to the Zealot's house alone. It is getting dark and the evening is quiet and serene after so much sunshine. Jesus looks in at the kitchen door, says hello and then goes upstairs, to meditate in the upper room, which has already been prepared for supper. He does not look very happy. He often sighs and walks to and fro in the large room, looking now and again at the surrounding country, which can be seen through the many doors of this large room, shaped like a cube above the ground floor. He goes out also and walks on the terrace making a tour of the house and He stops at the rear side looking at John of Endor who is kindly drawing water from a well and handing it to busy Salome. He looks, shakes His head and sighs.

The power of His glance draws the attention of John, who looks up and asks: «Master, do You want me?»

«No, I was only looking at you.»

«John is good. He helps me» says Salome.

«And God will reward him for that help too.»

200.2 [2] After these words Jesus goes back into the room and sits down. He is so engrossed in thought that He does not notice the noisy chattering of many voices and the shuffling of many feet in the entrance corridor and then two light footsteps climbing the outside staircase and approaching the large room. Only when Mary calls Him He looks up.

«Son, Susanna has arrived in Jerusalem with her family and she brought Aglae here at once. Do You wish to listen to her while we are alone?»

«Yes, Mother. At once. And do not let anyone come up until it is all over. I hope to deal with her before the others come back.

But please watch that there is no indiscreet curiosity... in no one... particularly with regards to Judas of Simon.»

«I will watch carefully...»

Mary goes out and shortly afterwards comes back holding by the hand Aglae, who is no longer wrapped in her large grey mantle with her veil pulled over her face and is not wearing high heeled sandals with complicated buckles and strips, which she wore before. She is now dressed like a Jewess, with low flat very plain sandals, like Mary's, a dark blue dress on which her mantle is draped, and a white veil which she is wearing in the style of common Jewish women, that is, simply covering her head with one edge falling on her shoulders so that her face is only partially veiled. Her plain dress, identical to the one worn by most women and the fact that she was with other Galileans prevented her from being recognised.

She enters with her head lowered, blushing at every step, and I think that she would have knelt down on the threshold, if Mary had not kindly pulled her towards Jesus.

«Here, Son, is the woman who has been looking for You for such a long time. Listen to her» says Mary when She is near Jesus and then withdraws, pulling the curtains over the wide open doors and closing the one which is near the staircase.

200.3

[3] Aglae puts down the little bag she was carrying on her shoulder, then she kneels down at Jesus' feet and bursts into tears. She prostrates herself on the floor, her head resting on her arms crossed on the floor.

«Do not weep thus. This is not the time for tears. You should have wept when you were hateful to God. Not now that you love Him and are loved by Him.»

But Aglae continues to weep...

«Do you not believe that it is so?»

She manages to speak through her sobs: «I love Him, it is true, as best I can... But although I know and believe that God is Bounty I cannot possibly hope to be loved by Him. I have sinned too much... Perhaps one day I will be loved... But I still have to weep so much... For the time being I am alone in my love. All alone... It is not desperate solitude of past years. It is a solitude full of longing for God, so it is no longer hopeless... but it is so sad...»

«Aglae, how little you still know the Lord! This longing for Him is the proof that God is replying to your love, that He is your friend, Who calls you, invites you and wants you. God is incapable of remaining insensitive to the desire of a creature, because He, the Lord and Creator of all creatures, excited that desire in that heart. He excited it because He loved with privileged love the soul that is now longing for Him. *The desire of God always precedes the desire of the creature,* because He is Most Perfect and therefore His love is by far more eager and ardent than the love of the creature.»

«But how can God love my filth?»

«Do not endeavour to understand with your intelligence. He is an abyss of mercy, which human intelligence cannot understand. But what the intelligence of man cannot understand, the intelligence of love, the love of the spirit does. It understands and confidently penetrates the mystery, which is God, and the mystery of the relationship of the soul with God. Enter, I tell you. Enter, because God wants it.»

«Oh! My Saviour! So I am really forgiven? I am really loved? Must I believe it?»

«Did I ever lie to you?»

«Oh! no, Lord! Everything You told me at Hebron came true. * You saved me because Your Name is salvation. You looked for me, a poor lost soul. You gave me the life of this soul, which I was carrying dead within me. You told me that if I had looked for You I would find You. And it was true. You told me that You are wherever man needs a doctor and medicine. And it is true. Everything, everything You told poor Aglae, from the words on that morning in June, to the other words at the Clear Water...»

«So you must believe these too.»

«Yes, I believe, I do believe! But say to me: "I forgive you"!»

«I forgive you in the name of God and of Jesus.»

200.4 «Thank You... [4]But now... What must I do? Tell me, My Saviour, what I must do to have Eternal Life. Man becomes corrupt only by looking at me... I cannot live in perpetual fear of being discovered and entrapped... During this journey I trembled every time a man looked at me... I do not want to sin anymore neither

---

* **You told me**, in 77.7.

do I want to cause others to sin. Tell me the road I must follow. I will follow it whatever it may be. You can see that I am strong also in privations... And even if I should die because of too many privations, I am not afraid. I will call death "my friend", because death will rid me of the dangers of the earth, and forever. Speak, my Saviour.»

«Go to a desert place.»

«Where, my Lord?»

«Wherever you wish. Where your spirit will lead you.»

«Will my spirit, which is just formed, be capable of so much?»

«Yes, because God is leading you.»

«And who will speak to me of God again?»

«Your risen soul, for the time being...»

«Will I see You again?»

«Never again in this world. But before long I will have redeemed you completely and then I will come to your spirit to prepare you to ascend to God.»

«How will my complete redemption take place if I do not see You again? How will You give it to me?»

«By dying for all sinners.»

«Oh! no! You must not die!»

«To give men the Life I must give Myself to death. That is why I came as a human being. Do not weep... You will soon join Me where I shall be after My sacrifice and yours.»

«My Lord! Will I die for You, too?»

«Yes, but in a different way. Your flesh will die hour by hour and because your will wants that. It has been dying for almost one year. When it is completely dead, I will call you.»

«Will I have the strength to destroy my guilty flesh?»

«In your solitude where Satan will attack you with livid violence the more you become worthy of Heaven, you will find an apostle of Mine, once a sinner and later redeemed.»

«Not the blessed apostle who spoke to me of You? He could not have been a sinner because he is too honest.»

«Not that one. Another one. He will reach you at the right moment. He will tell you what you cannot know just now. Go in peace. The blessing of God be with you.»

[5] Aglae, who has been kneeling all the time, bends to kiss the 200.5
feet of the Lord. She dares no more. She then picks up her sack

and turns it upside down. Some plain dresses, a little tinkling purse and an amphora of fine pink alabaster fall out of it.

Aglae puts the dresses into the sack, picks up the purse and says: «This is for the poor. It is what is left of my jewels. I kept only some coins for my journey... because, even if You had not told me. I intended going to a remote place. And this is for You. It is not so sweet as the perfume of Your holiness. But it is the best the earth can give. And I used it for the worst... Here. May God grant me to smell *at least* like this, in Your presence, in Heaven» and she removes the precious cap of the amphora and pours its contents onto the floor.

Waves of a strong scent of roses rise from the floor bricks, which become impregnated with the precious essence. Aglae puts away the empty amphora saying: «In remembrance of this hour» and she bends again to kiss Jesus' feet. She then stands up, withdraws backwards, goes out, closes the door...

I hear her steps receding towards the staircase, her voice exchanging a few words with Mary, then the noise of her sandals going down the steps and then nothing else. There is nothing left of Aglae except the little purse at Jesus' feet and the very strong scent in all the room.

Jesus gets up... he picks up the purse, puts it in His bosom, goes towards an opening looking onto the road and smiles seeing the woman going away, all alone, in her Jewish mantle, towards Bethlehem. He makes a gesture of blessing and goes towards the terrace and calls: «Mother.»

Mary goes upstairs quickly: «You made her happy, My Son. She has gone, with strength and peace.»

«Yes, Mother. When Andrew comes in, send him to Me before anybody else.»

200.6 [6] Some time goes by, then I hear the voices of the apostles, who have come back... Andrew goes upstairs: «Master, do You want me?»

«Yes, come here. No one will know, but it is only fair that I should tell you. Andrew, thank you in the name of God and of a soul.»

«Thanks? For what?»

«Can you not smell this perfume? It is a souvenir of the Veiled woman. She came. She is saved.»

Andrew turns as red as a cherry, he falls on his knees, and cannot find words... At last he says: «Now I am happy. Blessed be the Lord!»

«Yes, get up. Do not tell the others that she came.»

«I will be quiet, my Lord.»

«You may go. Listen: has Judas of Simon come yet?»

«Yes, he wanted to come with us, telling us... a lot of lies. Why does he do that, Lord?»

«Because he is a spoiled boy. Tell Me the truth: have you quarrelled?»

«No, My brother is too happy with his boy to be anxious to quarrel, and the others, You know... are more prudent. It is true, we are all disgusted, in our hearts. But after supper he is going away... Other friends... he says. Oh! and he despises prostitutes!...»

«Be good, Andrew. You must be happy, too, this evening...»

«Yes, Master. I also have a sweet, although invisible, paternity. I am going.»

[7] After some time the apostles come upstairs in a group with 200.7
the boy and John of Endor. The women follow them with dishes and lamps. The last to come are Lazarus and Simon. As soon as they enter the room, they exclaim: «Ah! it was coming from here!!!» and they smell the air saturated with the scent of roses, although the doors are wide open.

«But who scented this room thus? Perhaps Martha?» many of them ask.

«My sister has not left the house, today, after our meal» replies Lazarus.

«Who then? An Assyrian Satrap?» asks Peter facetiously.

«The love of a redeemed woman» Jesus says gravely.

«She might have spared this useless exhibition of redemption and given the poor what she spent. There are so many of them, and they know that we always give. I have not even a small coin left» says the Iscariot angrily. «And we have to buy a lamb, rent a room for the Supper and...»

«But I offered you everything...» says Lazarus.

«That is not fair. The rite loses its beauty. The Law says: "You shall take a lamb for you and your household". It does not say: "You shall accept a lamb".»

Bartholomew turns around all of a sudden, he opens his mouth, but closes it at once. Peter turns crimson in the effort to keep quiet. But the Zealot, who is in his own house, feels he can speak and says: «Those are rabbinical quibbles... May I ask you to forget about them and have, instead, respect for my friend Lazarus.»

«Well done, Simon.» Peter will burst if he does not speak. «Very good! I also think that *we* are forgetting too much that only the Master is entitled to teach...» Peter has to make an heroic effort to say: «we are forgetting» instead of saying: «Judas is forgetting.»

«It is true... but... I am nervous... I am sorry, Master.»

«Yes. And I also will reply to you. Gratitude is a *great virtue*. I am grateful to Lazarus. As that redeemed woman was grateful to Me. I pour on Lazarus the perfume of My blessing, also on behalf of those, among My apostles, who are not capable of doing so, *I, the head of you all*. The woman poured at My feet the perfume of her joy for being saved. She acknowledged the King, she came to the King, before many others upon whom the King bestowed much more love than upon her. Let her do as she wishes without criticising her. She will not be able to be present at My acclamation, or at My unction. Her cross is already upon her shoulders. Peter, you asked whether an Assyrian Satrap had come here. I solemnly tell you that not even the incense of the Magi, so pure and precious, was sweeter or more precious than this. Its essence was mixed with tears and that is why it is so intense: humility supports love and makes it perfect. Let us sit down to our meal, My friends...»

And with the offering of the food, the vision ends.

201. Marjiam's Examination for the Coming of Age.

26th June 1945.

201.1 [1] It must be Wednesday morning because the group of apostles and women, preceded by Jesus and Mary with the boy between them, is approaching the Gate of the Fish. Joseph of Arimathea, who went to meet them as he had promised, is also there. Jesus looks for Alexander, the soldier, but does not see him.

«He is not here today either... I wonder why...»

The crowd is so large that it is quite impossible to inquire of the soldiers, and in any case it might not be wise to do so, as the Jews are more intolerant than ever before festivities; they are also upset because of the capture of the Baptist and they accuse Pilate and his satellites of being accomplices. I realise that the situation is such because of the epithets that are exchanged during squabbles between soldiers and citizens at the Gate, where picturesque... rude insults crack every moment like fireworks.

The women from Galilee are scandalised and they wrap themselves closer in their mantles and veils. Mary blushes, but proceeds without hesitation, as straight as a palm tree, looking at Her Son, Who does not even attempt to make the over-excited Jews see reason or induce the soldiers to be merciful towards the Israelites. And as some rather unpleasant epithet is addressed to the Galilean group, Joseph of Arimathea moves forward towards Jesus and is recognised by the crowd who become silent out of respect for him.

At last the Gate of the Fish is behind them, and the great crowd of people, pouring into the town in waves, rushes along the streets, along with donkeys and herds...

[2] «Master, we are here!» shouts Thomas, who is on the other 201.2
side of the Gate with Philip and Bartholomew.

«Is Judas not here?», «Why are you here?» ask many.

«No. We came here at daybreak, because we were afraid that You might come earlier. But we have not seen him. I met him yesterday, he was with Sadoc, the scribe, you know, Joseph? The old, very lean man, with a wart under his eye. And there were other people with him... young people. I shouted to him: "Hallo, Judas". But he did not reply, pretending he did not know me. I said: "But what's the matter with him?" and I followed him for a few yards. He left Sadoc, in whose company he looked like a Levite, and went with the other men of his own age... who were certainly not Levites... And now he is not here... And he knew that we had decided to come here!»

Philip does not say anything. Bartholomew tightens his lips so much that they can no longer be seen, in an effort to stifle his opinion, which is rising from his heart.

«Very well! Let us go just the same! I will certainly not weep because of his absence» says Peter.

«Let us wait for a little while. He may have been held up» says Jesus seriously.

They lean against the wall, on its shady side, the women in one group, the men in another.

They are all wearing their best clothes. Peter, especially, is really magnificent. He is showing off brand new snow-white headgear, adorned with a galloon embroidered in red and gold. He is wearing his best tunic, a very dark garnet-red, adorned with a new belt identical in style with the decoration of his headgear. A knife, like a dagger, with an engraved hilt and an open-work brass sheath, through which the blade shines, hangs from his belt. The others are also armed more or less in the same fashion. Only Jesus is without a weapon. He is wearing a pure white linen tunic and a fleur-de-lis blue mantle, which Mary has certainly woven for Him during the winter months. Marjiam's dress is pale red with a festoon in a darker shade around the neck, cuffs and hem. A similar galloon is embroidered around the waist and the hem of the mantle, which the boy is carrying on his arm and caresses happily. Now and again he raises his head and his little face looks half smiling and half worried... Also Peter has a little parcel in his hand and he holds it very carefully.

201.3 [3] Some time goes by... but there is no sign of Judas.

«He did not deign...» grumbles Peter, and perhaps he would say something else, but John, the apostle, says: «Perhaps he is waiting for us at the Golden Gate...»

They go to the Temple. But Judas is not there.

Joseph of Arimathea loses patience. He says: «Let us go.»

Marjiam turns rather pale and kisses Mary saying: «Pray... pray for me!»

«Yes, My dear. Do not be afraid. You are so clever...»

Marjiam then clings to Peter. He presses Peter's hand nervously and as he still does not feel safe, he would like to take Jesus' hand.

«I am not coming, Marjiam. I am going to pray for you. I will see you later.»

«You are not coming? Why, Master?» asks Peter who is greatly surprised.

«Because it is better thus...» Jesus is very serious, I would say that He looks sad. And He concludes: «Joseph, who is a just man, can but approve of My decision.»

In fact Joseph does not utter one word and his silence, with an eloquent sigh, confirms his agreement.

«Well, then... let us go... » Peter is somewhat distressed.

Marjiam then clings to John. And they set out, preceded by Joseph to whom people bow deeply showing their respect. Also Simon and Thomas go with them. The others remain with Jesus.

[4]They enter the hall which Jesus also entered once. A young 201.4
man, who is writing in a corner, springs to his feet on seeing Joseph and he bows so profoundly as almost to touch the floor.

«God be with you, Zacharias. Please call Asrael and Jacob at once.»

The young man goes out and comes back almost at once with two men who are rabbis, or members of the synagogue, or scribes, I do not know. Two sullen personages whose haughtiness subsides only in Joseph's presence. Eight other less imposing men follow them. They sit down leaving the postulants, Joseph of Arimathea included, standing.

«What do you want, Joseph?» asks the senior examiner.

«I wish to present to your wisdom this son of Abraham who has reached the age prescribed to come under the Law and comply with it by himself.»

«Is he a relative of yours?» and they look at one another amazed.

«We are all relatives in God. But the boy is an orphan, and this man, whose honesty I guarantee, has adopted him as he does not wish to be without descendants.»

«Who is the man? Let him reply himself.»

«Simon of Jonas, from Bethsaida in Galilee, married with no children, a fisherman for the world, a son of the Law for the Most High.»

«And you, a Galilean, are taking this paternity upon yourself? Why?»

«It is written in the Law that we must take care of orphans and widows. That is what I am doing.»

«Can he possibly know the Law so well as to deserve to... But, boy, tell me. Who are you?»

«Jabez Marjiam of John, from the country near Emmaus, I was born twelve years ago.»

«So you are a Judaean. Is it lawful for a Galilean to take care of him? Let us look up the laws.»

«But what am I? A leper or am I cursed?» Peter begins to boil with anger.

«Be quiet, Simon, I will speak for him. I told you that I am standing surety for this man. I know him as if he were of my own household. Joseph the Elder would never propose anything against the Law or the laws. Please examine this child with justice and dispatch. The yard is full of children waiting to be examined. Please make haste, for everybody's sake.»

«But who can prove that the child is twelve years old and was redeemed from the Temple?»

«You can prove it looking up the documents. It is a piece of boring research, but can be done. Boy, did you tell me that you were the first-born?»

«Yes, sir. You will be able to see that, because I was consecrated to the Lord and redeemed with the prescribed offerings.»

«Let us look for these details then...» says Joseph.

«It is not necessary» reply coldly the two captious examiners.
201.5 [5]«Come here, child. Say the Decalogue» and the boy replies without any hesitation. «Give me that roll, Jacob. Read, if you can.»

«Where, rabbi?»

«Wherever you wish. What comes first under your eyes» says Asrael.

«No. Here. Give it to me» says Jacob. He then unfolds the roll and says: «Here.»

« "He then said to them secretly: 'Bless the Lord of Heaven, utter His praise before all the living, because He has been merciful with you. It is right to keep the secret of a king, but it is also right to reveal... ' ".»

«That is enough, quite enough! What are these?» asks Jacob, showing the fringes of his mantle.

«The sacred fringes, sir: we wear them to remember the precepts of the Most High Lord.»

«Is it lawful for an Israelite to eat any meat?..» asks Asrael.

«No, sir. Only the ones which are declared clean.»

«Tell me the precepts...»

And the docile child begins the string of: «You shall not...»

«That is enough! As a Galilean, he knows even too much. Man, it is for you now to swear that the boy is of age.»

Peter, with the best grace of which he is still capable after so much rudeness, delivers his paternal speech: «As you have ascertained, my son, at the prescribed age, knows how to conduct himself, as he knows the Law, the precepts, habits, traditions, ceremonies, blessings, prayers. Therefore, as you have verified, both he and I can ask you to declare him of age. In actual fact, I should have stated that before; but the custom has been infringed here, and not by us Galileans, and the child was questioned before the father. But I say this to you: since you have judged him competent, from this moment I am no longer responsible for his actions, neither in the eyes of God nor of men.»

«Pass into the synagogue.»

The little procession passes into the synagogue, followed by the sullen looks of the rabbis, whom Peter has put in their place. While Marjiam is standing in front of the lecterns and lamps, they cut his hair, shortening it so that it covers his ears, whereas before it reached down to his shoulders. Peter then opens his little parcel and takes out of it a beautiful red woollen belt embroidered in gold-yellow and ties it around the boy's waist, and while the priests are tying little leather strips on his forehead and arm, Peter is busy fixing the sacred fringes on to the mantle which Marjiam has handed over to him. And Peter is deeply moved when he intones the hymn praising the Lord!...

[6] The ceremony is over. They slip out quickly and Peter says: 201.6
«Thank goodness! I could not stand it any longer! What do you think, Joseph? They did not even fulfil the rite. It does not matter. You, my son, have Who will consecrate you... Let us go and get the lamb for the sacrifice of praise to the Lord. A little lamb, as dear as you are. And I thank you, Joseph! Say "thanks" to this great friend. If you had not been there, they would have thoroughly abused us.»

«Simon, I am glad I have been useful to a just man like you, and I beg you to come to my house in Bezetha for dinner. Of course, you will bring all the others.»

«Let us go and tell the Master. For me... it is too great an honour!» says Peter humbly, but he is beaming with joy.

They go through the yards and the halls once again to the yard of the women, where Marjiam's friends congratulate him. The men then go into the hall of the Israelites where Jesus is present with His disciples. They all join together in a dignified happy union, and while Peter goes to sacrifice the lamb, they all proceed through porches and yards to the first enclosure.

201.7 [7] How happy is Peter with his boy, who is now a perfect Israelite! He is so happy that he does not notice the wrinkle that furrows Jesus' forehead. So happy that he does not notice the rather oppressive silence of his companions. It is only in the hall of Joseph's house — when the boy, who is asked the ritual question as to what he wants to do in future, replies: «I will be a fisherman like my father» — that Peter, weeping, remembers and understands...

«But... Judas has spoiled our feast with a drop of poison... And You are upset, Master... and that is why the others are sad. Forgive me if I did not notice it before... Ah! Judas!...»

I think that everybody's heart is sighing like Peter's. But Jesus, to remove the poison, strives to smile and says: «Do not worry, Simon. We miss only your wife... I was also thinking of her; she is so good and is always sacrificed. But she will soon have her joy, unexpected but so welcome. Let us think of the good that is in the world. Come. So Marjiam answered all the questions correctly? I knew he would...»

Joseph comes back into the hall after giving instructions to his servants. «I thank you all» he says «for making me feel young again with this ceremony and for the honour of having in my house the Master, His Mother, His relatives and you all, my dear fellow disciples. Come into the garden. It is cool and the flowers...» and it all ends.

202. At the Temple on the Eve of Passover. Judas of Iscariot Justly Reproached. The Arrival of Johanan's Peasants.

27th June 1945.

202.1 [1] It is the eve of Passover. Jesus is alone with His apostles, because the women have not joined the group, and He is waiting for Peter, who has taken the lamb of Passover to be sacrificed. While they are waiting and Jesus is speaking to Marjiam of Solomon, Judas crosses the large yard. He is with a group of young men speaking, gesticulating ostentatiously and assuming an inspired attitude. He shakes his mantle continuously, then drapes it round himself posing skilfully. I do not think that Cicero looked so stately when delivering his orations...

«Look, Judas is over there!» says Thaddeus.

«He is with a group of saforim» remarks Philip.

And Thomas says: «I am going to hear what he is saying» and he runs away before Jesus may express a foreseeable «don't».

Oh! Jesus' countenance! A countenance of suffering and of severe judgement. Marjiam, who was looking at Him while He was speaking kindly and somewhat sadly of the great king of Israel, notices, the sudden change, is almost frightened by it and shakes Jesus' hand to call Him back to His senses exclaiming: «Don't look! Don't look! Look at me, for I love You.»...

[2] Thomas is successful in reaching Judas without being seen by 202.2
him and follows him for a few steps. I do not know what he hears, but I know that he bursts into a sudden thundering exclamation. which causes many people to turn around, and in particular Judas, who becomes livid with rage: «How many rabbis there are in Israel! I congratulate you, new light of wisdom!»

«I am not a flint-stone. I am a sponge. And I absorb. And when the desire of those starving for wisdom demands it, I squeeze out all my juices of life to give them...» Judas is pompous and contemptuous.

«You sound like a perfect echo. But an echo can only exist, if it is near the Voice. Otherwise it fades away, my friend. You seem to be going away from it. He is over there. Are you not coming?»

Judas changes colour, with the rancorous disgusting countenance of his worst moments. But he controls himself. He says: «Goodbye, my friends. Here I am with you, Thomas, my dear friend. Let us go to the Master at once. I did not know that He was here in the Temple. If I had known, I would have looked for Him» and he clasps Thomas' shoulders with his arm, as if he were very fond of him.

But Thomas, who is placid but not foolish, is not deceived by such protestations... and asks rather astutely: «What? Don't you know that it is Passover? And do you think that the Master is not faithful to the Law?»

«Oh! Never on your life! But last year He went about, and spoke... I remember this very day. He attracted me by means of His royal authoritativeness... Now... He looks to me like one who has lost vigour. Don't you think so?»

«No, I don't. I think He looks like one who has lost esteem.»

«Yes, in His mission, you are quite right.»

«No. You have misunderstood. He has lost men's esteem. And you are one of those responsible for that. Shame on you!» Thomas no longer smiles. He is serious and his words lash Judas like a whip.

«Watch how you speak!» threatens the Iscariot.

«Watch how you behave. We are two Jews here, with no witnesses. And that is why I am speaking to you. And I say once again: "Shame on you!". And now be quiet. Don't feign tragedy and don't start lamenting, otherwise I will speak in front of
202.3 everybody. [3]There is the Master and your companions. Control yourself.»

«Peace to You, Master...»

«Peace to you, Judas of Simon.»

«It is a great pleasure for me to find You here... I would like to speak to You...»

«Do so.»

«You know... I wanted to tell You... Can You not listen to me aside?»

«You are among your companions.»

«But I wanted You only.»

«At Bethany I am alone with those who want Me and look for Me, but you do not look for Me. You avoid Me...»

«No, Master. You cannot say that.»

«Why did you offend Simon and Me yesterday, and Joseph of Arimathea, your companions and My Mother and the other women as well?»

«I did? But I did not see you!»

«You did not want to see us. Why did you not come, as we had arranged, to bless the Lord because of an innocent child who was being accepted by the Law? Tell Me! You did not even feel the need to inform us that you were not coming.»

«There is my father!» shouts Marjiam who sees Peter coming

back with his lamb, which has been slaughtered, eviscerated and wrapped once again in its skin. «Oh! Micah and the others are with him! I am going, can I go and meet them and hear of my old father?»

«Yes, son, go» says Jesus caressing him. And touching John of Endor on his shoulder, he says to him: «Please, go with him and... keep them there for a little while.» And He addresses Judas once again: «Tell Me! I am waiting for your reply.»

«Master... a sudden obligation... an unbreakable one... I was very sorry... But...»

«But was there not one person in Jerusalem who could bring your justification, supposing you had one? And even that would have been a fault. I remind you that recently a man did not bury his father to follow Me, and that these brothers of Mine left their father's house, amongst imprecations, to follow Me, and that Simon and Thomas, and Andrew, James, John, Philip and Nathanael with them, left their families and Simon Cananean left his wealth to give it to Me and Matthew his sins to follow Me. And I could go on mentioning one hundred more names. There are people who leave their lives, *their very lives*, to follow Me to the Kingdom of Heaven. But since you are so selfish, at least be polite. You have no charity, at least be courtly. Since you like them, imitate the false Pharisees who betray Me, who betray us behaving like well-bred people. It was your duty to be free to be with us yesterday, so as not to offend Peter, for whom I demand respect *from everybody*. But if you had at least sent notice...»

«I made a mistake. [4]But now I was coming to You on purpose, 202.4
to tell You that for the same reason I cannot come tomorrow. You know... I have friends of my father and...»

«That is enough. Go with them. Goodbye.»

«Master... are You angry with me? You told me that You would act as my father... I am a reckless son, but a father forgives...»

«I forgive you. But go away. Do not keep your father's friends waiting, as I do not keep waiting the friends of holy Jonah .»

«When are You leaving Bethany?»

«At the end of the Feast of Unleavened Bread. Goodbye.»

Jesus turns around and goes towards the peasants who are in an ecstasy over Marjiam who is so changed. He takes a few steps then stops because of Thomas' remark: «By Jehovah! He wanted to see in You the authoritativeness of a King! He got what he wanted!...»

«I beg you all to forget the incident, as I am striving to forget it. I order you to make no mention of it to Simon of Jonah, John of Endor and the little one. For reasons which you can easily understand, it is better not to grieve or scandalise those three. And no word about it at Bethany, with the women. My Mother is there, do not forget it.»

«Do not be concerned, Master.»

«We will do all we can to make amends.»

«And to comfort You» they all say.

202.5 «Thank you... [5]Oh! Peace to you all. Isaac found you. I am glad. Enjoy your Passover in peace. My shepherds will be as many good brothers to you. Isaac, before they go away, bring them to see Me. I want to bless them once again. Have you seen the boy?»

«Oh! Master! How well he is! He is already much healthier! We will tell the old man. He will be so happy. This just man has told us that Jabez is now his son... It is a gift of Providence! We will tell him everything.»

«Also that I am a son of the Law. And that I am happy. And I always remember him. And he must not weep for me or for my mother. She is near me and she is near him like an angel and he will always have her, also in the hour of death, and if Jesus has already opened the gates of Heaven, well, then mummy will come to meet the old father and she will be more beautiful than an angel and will take him to Jesus. Jesus told me. Will you tell him? Will you be able to tell him properly?»

«Certainly, Jabez.»

«No. Now I am Marjiam. The Lord's Mother gave me that name. It is as if you said Her name. She loves me so much. She puts me to bed in the evening and She makes me say the prayers which She made Her Child say. And She wakes me up with a kiss, She dresses me and teaches me many things. Also Jesus does. But they teach me so gently that I learn without any difficulty. My Master!!!» The child presses against Jesus with an attitude of adoration and love that is really moving.

«Yes, tell him everything, and also not to give up hope. This angel prays for him and I bless him. I bless you, too. Go. Peace be with you.»

203. The Prayer of the "Our Father".

28th June 1945.

1 Jesus comes out with His apostles from a house near the walls 203.1
and I think that they are still in the Bezetha district, because to go outside the walls, one must pass again by Joseph's house, near the Gate, which I hear people call Herod's Gate. The town is semi-deserted in the placid moonlit evening. I understand that they have celebrated Passover in one of Lazarus' houses, which, however, is not the one of the Last Supper. They are, in fact, poles apart. One in the north, the other in the south of Jerusalem.

On the doorstep Jesus takes leave, with His usual kindness, of John of Endor, who is to take care of the women and whom He thanks for accepting that task. He kisses Marjiam, who has also come to the door and then sets out for Herod's Gate.

«Where are we going, Lord?»

«Come with Me. I am taking you to crown Passover with a rare longed for pearl. That is why I wanted to be alone with you. My apostles! Thank you, My friends, for your great love for Me. If you could see how it comforts Me, you would be amazed. See: I proceed among continuous frictions and disappointments. Disappointments for you. You must convince yourselves that I am never disappointed, because I have not been granted the gift of ignoring... That is another reason why I advise you to agree to be guided by Me. If I allow this or that thing, do not hinder it. If I do not interfere to put an end to something, do not endeavour to do it yourselves. Each thing is to be done at the right moment. Trust Me, in everything.»

They are at the north-east corner of the circuit of the walls; they turn around it and proceed along the hill of Moriah to a point where they can cross the Kidron by a little bridge.

«Are we going to Gethsemane?» asks James of Alphaeus.

«No. Farther up. To the Mount of Olives.»

«Oh! It will be lovely!» says John.

«The boy would have liked it too» whispers Peter.

«Oh! There will be many more opportunities for him to come here! He was tired. He is only a boy. I want to give you a *great* thing because the right moment has now come for you to have it.»

2 They climb up among the olive-trees, leaving Gethsemane on 203.2

the right, until they reach the top of the mountain, where the leaves of the olive-trees are rustling in the wind.

Jesus stops and says: «Let us stop... My dear disciples who are to continue My work in future, come near Me. Many a time you have said to Me: "Teach us to pray as You pray. Teach us, as John taught his disciples, so that we may pray with the same words as our Master". And I always replied to you: "I will do that when I see in you the minimum sufficient preparation so that the prayer may not be a vain formula of human words, but a real conversation with the Father". That moment has now come. You now possess what is necessary to know the words worth being said to God. And I want to teach you them this evening, in peace and in our mutual love, in the peace and love of God and with God, because as true Israelites we have fulfilled the Passover precept and we have complied with God's commandment concerning
203.3 love for God and our neighbour. [3]One of you has suffered very much during the past days. He suffered undeservedly, also because of his effort to repress his indignation aroused by the undeserved deed. Yes, Simon of Jonah, come here. Not one throb of your honest heart has been concealed from Me, neither has there been any grief that I have not shared with you. Both I and your companions...»

«But You, my Lord, have been offended more than I was! And that was for me a greater pain,... no... a more sensitive... no, not that... a more... more. Well: that Judas should have loathed to be present at my feast, has hurt me as a man. But to see You grieved and offended has hurt me in a different way and I suffered twice as much... I... I do not want to boast and show off by using Your words... But I must say, and if it is due to pride in me, tell me, I must say that I suffered with my soul... and it hurts more.»

«It is not pride, Simon. You suffered spiritually, because Simon of Jonah, a fisherman in Galilee, is changing into Peter of Jesus, the Master of the spirit, so that also His disciples are becoming active and wise in the spirit. It is for this progress of Yours in the life of the spirit, it is because of such progress of you all, that I want to teach you the prayer this evening. How much you have changed after the solitary retreat!»

«Everybody, Lord?» asks Bartholomew who sounds rather incredulous.

«I understand what you mean... But I am speaking to you eleven. Not to anyone else...»

«But what is the matter with Judas of Simon, Master? We do not understand him any more... He seemed so changed, but now, since we left the lake...» says Andrew desolately.

«Be quiet, brother. I have the key to the mystery! A little bit of Beelzebub has stuck to him. He went to look for it in the cave at Endor to astonish us... and he was served as he deserved! The Master said it on that day... At Gamala the demons rushed into the pigs. At Endor the demons came out of that poor wretch of John into him... We know that... we know that... Let me tell them, Master! I have it here, in my throat, and if I do not say it, it will not come out and it will poison me...»

«Be good, Simon!»

«Yes, Master... and I would assure You that I will not be rude to him. But I say and think that since Judas is a vicious fellow — and we all know that — he is somewhat similar to a pig... and obviously demons willingly choose pigs when... changing their dwelling places. There it is: I have said it.»

«Do you think it is thus?» asks James of Zebedee.

«What else can it be! There is no other reason why he should be so difficult. He is worse now than he was at the Clear Water! And there one might have thought that the place and the season made him so nervous. But now...»

4 «There is another reason, Simon...» 203.4

«Tell us, Master. I will be happy to change my mind about my companion.»

«Judas is jealous. He is agitated because he is jealous.»

«Jealous? Of whom? He is not married, and even if he were, and went with women, I think that none of us would be rude to a fellow disciple...»

«He is jealous of Me. Just think: Judas changed after Endor and after Esdraelon. That is, when he saw that I was taking care of John and of Jabez. But now that John, above all, John, will be going away, as he will be leaving Me and staying with Isaac, you will see that Judas will become merry and good once again...»

«Well!... But You are not going to tell me that he is not possessed by a little demon. And above all... No, I will say it! And above all You will not tell me that he has improved during these last months. I was jealous as well, last year... I would not have liked anybody except the six of us, the first six, do You remember? Now, now... Let me invoke God just this once as witness to what I am going to say. Now I say that the more the disciples increase in numbers around You, the happier I am. Oh! I would like to bring all men to You and I would also like to have all the necessary means to help those who are in need, so that misery may not hinder anyone from coming to You. God sees whether I am telling the truth. But why am I thus now? Because I let You change me. He... has not changed. On the contrary... Yes, Master... A little demon has possessed him...»

«Do not say that. Do not think that. Pray that he may be cured. Jealousy is a disease...»

«Of which one can be cured beside You, if one wants to. Ah! I will put up with him, for Your sake... But, how difficult it is!...»

«I gave you a prize for that: the boy. And now I will teach you how to pray...»

«Oh! yes, Brother. Let us speak of that... and let us remember my namesake only as one who is in need of prayer. I think he has already had his punishment. He is not with us just now!» says Judas Thaddeus.

203.5 [5] «Listen. When you pray, pray thus: "Our Father, Who are in Heaven, may Your name be held holy, Your Kingdom come on earth as it is in Heaven, and may Your will be done on earth as it is in Heaven. Give us today our daily bread, forgive us our debts as we forgive those who are in debt to us, and do not put us to the test, but save us from the Evil One".»

Jesus has stood up to say the prayer and everybody has imitated Him, attentively and moved.

«Nothing else is required, My friends. Everything man needs for his spirit and his flesh and blood is contained in these words as in a golden ring. With this prayer you ask for what is useful to the former and the latter two. And if you do what you ask for, you will gain eternal life. It is so perfect a prayer that neither the storms, heresies nor the course of ages will undermine it. Christianity will be split by Satan's bite and many parts of My mystic body will be torn off and separated, forming independent cells in the vain desire to form a body as perfect as the mystical Body of Christ will be, which is the one formed by all the faithful believers united in the apostolic Church, the only true Church, as long as the earth exists. But those separated little cells, devoid of the gifts, which I will leave to the Mother Church to nourish My children, will always be denominated Christian, because of their worship of the Christ, and in their error they will always remember that they derive from the Christ. Well, they will pray with this universal prayer as well. Remember it carefully. Meditate on it continuously. Practise it in your actions. You need nothing else to sanctify yourselves. If one were alone, in a heathen place, without churches, without books, one would already have all the knowledge to meditate on in this prayer and a church in his heart for this prayer. One would have a safe rule of sanctification.

[6] "Our Father". 203.6

I call Him: "Father". Father of the Word, Father of the Incarnate. That is how I want you to call Him because you are all one with Me, if you remain in Me. Once man had to prostrate himself with his face on the ground to whisper, trembling with fear: "God!" He who does not believe in Me and in My word is still in such paralyzing fear... Watch the interior of the Temple. Not God, but the very remembrance of God is concealed from the eyes of the faithful by a triple veil. He who prays is separated by remoteness and veils, everything has been devised to say to him: "You are mud. He is Light. You are contemptible. He is Holy. You are a slave. He is King".

But now!... Stand up! Come near Me! I am the Eternal Priest. I can take you by the hand and say: "Come". I can grasp the veils and draw them, and thus throw open the inaccessible place closed so far. Closed? Why? Closed by Sin, yes. But even more closed by the dispirited thought of man. Why closed if God is Love, if God is Father? I can, I must, I want to take you not into the dust, but into the azure; not far, but near; not as slaves, but as children onto the heart of God.

Say: "Father! Father!". And never tire repeating this word. Do you not know that every time you say it, Heaven shines because of God's joy? If you said with true love no other word but that one, you would be saying a prayer pleasing to the Lord. "Father! Father!" the little ones say to their fathers. It is the first word they say: "Mother, father". You are the little children of God. I created you from the old man you were and whom I destroyed by means of My love to give birth to the new man, the Christian. Call, therefore, the Most Holy Father Who is in Heaven, with the first word that little children learn.

203.7 [7] "May Your Name be held holy".

Oh! Name, which is holier and sweeter than any other name and which the fear of the guilty taught you to conceal under a different one. No, no longer Adonai. He is God. He is the God Who in an excess of love created Mankind. And Mankind, from now onwards, with lips cleansed by the purification that I am preparing, should call Him by His Name, awaiting to fully comprehend the true meaning of the Incomprehensible One, when the best children of Mankind, united to Him, will rise to the Kingdom that I have come to establish. *

203.8 [8] "May Your Kingdom come on earth as it is in Heaven".

Desire its coming with all your strength. If it came, it would be the joy of the earth. The Kingdom of God in hearts, in families, among citizens and nations. Suffer, work, sacrifice yourselves for this Kingdom. Let the earth be a mirror reflecting the life of Heaven in each individual. It will happen. All this will happen one day. Centuries of tears and blood, of errors, persecutions, of darkness relieved by flashes of light radiating from the mystical Light of My Church will precede the moment in which the earth will possess the Kingdom of God. Oh! My Church: although a boat, it will never be sunk, as it is also a cliff unshakeable by breakers and will hold high the Light, My Light, the Light of God. And it will then be like the intense blazing of a star which, having reached the perfection of its existence, disintegrates, an immeasurable flower of the ethereal gardens, to breathe its existence and love at the feet of its Creator, in a rutilant throb. But it will most certainly come. And then there will be the perfect, blessed eternal Kingdom of Heaven.

203.9 [9] "And may Your will be done on earth as it is in Heaven".

The submission of one's will to the will of another person can be accomplished only when one reaches perfect love for that creature. The submission of one's will to God's can be achieved

---

* **that I have come to establish**. M.V. noted on typewritten copy: *"As Jesus revealed the Father" (John 1:18) during his ministry as Master, and in the way He could reveal it to the living, it will still be through the Word, Son of the Father, that the citizens of the Kingdom of God will have knowledge of God.*

only when one achieves possession of the theological virtues in a heroic degree. In Heaven, where everything is faultless, God's will is done. You, children of Heaven, must learn to do what is done in Heaven.

10 "Give us today our daily bread". 203.10

When you are in Heaven, God alone will be your nourishment. Beatitude will be your food. But here, you still need bread and since you are the children of God, it is only fair to say: "Father, give us some bread". Are you afraid He will not hear you? Oh! No! Just think: If one of you has a friend and, if he finds out that he has no bread to offer another friend or relative, who has arrived in the middle of the night, and he goes to his friend saying: "Lend me three loaves, because a guest has arrived and I have nothing to give him to eat", can he possibly hear his friend answer him from inside the house: "Do not bother me, I have already bolted the door and my children are already sleeping beside me. I cannot get up and give you what you want"? No. If he has gone to a *true* friend and if he insists, he will receive what he asks for. He would receive it even if he went to someone who was not a very good friend. He would be satisfied because of his insistence, as his friend, of whom he asked the favour, will hasten to give him what he wants, so that he may no longer be bothered.

But when you pray the Father, you do not turn to a friend of the earth, but you apply to the Perfect Friend Who is the Father of Heaven. That is why I say to you: "Ask, and it will be given to you, search, and you will find, knock and the door will be opened to you". For the one who asks will receive, the one who searches always finds, the one who knocks will have the door opened to him. What father among you would hand his son a stone when he asked for bread? Or hand him a snake instead of a roasted fish? A father who did that to his own children would be a criminal. I have already told you and I will repeat it to convince you to be good and trustful. As a sound-minded person would not give a scorpion instead of an egg, with what greater bounty will God give you what you ask for! Because He is good, whereas you are more or less wicked. Ask, therefore, the Father for your bread with humble filial love.

11 "Forgive us our debts as we forgive those who are in debt to 203.11
us".

There are material debts and spiritual ones. There are also moral debts. The money or the goods that one has received as a loan and must give back, are a material debt. Esteem extorted and not given back and love wanted and not returned are a moral debt. To obey God, from Whom one would exact much giving Him very little, and to love Him are a spiritual debt. He loves us and is to be loved, as a mother, a wife, a son, from whom so much is exacted, are to be loved. A selfish man wants to receive, but does not give. But an egoist is poles apart from Heaven. We are in debt to everybody. From God to a relative, from a relative to a friend, from a friend to our neighbour, to a servant, to a slave, because they are all beings like ourselves. Woe to him who does not forgive! He will not be forgiven. God, out of justice, cannot remit the debt of a man who is in debt to Him, the Most Holy One, if man does not forgive his fellow man.

203.12 [12] "Do not put us to the test, but save us from the Evil One".

The man who did not feel the need to share the Passover supper with us, asked Me, less than a year ago: "What? You asked not to be tempted and to be helped against temptation?". There were only the two of us... and I replied. Later we were four, in a lonely area, and I replied once again. But still to no avail, because when dealing with an unyielding spirit it is necessary to open a breach by demolishing the evil fortress of his stubbornness. And I will, therefore, repeat it once, ten times, one hundred times until everything is accomplished.

But since you are not hardened by strange doctrines or by even stranger passions, I beg you to pray thus. Pray with humility that God may avert temptations from you. Oh! humility! To know oneself for what one is! Without losing heart, but to know oneself! Say: "I may give in, even if I do not think I could do it, because I am but an imperfect judge of myself. Therefore, Father, if possible, deliver me from temptations by keeping me so close to You as not to allow the Evil One to harm me". Because, remember, it is not God Who tempts you to evil things, but it is the Evil One who tempts you. Pray the Father that He may support your weakness so that it may not be led into temptation by the Evil One.

203.13 [13] I have told you everything, My beloved ones. This is My second Passover among You. Last year we shared only our bread and the lamb. This year I give you My prayer. I will have other gifts for My future Passovers amongst you, so that, when I shall have gone where the Father wants Me, you may have a reminder of Me, the Lamb, at every feast of the Mosaic lamb.

Get up and let us go. We shall go back to town at dawn. Or rather: tomorrow, you, Simon, and you, My brother (and He points to Judas), will go to fetch the women and the boy. You, Simon of Jonah, and you all, will stay with Me until they come back. Then we shall all go to Bethany together.»

And they go down to Gethsemane, where they enter the house to rest.

204. Faith and Soul Explained to the Gentiles Through the Parable of the Temples.

29th June 1945.

[1] In the peace of the Sabbath Jesus rests near a flax field in 204.1
bloom belonging to Lazarus. Rather than «near» I should say that He is «immersed» in the tall flax, and sitting on the edge of a furrow He is engrossed in thought. Only an odd silent butterfly flutters near Him or a lizard rustles nearby, looking at Him with its jet-black eyes, raising its little triangular head with its light throbbing throat. There is nothing else. In the late afternoon, the least sigh of wind has also become silent among the tall stalks.

From far away, perhaps from Lazarus' garden, the song of a woman can be heard and the joyful shouting of the boy who is playing with someone. Then one, two, three voices call: «Master! Jesus!»

Jesus arouses Himself and stands up. Although the fully grown flax is very tall, Jesus emerges a good height above the blue-green sea.

«There He is, John!» shouts the Zealot.

And John in turn calls: «Mother! The Master is here, in the flax field.»

And while Jesus approaches the path leading to the houses, Mary arrives.

«What do You want, Mother?»

«My Son, some Gentiles have come with some ladies. They say

that they heard from Johanna that You were here. They also said that they have been waiting for You all these past days near the Antonia...»

«Ah! I know! I will come at once. Where are they?»

«At Lazarus' house, in his garden. He is loved by the Romans and does not feel the repugnance towards them that we do. He let them go into the large garden with their carts, so that no one would be scandalised...»

204.2 «All right, Mother. [2]They are Roman soldiers and ladies. I know.»

«And what do they want from You?»

«What many in Israel do not want: light.»

«But how and what do they believe You are? God perhaps?»

«Yes, in their way of thinking. It is easier for them to accept the idea of the incarnation of a god in mortal flesh, than it is for us.»

«So they believe in Your faith...»

«Not yet, Mother. I must destroy theirs, first. For the time being they consider Me a wise man, a philosopher, as they say. But both their desire to become acquainted with philosophical doctrines and their inclination to believe the incarnation of a god as possible, are of great help to Me in leading them to the true Faith. Believe Me, they are more ingenuous in their way of thinking, than many Israelites.»

«But are they sincere? It is rumoured that the Baptist...»

«No. Had it been for them, John would be free and safe. Non-rebellious people are left in peace. On the contrary I can assure You that for them to be a prophet — they say a philosopher because the loftiness of supernatural wisdom is still philosophy to them — is a guarantee of respect. Do not worry, Mother. No harm will come to Me from that end...»

«But the Pharisees... if they find out, what will they say also about Lazarus? You are You... and You *are* to bring the Word to the world. But Lazarus!... They already offend him so much...»

«But they cannot touch him. They know that he is protected by Rome.»

«I leave You, Son. Here is Maximinus, he will take You to the Gentiles» and Mary, Who had walked beside Jesus all the time, withdraws quickly, and goes towards the Zealot's house. Jesus on the other hand, goes through a little iron door in the garden wall, into a distant part of the garden, where it actually becomes an orchard and precisely near the place where Lazarus will be buried later.

Lazarus is also there, but no one else. «Master, I took the liberty of giving them hospitality...»

«You did the right thing. Where are they?»

«Over there, in the shade of the boxes and laurels. As You can see they are at least five hundred steps from the house.»

«That is all right... [3]May Light come to you all.» 204.3

«Hail, Master!» greets Quintilian, who is wearing civilian clothes.

The ladies stand up to greet Jesus. They are Plautina, Valeria and Lydia; there is also another elderly woman, but I do not know who she is or whether she is of the same rank as the others. They are all wearing very plain clothes without any sign of distinction.

«We were anxious to hear You, but You never came. I was on duty when You arrived. But I never saw You.»

«Neither have I seen at the Gate of the Fish a soldier, who was a friend of Mine. His name was Alexander...»

«Alexander? I am not sure whether he is the one I am thinking of. I know that some time ago, in order to calm the Jews, we had to remove a soldier who was guilty of... speaking to You. He is now at Antioch. But perhaps he will come here again. How boring they are... they want to rule even now that they are subject! One has to be clever to avoid greater trouble... They make life difficult for us, believe me... But You are good and wise. Will You speak to us? I may be leaving Palestine soon, and I would like to have something to remind me of You.»

«Yes, I will speak to you. I never disappoint anyone. What do you wish to know?»

Quintilian looks at the ladies inquisitively.

«Whatever You wish, Master» says Valeria.

[4]Plautina stands up again and says: «I have been thinking a 204.4
lot... there is so much I would like to know... everything, to be able to judge. But if I may ask, I would like to know how can a faith, Yours, for instance, be built on a ground which You said is devoid of true faith. You said that our beliefs are vain. So we

have nothing. How can we achieve something?»

«I will take as an example something that you have. Your temples. Your really beautiful sacred buildings, the only imperfection of which is that they are dedicated to Nothing, can teach you how one can achieve faith and where to place it. Watch. Where are they built? Which place, if at all possible, is chosen for them? How are they built? The place is generally spacious, open and elevated. And when it is not spacious and open, it is made so by demolishing what encumbers and obstructs it. If it is not elevated, they increase its height by means of a stereobate more elevated than the normal three steps used for temples placed on a natural elevation. They are generally surrounded by a sacred enclosure, formed by colonnades and porches inside which are enclosed the trees sacred to the gods, fountains and altars, statues and stelae and are usually preceded by a propylaeum beyond which is the altar where prayers to the deity are said. In front of it there is the place for the sacrifice, because the sacrifice precedes the prayer. Very often, and particularly in the more magnificent ones, a peristyle encircles them with a garland of precious marbles. Inside there is the front vestibule, outside or inside the peristyle, the cell of the deity and the rear vestibule. Marbles, statues, pediments, acroteria and gables, all polished, precious and decorated, make the temple a most noble building also for the coarsest sight. Is it not so?»

«Yes, it is, Master. You have seen and studied them very well» confirms Plautina praising Jesus.

«But we know that He never left Palestine!?» exclaims Quintilian.

«I never left Palestine to go to Rome or Athens. But I am acquainted with Greek and Roman architecture and I was present when the genius of man decorated the Parthenon because I am wherever there is life or a manifestation of life. Wherever a wise man meditates, a sculptor sculptures, a poet writes, a mother sings over a cradle, a man toils in fields, a doctor fights diseases, a living being breathes, an animal lives, a tree vegetates, I am there together with Him from Whom I come. In the rumble of the earthquake or in the peal of thunder, in the light of stars or in flood-tide and ebb-tide, in the flight of eagles or in the buzzing of mosquitoes, I am there with the Most High Creator.»

«So... You... You know everything. Both thoughts and deeds of men?» asks Quintilian again.

«Yes, I do.»

The Romans look at one another amazed. [5]There is a long silence then Valeria timidly begs: «Expand on Your idea, Master, so that we may know what to do.» 204.5

«Yes. Faith is built as they build the temples of which you are so proud. They make space for the temple, they free it from obstructions, they elevate it.»

«But where is the temple in which one should put faith, the true deity?» asks Plautina.

«Faith, Plautina, is not a deity. It is a virtue. There are no deities in true faith. There is only One and True God.»

«So... He is up there, in His Olympus, all by Himself? And what does He do if He is alone?»

«He is Self-sufficient and takes care of everything in creation. I have just told you that God is also present in the buzzing of a mosquito. He does not get bored, do not worry. He is not a poor man, the master of an immense empire in which he feels he is hated and lives trembling with fear. He is Love and lives loving. His Life is continuous Love. He is Self-sufficient because He is infinite and most powerful, He is Perfection. So numerous are the things created that live because of His continuous will, that He has no time to grow weary. *Tedium is the fruit of idleness and vice*. In the Heaven of the True God there is neither idleness nor vice. Soon, in addition to angels which now serve Him, He will have a great crowd of just people rejoicing in Him and the crowd will grow greater and greater with the future believers in the True God. »

«Are the angels genii?» asks Lydia.

«No, they are spiritual beings like God Who created them.»

«What are genii, then?»

«As you imagine them, they are falsehood. They do not exist, as you imagine them. But owing to the instinctive need of men to search for the truth, you have also realised that man is not only flesh and that there is something immortal in his perishable body. And that is the consequence of the incentive of the soul, which is alive and present also in heathens, and suffers in them, as it is disappointed in its desires, because it is famished longing for the True God Whom it remembers in the body in which it dwells and which is guided by a pagan mind. And the same applies to towns and nations. And thus you believe, you feel the need to believe in "genii". And thus you give yourselves an individual genius, a family, a town, a national genius. You have the "genius of Rome", the "genius of the emperor". And you worship them as lesser deities. Come to the true faith. You will become acquainted and friendly with your angel, whom you will venerate, but not worship. Only God is worshipped.»

204.6 [6] «You said: "Incentive of the soul which is alive and present also in heathens, and suffers in them because it is disappointed". But from whom does the soul come?» asks Publius Quintilian.

«From God. He is the Creator.»

«But are we not born of woman through union with man? Also our gods are born thus.»

«Your gods do not exist. They are phantoms of your mind which needs to believe. Because *such need is more peremptory than the need to breathe*. Also he, who says he does not believe, does believe. He believes in something. The simple statement: "I do not believe in God" presupposes another faith. In oneself, perhaps, or in one's proud mind. But one always believes. It is like thinking. If you say: "I do not want to think", or: "I do not believe in God", by those two simple sentences you prove that you are thinking that you do not want to believe in Him Whom you know to exist and that you do not want to think. With regards to man, to express the concept correctly you must say: "Man, like all animals, is born through the union of male and female. But the soul, that is the thing which distinguishes the animal-man from the animal-brute, comes from God. He creates it as and when a man is procreated, or rather: when he is conceived in a womb and He infuses it in the body which otherwise would be only animal".»

«And have we got it? We pagans? According to Your fellow-countrymen it would not appear to be so...» says Quintilian ironically.

«Every man born of woman has it.»

«But You said that sin kills it. If so, how can it be alive in us sinners?» asks Plautina.

«You do not sin against faith, because you believe that you are in the Truth. When you become acquainted with the Truth and you persist in your error, then you will commit sin. Likewise, many things which are sinful for Israelites, are not so for you. Because no divine law forbids you. One sins when one consciously rebels against the order given by God and says: "I know that what I am doing is wrong. But I want to do it just the same". God is just. He cannot punish one who does the wrong thing thinking that he is doing the right one. He punishes those, who being able to tell Good from Evil, choose the latter and persist in it.»

«So we have a soul and it is alive and present in us?»

«Yes, it is so.»

«And it suffers? Do You really think that it remembers God? We do not remember the womb that bore us. We could not tell what its inside was like. If I have understood You correctly, the soul is spiritually born of God. Can it possibly remember Him if our body does not remember the long time it was in a womb?»

«The soul is not material, Plautina. An embryo is. In fact the soul is infused when the foetus is already formed. The soul is, like God, eternal and spiritual. It is eternal from the moment it is created, whereas God is the Most Perfect Eternal Being and thus has no beginning in time and will have no end. The *soul,* the lucid, intelligent, spiritual work of God, *does remember.* And it suffers, because it longs for God, the True God, from Whom it comes, and it hungers for God. That is why it spurs the torpid body to endeavour to approach God.»*

[7] «So we have a soul as those whom you call "the just people" of 204.7
your nation have? Exactly the same?»

«No, Plautina. It depends on what you mean. If you mean according to its origin and nature, it is exactly the same as the souls of our saints. But if you refer to its formation, then I say that it is different. And if you mean according to the perfection reached before death, then it may be completely different. But that does not apply to you heathens. Also a son of our people can be completely different from a saint, in future life. *A soul is subjected to three phases,* The first is creation. The second a new creation. The third is perfection. The first is common to all men. The second is peculiar to just people who through their will el-

* **The soul... does remember**. An illuminating description of the so-called "memory of souls" that is different from the one conceived by Socrates, is that of 8th September 1945 and is found in the volume "The Notebooks. 1945-1950".

evate their souls to a more complete revival, joining their good deeds to the perfection of God's work, whereby their souls are spiritually more perfect and form a connection link between the first and third ones. The third is peculiar to the blessed souls, or saints, if you prefer so, who have exceeded by a thousand degrees the initial stage of their souls, a stage suitable to man, and have transformed them into something suitable to rest in God.»

204.8 [8] «How can we make room, clearance and elevation for our souls?»

«By demolishing the useless things you have in your "ego". Clear it of all wrong knowledge, and with the debris make the elevation for the sovereign temple. A soul is to be carried higher and higher, on the three steps. Oh! you Romans love symbols. Look at the three steps in a symbolic light. They can tell you their names: penance, patience, perseverance. Or: humility, purity, justice. Or: wisdom, generosity, mercy. Or, finally, the splendid trinomial: faith, hope, charity. Look also at the symbol of the ornate strong enclosure which encircles the area of the temple. You must surround your soul, the queen of the body, the temple of the Eternal Spirit, with a barrier which may protect it without obstructing light or oppressing it with ugly sights. An enclosure that must be safe and free from the love and desire of what is inferior: flesh and blood, and must aim at what is superior: the spirit. The chisel of freedom is your will-power, which will smooth corners, and remove clefts, stains and flaws in the marble of your *ego,* so that it may be perfect around your souls. And at the same time, the enclosure protecting the temple is to be used by you as a merciful shelter for the more unhappy people who do not know what Charity is. The porches: they are the effusion of love, of piety, of your desire that more people may come to God, and are like the loving arms stretched like a veil over the cradle of an orphan. And beyond the enclosure: the most beautiful and most scented trees are a homage to the Creator. The trees, planted on a soil previously barren and subsequently cultivated, symbolise all kinds of virtues and form the second living flowery enclosure around the sanctuary; and among the trees, that is among the virtues, there are the fountains, a further effusion of love and another purification before approaching the propylaeum near which one must sacrifice one's carnality and repudiate

all forms of lust before ascending the altar. And then you may proceed further, to the altar and lay your offer on it and finally, crossing the vestibule, you may approach the cell, where God is. And what will the cell be like? Abundance of spiritual wealth, because you can never adorn God too much. Have you understood? You asked Me how Faith is built. I said to You: "Following the method used to build temples". You can see that it is true.[9] Is 204.9
there anything else you wish to ask Me?»

«No, Master. I think that Flavia has written what You said. Claudia wants to know. Have you written everything?»

«I have written everything most accurately» replies the woman handing over the waxed tablets.

«We will have time to read them again», says Plautina.

«It is wax. It is easily cancelled. Write everything in your hearts. It will never cancel.»

«Master, they are encumbered with vain temples. We are throwing Your words against them to demolish them. But it is a long tasks» says Plautina sighing. And she concludes: «Remember us in Your Heaven...»

«You may rest assured that I will. I leave you. I want you to know that your visit has been very dear to Me. Goodbye, Publius Quintilian. Remember Jesus of Nazareth.»

The ladies say goodbye and are the first to go away. Then Quintilian, who is somewhat pensive, leaves. Jesus watches them go away with Maximinus who leads them back to their wagons.

10 «What are You thinking of, Master?» asks Lazarus. 204.10

«That there are many unhappy people in the world.»

«And I am one of them.»

«Why, My dear friend?»

«Because everybody comes to You, except Mary. Is she the greatest ruin?»

Jesus looks at him and smiles.

«You are smiling? Are You not sorry that Mary cannot be converted? Are You not sorry that I am suffering? Martha has done nothing but weep since Monday evening. Who was that woman? Don't You know that for the whole day we hoped it was she?»

«I am smiling because you are an impatient child... And I am smiling because I think that you are wasting energy and tears. Had it been she, I would have rushed to tell you.»

«So it was not she?»

«Oh! Lazarus!...»

«You are right. Patience! Still patience!... Master, here are the jewels that You gave me to sell. They have become money for the poor. They were beautiful. Ladies' jewels.»

«They belonged to "that" woman.»

«I thought so. Ah! Had they been Mary's... But she!... I am losing hope, my Lord!...»

Jesus embraces him without speaking for a little while. He then says: «Please do not mention those jewels to anybody. She must disappear, without being admired or desired any longer, like a cloud driven elsewhere by the wind, without leaving any trace in the blue sky.»

«You may be sure, Master... and, in exchange, bring me Mary, our unhappy Mary...»

«Peace be with you, Lazarus. I will keep My promise.»

205. First Assignment to John of Endor. The Parable of the Prodigal Son.

30th June 1945.

205.1 [1] «John of Endor, come here with Me. I must speak to you» says Jesus looking out of the door.

The man hastens towards Jesus leaving the boy to whom he was explaining something. «What do You want to tell me, Master?» he asks.

«Come upstairs with Me.»

They go up to the terrace and they sit down in the most sheltered part, because the sun is already strong, although it is still morning. Jesus runs His eyes over the cultivated country, where day by day the corn is becoming golden and fruit is ripening on trees. He seems to be wishing to derive some thought from that vegetable metamorphosis.

«Listen, John. I think that Isaac is coming today to bring Me Johanan's peasants before they leave. I told Lazarus to lend Isaac a wagon to quicken their return and thus avoid a delay which would cause them to be punished. And Lazarus has agreed, because he does everything I tell him. But I want something else from you. I have here a sum of money given to Me by a person for the poor of the Lord. Usually one of My apostles is responsible for keeping the money and giving alms. Generally it is Judas of Kerioth; sometimes one of the others. But Judas is not here. And I do not want the others to know what I want to do. I would not have told Judas either. You will do it, in My name...»

«I, my Lord?... I?... Oh! I am not worthy!...»

«You must accustom yourself to working in My name. Is that not why you came?»

«Yes, but I thought I had to work to rebuild my poor soul.»

«And I will give you the means. Against what did you sin? Against Mercy and Love. You demolished your soul by means of hatred. You will rebuild it through love and mercy. I will give you the material. I will make use of you especially for deeds of mercy and love. You are also capable of curing, and of speaking. So you are qualified to take care of physical and moral miseries and you are capable of doing it. You will start with this action. Here is the purse. You will give it to Micah and his friends. Divide it into equal parts. But divide it as I will tell you. Make ten parts and give four to Micah, one for himself and one each to Saul, Joel and Isaiah. Give the other six to Micah with instructions to give them to Jabez' old father, for himself and his companions. They will thus be able to have some comfort.»

«All right. But what shall I tell them to justify it?»

«Say: "This is to remind you to pray for a soul that is redeeming itself" .»

«But they may think that it is I! It is not fair!»

«Why? Do you not want to redeem yourself?»

«It is not fair that they should think that I am the donor.»

«Never mind, do as I tell you.»

«I will obey... but at least let me give something as well. In any case... now I do not need anything anymore. I do not buy books and I have no poultry to feed. I am satisfied with very little. Take this, Master. I am keeping a minimum for my sandal expenses...» and from a purse attached to his belt he takes out some coins which he adds to Jesus' money.

«May God bless you for your mercy... [2]John, before long we 205.2
shall be parting, because you will be going with Isaac.»

«I am sorry about that, Master. But I will obey.»

«I am sorry as well to send you away. But I need itinerant disciples so badly. I am no longer sufficient. I will soon be sending the apostles and then the disciples. And you will do a lot of good. I will keep you for special missions. In the meantime you will become formed with Isaac. He is so good and the Spirit of God has really instructed him during his long disease. And he is the man who has always forgiven everything... On the other hand, the fact that we have to part does not mean that we shall never meet again. We shall often meet, and every time we are together, I will speak just for you, remember that...»

John bends very low, he hides his face in his hands, bursts into bitter tears and moans: «Oh! Then tell me at once something to persuade me that I have been forgiven... that I can serve God... If You knew how I see my soul, now that the smoke of hatred has vanished... and how I think of God...»

«I know, do not weep. Be humble, but do not be disheartened. *Disheartenment is still pride*. Be humble, that is all. Cheer up, do not weep...»

John of Endor slowly calms down...

When Jesus sees that he has become calm, He says: «Come, let us go under that thicket of apple-trees and gather our companions and the women. I will speak to everybody, but I will tell you how God loves you.»

They go down, assembling the others as they procede, and they all sit down in a circle in the shade of the apple orchard. Also Lazarus, who was speaking to the Zealot, joins the company. They are about twenty people in all.

205.3 [3] «Listen. It is a beautiful parable that will guide you with its light in many cases.

A man had two sons. The elder was a serious, affectionate, obedient worker. The younger was more intelligent than his brother who was actually somewhat dull and preferred to be guided rather than tire himself making decisions by himself, but he was also rebellious, absent-minded, fond of luxury, pleasure loving, a squanderer and idle. Intelligence is a great gift of God. But it is a gift to be used wisely. Otherwise it is like certain medicines that, when taken in the wrong way, kill instead of curing. His father, as it was his right and duty, used to recall him to a more sensible life. But it was all in vain, the only result was that he answered back and became more obstinate in his wicked ideas.

Finally one day, after a fierce quarrel, the younger son said: "Give me my part of the estate. So I will no longer hear your reproaches and my brother's complaints. Let each have his own and no more about it". "Be careful" replied the father, "because you will soon be ruined. What will you do then? Consider that I will not be unfair to favour you and I will not take a farthing off your brother to give it to you". "I will not ask you for anything. You may be sure. Give me my part".

The father had the estate and valuables assessed, and since money and jewels were worth as much as the real estate, he gave the elder brother the fields and vineyards, the herds and olive-trees, and the younger one the money and jewels, which the young man changed immediately into money. And after doing that in a few days, he went to a distant country where he lived like a lord, squandering all his money on a life of debauchery, making people believe that he was the son of a king, because he was ashamed to admit that he was a countryman and thus he disowned his father. Banquets, friends, women, robes, wines, games... he led a loose life. He soon saw that his money was coming to an end and that poverty was in sight. And to make matters worse, the country experienced a severe famine, which compelled him to spend his last penny. [4]He would have liked to go 205.4
back to his father. But he was proud and decided not to. So he went to a wealthy man of the country, a friend of his in his happy days, and he begged him saying: "Take me among your servants, remembering the days when you enjoyed my wealth". See how foolish man is! He prefers the lash of a master rather than say to his father: "Forgive me. I made a mistake!". The young man had learned many useless things with his bright intelligence, but he did not want to learn the saying of Ecclesiasticus: "How ill-famed is he who deserts his father and how accursed of the Lord is whoever angers his mother". He was intelligent, but not wise.

The man that he turned to, in exchange for the grand time he had enjoyed with the foolish young man, sent him to look after his pigs, because it was a pagan country and there were many pigs. So he was sent to pasture the herds of pigs in the farm. Filthy, in rags, stinking and starving — food in fact was scarce for all the servants and particularly for the lowest ones and he, a foreign ridiculed herdsman of pigs was considered such — he saw the pigs glut themselves with acorns and sighed: "I wish I could fill my stomach with this fruit! But they are too bitter! Not even starvation can make them palatable". And he wept remembering the sumptuous banquets when he acted the "grand seigneur" only a short while before, laughing, singing, dancing... and then he would think of the honest substantial meals at his far away home, of the portions his father used to make impartially for everybody, keeping for himself the smallest one, happy to see the healthy appetite of his and he remembered the helpings his just father gave the servants and he sighed: "My father's servants, even the lowest, have plenty of bread... and I am dying here of starvation...". A long meditation, a long struggle to subdue his pride...

205.5 [5] At last the day came when his humility and wisdom revived and he got up and said: "I will go back to my father! This pride of mine is silly, as it deprives me of my freedom. And why? Why should I suffer in my body and even more in my heart when I can be forgiven and receive comfort? I will go back to my father. That is settled. And what shall I say to him? What has matured in my heart here, in this abjection, in this filth, suffering the pangs of hunger! I will say to him: 'Father, I have sinned against Heaven and against you, I am no longer worthy of being called your son; treat me therefore as the least of your servants, but bear me to stay under your roof. That I may see you moving about... I cannot say to him: '... because I love you'. He would not believe me. But my behaviour will tell him and he will understand and before dying he will bless me once again... Oh! I hope so. Because my father loves me". And when he went back to town in the evening he gave up his job and begging along the way he went back home. And he saw his father's fields... and the house... and his father supervising the work... he was old, emaciated by grief but always kind and good... The guilty son seeing that ruin caused by him stopped frightened... but the father, looking around, saw him and ran to meet him, because he was still far away. And when he reached him, he threw his arms around his neck and kissed him. Only the father had recognised his son in the dejected beggar and he was the only one to be moved with love.

The son, clasped in his father's arms, with his head resting on his father's shoulder, whispered sobbing: "Father, let me throw myself at your feet". "No, son! Not at my feet. Rest on my heart, which has suffered so much because of your absence, and now needs to revive feeling your warmth on my chest". And the son, crying louder, said: "Oh! father! I have sinned against Heaven and against you, I am no longer worthy to be called son by you. But allow me to live among your servants, under your roof, seeing you, eating your bread, serving you, and you will be the breath of my life. Every time I take a morsel of bread, every time you breathe, my heart, which is so corrupt, will change and I will become honest..."

But the father, embracing him all the time, led him towards the servants, who had gathered together watching in the distance and he said to them: "Quick, bring the best robe, and basins of scented water here, and wash him, spray him with scents, clothe him, put new sandals on his feet and a ring on his finger. Bring a fattened calf and kill it. And prepare a banquet. Because this son of mine was dead and has come back to life, he was lost and has been found. Now I want him to find the innocent love of a child once again, and my love and the celebration of the household for his return, must give it to him. He must realise that he is always my dear last-born child, as he was in his childhood a long time ago, when he used to toddle beside me making me happy with his smile and his prattling". And the servants did so.

[6] The elder son was out in the country and he did not know any- 205.6
thing until his return. Coming towards the house in the evening, he saw that it was brightly lighted and he heard the sound of instruments and dancing coming from it. He called a servant who was bustling about and asked him: "What is happening?". And the servant replied: "Your brother has come back! Your father had the fattened calf killed because his son has come back to him safe and cured of his wickedness and he ordered a celebration. They are only waiting for you to start". But the first-born was angry because he thought that such a feast for his younger brother was unfair, as he was not only younger, but had also been wicked. And he did not want to go in, on the contrary he was about to walk away from the house.

But the father, informed of the situation, ran out and reached him and endeavoured to convince him, begging him not to spoil his joy. The elder brother replied to his father: "And you expect me not to be upset? You are unfair to your first-born and you hold him in contempt. I have served you since I was able to work, and I have done that for many years. I have never disobeyed an order of yours, not even a simple desire. I have always been near you, and I have loved you for two, to make you recover from the wound inflicted on you by my brother. And you have not even given me a lamb to have a feast with my friends. You are now honouring my brother and you have killed the best calf for him, who offended and abandoned you, and has been a lazy spendthrift and has now come back because he was driven by starvation. It is really worth while being a hard honest worker! You should not have done that to me".

The father then, clasping him to his heart, said: "Son! Can you believe that I do not love you, because I do not celebrate your behaviour? Your deeds are holy by themselves, and the world praises you because of them. Your brother, instead, needs to be rehabilitated both in the eyes of the world and in his own. And do you think that I do not love you because I give you no visible prize? But day and night, in every moment of my life, you are present to my heart, and I bless you every moment. You have the continuous reward of being always with me, and what is mine is yours. But it was fair to have a feast, a celebration for your brother who was dead and has come back to good life, who was lost and has come back to our love". And the first-born yielded to his father's desire.

205.7 [7] And that, My friends, is what happens in the House of the Father. And whoever feels that he is like the younger son of the parable must believe that if he imitates him in going to the Father, the Father will say to him: "Not at My feet. But rest on My heart, which has suffered because of your absence and is now happy because you have come back". He who is in the situation of the first-born and without any fault against the Father, must not be jealous of the Father's joy, but must take part in it and love the redeemed brother.

That is all. You, John of Endor and you, Lazarus, please remain here. The others can go and set the tables. We shall not be long.»

They all withdraw. When Jesus, Lazarus and John are alone, Jesus says to them: «That is what will happen to the dear soul you are awaiting, Lazarus, and that is what is happening to yours, God's bounty has no limit...»

[8]... The apostles, together with Mary and the women, go towards the house, preceded by Marjiam who runs ahead frisking. 205.8
But he soon comes back and takes Mary by the hand saying to Her: «Come with me. I have something to tell You, when we are alone.» And Mary follows him. They turn towards a well, situated in a corner of the little yard and completely covered by a thick bower that from the ground climbs up towards the terrace forming an arch. Behind it, there is the Iscariot.

«Judas, what do you want? Go, Marjiam... Speak. What do you want?»

«I am guilty... I dare not go to the Master or face my companions... Help me...»

«I will help you. But do you not consider how much grief you cause? My Son wept because of you. And your companions suffered. But come. No one will say anything to you. And, if you can, do not commit the same sins again. It is shameful for a man and a sacrilege against the Word of God.»

«And will You forgive me, Mother?»

«I? I count for nothing as far as you are concerned, since you think you are so great. I am the least of the servants of the Lord. How can you worry about Me, if you feel no pity for My Son?»

«Because I have a mother as well, and if You forgive me, I will feel as if she did, too.»

«She does not know about this fault of yours.»

«But she made me swear I would be good to the Master. I am a perjurer. I can feel the soul of my mother reproaching me.»

«You feel that, do you? But do you not feel the lament and the reproach of the Father and of His Word? You are disgraceful, Judas! You cause grief to yourself and to those who love you.»

Mary is very serious and sad. She speaks without bitterness but with much seriousness. Judas weeps.

«Do not weep. Improve yourself. Come» and She takes him by the hand and enters the kitchen.

Everybody is filled with astonishment. But Mary wards off any possible uncharitable remark. She says: «Judas has come back. Behave as the first-born did after his father's speech. John, go and tell Jesus.»

John of Zebedee runs away. Silence hangs heavy on the kitchen... Then Judas says: «Forgive me, all of you, and you, Simon, first of all. Your heart is so paternal. And I am an orphan, too.»

«Yes, I forgive you. Please, say no more about it. We are brothers... and I do not like these ups and downs of forgiveness and relapses. They humiliate both the offender and the forgiver. Here is Jesus. Go to Him. That's all.»

Judas goes away and Peter, not being able to do anything else, starts chopping wood with keen impetuosity...

206. Two Parables of the Kingdom of Heaven: the Ten Virgins and the Royal Wedding. The Stay in Bethany Ends.

1st July 1945.

206.1 [1] Jesus is speaking in the presence of Johanan's peasants, of Isaac and many disciples, of the women amongst whom there is the Blessed Virgin Mary and Martha, and of many people from Bethany. All the apostles are present. The boy, sitting in front of Jesus, does not miss one word. I think Jesus has just begun to speak because people are still arriving...

Jesus says: «... it is because of this sensation of fear that I realise is so sharp in you, that today I wish to tell you a sweet parable. Sweet for the men of goodwill, bitter for the others. But the latter can remove the bitterness. Let them become men of goodwill, and the reproach, provoked in their consciences by the parable, will no longer exist.

206.2 [2] The Kingdom of Heaven is the house of the nuptials of God with souls. The moment a soul enters it, is the day of the nuptials.

Now listen. It is a custom with us that virgins escort the bridegroom when he arrives, to take him with lights and songs to the nuptial house together with his sweet bride. When the procession leaves the house of the bride, who wearing a veil and deeply moved turns her steps to the place where she will be queen, that is, to a house which is not hers, but will become hers the moment she becomes one body with her husband, the procession of the virgins, who are generally friends of the bride, runs to meet the happy couple, forming a circle of lights around them.

Now it happened that in a town there was a wedding. While the bride and bridegroom were making merry with relatives and friends in the house of the bride, ten virgins went to their place, that is, to the hall in the groom's house, to be ready to go out and meet him when the sound of cymbals and songs warned them that the young couple had left the bride's house to come to the groom's. But the feast in the house of the nuptials extended and night fell. As you know, the virgins always keep their lamps lit, so that they do not waste time at the right moment. Now, of these ten virgins, five were wise and five were foolish, and all their lamps were lit and shining. The wise ones, full of wisdom, had provided themselves with small flasks full of oil, to fill up their lamps in the event they should have to wait longer than expected, whereas the foolish ones had only filled their little lamps.

One hour went by after the other. Cheerful conversation, tales and jokes made their waiting pleasant. But later they did not know what to say or what to do, and weary and tired, the ten girls sat down more comfortably and slowly fell asleep with
their lamps lit and close to them. [3]At midnight a cry was heard: 206.3
"The bridegroom is coming, go and meet him!". The ten girls got up on hearing the order, took their veils and garlands, adorned themselves and ran to the shelf where the lamps were. The light of five of them was already fading... The wicks, no longer sustained with oil, which was finished, were smoky, their light was becoming fainter and fainter and they would go out at the least whiff of air, whereas the flames of the other five lamps, which had been refilled by the wise virgins before they fell asleep, were still bright and became even brighter when more oil was added to the lamps.

"Oh" begged the foolish girls "give us some of your oil, otherwise our lamps will go out as soon as we move them. Yours are already so beautiful!..." . But the wise virgins replied: "The wind is blowing in the night outside and heavy drops of dew are falling. There is never enough oil to give a flame strong enough to withstand the wind and dampness. If we give you some, also our lights will begin to fade away. And the procession of the virgins would be really a sad one without the flickering flames of lamps! Go, run to the nearest vendor, beg, knock, make him get up to give you some oil". And the foolish girls, panting, creasing their veils, staining their dresses, losing their garlands while pushing one another and running, followed the advice of their companions.

But while they were on their way to buy some oil, the bride and the bridegroom appeared at the end of the street. The five virgins, with their lamps lit, ran to meet them and the young couple entered the house in the midst of them for the final ceremony, when the virgins at the end would escort the bride to the nuptial room. The door was closed behind them and those who were outside were left out. And that was the case of the five foolish bridesmaids, who at last arrived with the oil, but found the door closed and in vain they knocked, hurting their hands and moaning: "Lord, lord, open the door for us! We were in the wedding procession. We are the propitiatory virgins chosen to bring honour and good luck to your wedding". But the bridegroom, leaving for a moment the closest guests whose leave he was taking while the bride was entering the nuptial room, from the upper part of the house said to them: "I tell you that I do not know you. I do not know who you are. I did not see you rejoicing around my beloved bride. You are usurpers. You are therefore left out of the nuptial house". And the five foolish girls, weeping, went away along the dark streets, with their useless lamps, their creased dresses and torn veils, while their garlands were practically destroyed or lost.

206.4 [4] And now listen to the meaning of the parable. I told you at the beginning that the Kingdom of Heaven is the house of the nuptials of God with souls. *All* the faithful are called to the celestial wedding because God loves all His children. Sooner or later everybody arrives at the moment of the nuptials and it is a great fortune to arrive.

But listen further. You know how girls consider it an honour and fortune to be invited as bridesmaids of the bride. Let us see whom the various people represent and you will understand better. The Bridegroom is God. The bride is the soul of a just person who, after the period of engagement in the house of the Father, that is under the protection of and in obedience to God's doctrine, living according to justice, is taken to the house of the Bridegroom for the wedding. The virgin-maids are the souls of the

faithful, who following the example set by the bride — the fact that she was chosen by the Bridegroom because of her virtues means that she was a living example of holiness — endeavour to achieve the same honour by sanctifying themselves. [5]They are in 206.5
a *white, clean, fresh dress, with white veils, crowned with flowers*. They are holding *lighted lamps* in their hands. The lamps are very clean, and the wicks are nourished with the purest oil so that they may not be unpleasant.

In a white dress. Justice steadily practised gives a white dress and the day will soon come when it will be most white, without even the most remote remembrance of stain, it will be of supernatural, angelical whiteness.

In a clean dress. One must always keep the dress clean through humility. It is so easy to dim the purity of the heart. And those whose hearts are not pure cannot see God. Humility is like water that washes. A humble man soon notices that he has darkened his robe, because his eyes are not dimmed by the fumes of pride and thus he runs to his Lord and says: "I have stained the purity of my heart. I weep at Your feet to be cleansed. Oh! my Sun, purify my heart through Your benign forgiveness and Your paternal love!"

In a fresh dress. Oh! the freshness of a heart! Children have it by gift of God. The just have it by gift of God and through their own will. Saints have it by gift of God and through their will elevated to heroism. But will a sinner, whose soul is torn, burnt, poisoned and disgraced, ever be able to have a fresh robe? Oh! of course he will. He begins to have it the moment he looks at himself with disgust. He increases its freshness when he decides to change life. He brings it to perfection when through penance he washes, detoxicates, cures and recomposes his poor soul. And with the help of God, Who does not refuse assistance to anyone who asks Him for holy help, and through his own will elevated to super-heroism — because it is not necessary for him to protect what he has, *but to rebuild what he destroyed* and thus he must work twice, three times, seven times as much — and with untiring penance, relentless against his sinful *ego,* he will take his soul back to the freshness of a child's soul. A new freshness, made precious by experience, which makes him the master of other people who were once like him, that is, sinners.

With white veils. Humility! I said: "When you pray or do * penance, do not let the world see you". In the Wisdom Books it is written: "It is right to keep the secret of the King". * *Humility is the candid veil worn to defend the good we do and the good God grants us.* We must not be proud of the privileged love granted to us by God, nor seek foolish human glory. The gift would be taken away at once. But from the depth of our hearts we must sing to our God: "My soul proclaims Your greatness, o Lord... because You have looked upon Your lowly handmaid".»

Jesus makes a short pause and casts a glance at His Mother, Who blushes under Her veil and bends forward as if She wanted to tidy the hair of the boy sitting at Her feet, but in actual fact to conceal her deep-felt remembrance...

Crowned with flowers. A soul *must* weave its daily garland of virtuous deeds, because nothing withered or slovenly looking is to appear in the presence of the Most High. I said daily. Because a soul does not know when God-Bridegroom may appear and say: "Come". Therefore you must never tire renewing the garland. Be not afraid. Flowers wither. But the flowers of virtuous wreaths *do not wither.* God's angel, whom every man has at his side, picks up these daily wreaths and takes them to Heaven. And they will be there in the throne for the new blessed soul when it enters the nuptial house as the bride.

206.6 [6] *Their lamps are lit.* They have them to honour the Bridegroom and to see the way. How refulgent faith is, and what a kind friend it is! It gives a flame as bright as a star, a flame that smiles because it is sure in its certainty, a flame that also brightens the instrument supporting it. Also the flesh of man nourished with faith seems to become brighter and more spiritual, even in this world, free from premature withering. Because he who believes holds onto God's words and commandments in order to possess God, his ultimate aim, and therefore he shuns corruption, he is not perturbed or afraid, he feels no remorse, he is not compelled to make an effort to remember lies or to conceal evil deeds and remains young and handsome by means of the beautiful incorruptibility of saints: flesh and blood, mind and heart free from lust to contain the oil of faith, to give light without smoke. A con-

---

* **I said** in 172.5/8.

* **is written** in *Tobia 12:7.*

stant will to feed that light forever. Everyday life, with its disappointments, ascertainments, contacts, temptations, disagreements, tends to diminish faith. No! It must not happen. Go every day to the source of the sweet, sapiential oil of God. A lamp with little oil can be put out by the least puff of wind or by the heavy dew of the night. The night... The hour of darkness, of sin, of temptation comes for everybody. It is night for the soul. But if the soul is filled to the brim with faith, its flame cannot be put out by the wind of the world or by the fog of sensuality.

And finally vigilance, vigilance, vigilance. He who is unwarily trustful and says: "Oh! God will come on time, while my light is still on", and makes up his mind to go to sleep instead of keeping awake, and goes to sleep without providing what is necessary to get up and be ready at the first call, and he who waits until the last moment to procure the oil of faith or the strong wick of goodwill, runs the risk of *being left out* when the Bridegroom arrives. Be vigilant, therefore with prudence, perseverance, purity, confidence, so that you may always be ready for God's call, because you really do not know when He will come.

[7] My dear disciples, I do not want you to be afraid of God, on the contrary I want you to have faith in His goodness. Both you who will remain here, and you who will be going away, must consider that, if you do what the wise virgins did, you will be invited not only to escort the Bridegroom, but like the virgin Esther, who became queen in the place of Vashti, you will be chosen and elected to be brides, as the Bridegroom "found more approval and favour with you than with anybody else". I bless you, who are about to go away. Take My words with you for yourselves and for your companions. May the peace of the Lord always be with you.» 206.7

Jesus goes near the peasants to say goodbye to them once more, but John of Endor whispers to him: «Master, Judas is here now...»

«It does not matter. Take them to the wagon and do as I told you.»

The people at the meeting slowly go away. Many talk to Lazarus... And Lazarus turns towards Jesus, Who after leaving the

* **became queen** as narrated in: *Esther 2:1-18*. Ester is also mentioned in 136.2 and 414.1.

peasants was going towards him, and says: «Master, before leaving us, speak to us again... It is the desire of the hearts of the people of Bethany.»

«Night is falling. But it is placid and serene. If you wish to gather on the cut hay, I will be speaking to you before leaving this friendly town. Or we can meet tomorrow, at dawn. Because the hour of farewell has come.»

«Later! This evening!» they all shout.

«As you wish. Go now. I will speak to you half way through the first watch»...

206.8 [8] ... and in fact, untiring, Jesus sets out towards the middle of a recently cut meadow, on which the withering hay forms a sweet smelling soft rug, while the sun sets and also its glow disappears and crickets begin their early uncertain solitary chirping. He is followed by the apostles, the Maries, Martha and Lazarus and their household, Isaac and his disciples, and I would say by all the people of Bethany. Among the servants there is the old man and the woman, the two who on the Mount of Beatitudes found comfort for the rest of their days.

Jesus stops to bless the patriarch, who kisses His hand weeping, and caresses the boy walking beside Jesus and says to him: «"You are happy that you can follow Him all the time! Be good, be careful, son. You are very lucky! Very lucky, indeed! A crown is hanging over your head... You are blessed!»

206.9 [9] When they are all settled, Jesus begins to speak.

«After the departure of our dear friends, who needed to be confirmed in the hope, or better still, in the certainty that little knowledge is required to be admitted to the Kingdom, that only a minimum truth on which one's goodwill may work is sufficient, I will now speak to you, who are much happier than they are, because you enjoy much more material comfort and you have greater help from the Word. Only by thought I can extend My love to them. Here, My love reaches you also through My word. Therefore, you are to be treated both here on the earth and in Heaven with greater strength, because more will be asked of those to whom more was given. They, the poor friends who are going back to their prison, have the least welfare, and, on the contrary, the greatest sorrow. Therefore, there are only promises of benignity for them, because anything else would be superfluous. I solemnly tell you that their lives are penance and holiness, and nothing else is to be imposed upon them. And I also solemnly tell you, that like wise virgins, they will not let their lamps go out until the hour they are called. Let them go out? No. The light of their lamps is the only good they possess. They cannot let it go out.

[10] I solemnly tell you that as I am in the Father, so the poor are 206.10
in God. That is why I, the Word of the Father, wanted to be born poor and to remain poor. Because amongst the poor I feel closer to the Father Who loves the least people and is loved by them with all their strength. The rich have many things. The poor have but God. The rich have friends. The poor are alone. The rich have many comforts. The poor have none. The rich have many distractions. The poor have but their work. Money makes everything easy for the rich. The poor also have the cross of having to be afraid of diseases and famine, because they mean starvation and death to them. But the poor have God. Their Friend. Their Comforter. He Who distracts them from their painful present by means of heavenly hope. He, to Whom man can say — and *they* know how to say it, because they are poor, humble, alone –: "Father, support us in Your mercy".

What I say on this land of Lazarus, a friend of Mine and a friend of God although he is so rich, may seem strange. But Lazarus is an exception amongst the rich. Lazarus has been successful in achieving that most difficult virtue to be found on the earth, and even more difficult to be practised when it is recommended by other people. *The virtue of freedom from wealth.* Lazarus is just. He does not feel offended. He cannot be offended because he knows that he is the rich-poor man, and thus My concealed reproach does not affect him. Lazarus is just. And he knows that the world of great people is as I say. I therefore speak and say: I solemnly tell you that it is much easier for a poor man to be in God than it is for a rich one; and in the Heaven of My Father and yours, many seats will be occupied by those who on the earth were despised because they were the least amongst men, like trodden dust.

The poor keep in their hearts the pearls of the words of God. They are their only treasure. He who has only one precious thing, watches over it. He who has many, is bored and absent-minded, proud and sensual. That is why he does not admire with humble loving eyes the treasure given by God, and confuses it with other treasures, only apparently precious, treasures which are the riches of the earth and he thinks: "It is only out of kindness that I accept the words of one who is like me fleshwise!" and by means of strong flavours of sensuality he blunts his capability of savouring what is supernatural. Strong flavours!... Yes, very spicy to disguise their stench and their putrid flavour...

206.11 [11] But listen and you will understand better how worldly cares, riches and orgies prevent one from entering the Kingdom of Heaven.

Once a king celebrated the wedding of his son. You can imagine the feast at the palace. He was the only son and having reached the perfect age, he was getting married to his beloved bride. The father and king wanted the joy of his son to be surrounded with joy, as he was at last getting married to his dear fiancée. Among the many celebrations he gave a sumptuous dinner. And he prepared it in good time, looking after every detail, to ensure it was magnificent and worthy as the wedding of the king's son.

He sent out his servants early to tell friends and allies, as well as the mighty ones of his kingdom, that the wedding was to take place on a certain evening and that they were invited, and that they should come to form a worthy picture to the king's son. But friends, allies and mighty ones of the kingdom did not accept the invitation.

The king then, doubting that the first servants had not spoken clearly, sent out some more, who should insist saying: "Please, do come! Everything is now ready. The tables are laid in the hall, rare wines have been brought from everywhere, oxen and fattened cattle are already in the kitchen to be cooked, women slaves are kneading flour to make cakes and crushing almonds in mortars to make the finest delicacies flavoured with rare spices. The most clever dancers and musicians have been engaged for the feast. Come, therefore, or all the preparations will be useless!"

But friends, allies and great ones of the kingdom either refused or said: "We have other things to do", or pretended to accept the invitation, but then they attended to their own matters, some to their fields, some to their business, some to even less noble affairs. And finally there were some who, bored with so much insistence, took the servant of the king and killed him to keep him quiet, as he insisted saying: “Do not refuse the king’s invitation or you may find yourself in trouble”. The servants went back to the king and reported the situations and the king flared up in a temper and sent his soldiers to punish the murderers of his servants and chastise those who had scorned his invitation, whilst he intended to reward those who had promised to come.

But at the fixed hour on the evening of the feast, no one came.
[12]The king was very angry, he called his servants and said to 206.12
them: “On no account my son will be left without people who will give him a hearty welcome on the evening of his wedding. The banquet is ready, but the guests we invited are not worthy of it. And yet the nuptial banquet of my son is to take place. Go therefore to the squares, along the streets, stand at the crossroads, stop the passers-by, gather together those who are standing there, and bring them all here. Let the hall be filled with joyful people”.

The servants went. They went out along the streets, they spread out on the squares, they stood at crossroads, they gathered as many people as they could find, both good and bad, rich and poor, and took them to the royal palace, and they gave each of them the means to be worthy to enter the hall of the nuptial banquet. Finally they led them into the hall, which was full of jubilant people, as the king desired.

But when the king went into the hall to see whether the feast could begin, he saw one man who, notwithstanding the assistance given to him by the servants, was not wearing a wedding garment. He asked him: “How did you get in here, without a wedding garment?”. And the man did not know what to say, because he had no excuse. The king then called his servants and said to them: “Take this man, bind him hand and foot and throw him out of my palace, into the dark and icy mud. He shall stay there weeping and grinding his teeth as he deserved through his ingratitude and because he offended me and my son more than me, by entering the banquet hall with a poor dirty garment, whereas nothing must enter it but what is worthy of it and of my son”.

[13]As you can see, worldly cares, avarice, sensuality, cruelty 206.13

bring down the king's wrath on people and cause the children of such cares never to enter the King's palace again. And you can also see how among those who were invited, for the sake of his son, some were punished.

How many there are nowadays in this land, to whom God has sent His Word! God has really invited the allies, the friends, the great ones of His people, through His servants, and He will invite them again, and more urgently, as the hour of My Wedding approaches.

But they will not accept the invitation, because they are false allies, false friends and they are great only by name, because they are shallow. Jesus' voice is becoming louder and louder and His eyes are flashing like two gems, in the light of the fire lit between Him and His audience, to give light in the moonless night; the moon is in fact waning and will rise later.

Yes, they are shallow. And because of their shallowness, they do not understand that it is their duty and an honour for them to accept the King's invitation. Pride, harshness, lust act like a wall in their hearts. And — wicked as they are! — they hate Me and so they do not want to come to My wedding. They refuse to come. They prefer to be connected with filthy policy, with even filthier money and with the most filthy sensuality, rather than come to My wedding. They prefer shrewd calculations, conspiracies, underhand conspiracies, snares, crimes.

I condemn all that in the name of God. Consequently the voice that speaks and the feasts to which they are invited, are hated by them. Those who kill the servants of God are to be looked for among *this* people: the Prophets who have been the servants till now; My disciples who are the servants from now onwards. The swindlers of God who say: "Yes, we will come", whereas inwardly they think: "Never on your life!" are to be selected among *this* people. All that is in Israel.

And the King of Heaven will send to gather at the crossroads those who are not friends, not great ones, not allies, but only people passing by, so that His Son may have a worthy wedding celebration. And through Me, through Me the Son and the servant of God, the gathering has already begun. They will come, whoever they are... And they have already come. And I help them to be clean and properly dressed for the wedding feast. But there will be someone, who for his own misfortune, will also misuse the munificence of God, Who gives him scents and regal garments to make him appear what he is not, that is a rich and worthy person, and he will take abominable advantage of such bounty to seduce and make a profit... An individual with a wicked soul, embraced by the revolting octopus of all vices... and he will embezzle scents and garments to make an unlawful profit, as he will not use them for the wedding of the Son, but for his own wedding with Satan.

All that will happen. Because many are called but few are those, who knowing how to persevere in their vocation, are chosen. But it will also happen that those hyenas, who prefer putrid food to living nourishment, will be punished by being thrown out of the Banquet hall into the dark and mud of an eternal pond, in which Satan will grin horribly at each triumph over a soul and where there is an eternal sound of desperate weeping of the mad people who followed Crime instead of following Bounty Who had called them.

[14] Get up and let us go and rest. I bless you, citizens of Bethany. 206.14
I bless you all and I give you My peace. And I particularly bless you, Lazarus, My friend, and you, Martha. I bless My oId and new disciples, whom I will be sending into the world to invite people to the wedding of the King. Kneel down, that I may bless you all. Peter, say the prayer I taught you, and say it here, standing beside Me, because that is how it is to be said by those who are destined by God for that task.»

They all kneel down on the hay, only Jesus and Peter remain standing. Jesus, tall as he is, is most handsome in His linen robe, and Peter, in his dark brown tunic, deeply moved, says the prayer, almost trembling, in a voice which although not beautiful is manly, going very slow for fear he might make a mistake: «Our Father...» The sobs of men and women can be heard...

Marjiam, kneeling just in front of Mary Who is holding his hands joined, is looking at Jesus with an angelical smile and says in a low voice: «Look, Mother, how lovely He is! And how lovely also my father is! I seem to be in Heaven... Will my mother be here, watching?»

And Mary, in a whisper ending in a kiss, replies: «Yes, My dear. She is here. And she is learning the prayer.»

«And what about me? Will I learn it?»

«She will whisper it to your soul while you sleep, and I will repeat it to you during the day.»

The boy bends back his little dark-haired head, resting it on Mary's breast, and remains thus while Jesus blesses with the solemn Mosaic blessing.

Then they all get up and go to their homes: only Lazarus follows Jesus, entering Simon's house with Him, to remain a little longer together. All the others come in as well. The Iscariot places himself in a semi-dark corner and looks mortified. He dare not go near Jesus with the others...

206.15 [15] Lazarus congratulates Jesus. He says: «Oh! I am sorry to see You go away. But I am happier than I would have been, had I seen You go away the day before yesterday!»

«Why, Lazarus?»

«Because You looked so tired and sad... You did not speak, and You hardly ever smiled... Yesterday and today You have become once again my kind holy Master, and that makes me so happy...»

«I was so even if I was quiet...»

«You were. But You are serenity and word. That is what we want from You. We drink our strength at those sources. And now those sources seemed to be dried up. Our thirst was painful... You see that also the Gentiles are amazed, and they have come looking for them...»

The Iscariot, whom John of Zebedee had approached, dares to speak: «Of course, they also inquired of me... Because I was very often at the Antonia, hoping to see You.»

«You knew where I was» replies Jesus briefly.

«I did. But I was hoping You would not disappoint those who were expecting You. Also the Romans were disappointed. I do not know why You behaved like that...»

«And you are asking Me? Are you not aware of the humours of the Sanhedrin, of the Pharisees, and of others as well, with regards to Me?»

«What? Were You afraid?»

206.16 «I was disgusted. [16]Last year, when I was alone — all by Myself against the whole world, which did not even know whether I was a prophet — I bore evidence that I was not afraid. And you were a conquest of that audacity of Mine. I spoke openly against a whole world of howlers; I caused the voice of God to be heard by a people who had forgotten it; I cleansed the House of God of the material filth in it, without any hope of purifying it of the more serious moral filth nesting in it, because I am not unaware of the future of men. But I had to do My duty, because of My zeal for the House of the Eternal Lord, which had been converted into a place where swindlers, usurers and thieves bawled, and I did it to arouse from their torpor those whom centuries of priests' carelessness had caused to fall into spiritual lethargy. It was a cry to gather My people and take them to God... This year I have come back... And I saw that the Temple is still the same... *it is even worse*. It is no longer a den of thieves, but a place of conspiracy, it will later become the centre of Crime, then a brothel and finally it will be destroyed by a power greater than Samson's, crushing a caste unworthy of being called holy. It is useless to speak in that place, where, I would remind you, I was forbidden to speak. Faithless people, whose poisoned leaders dare to forbid the Word of God to speak in His House! I was forbidden. I was silent for the sake of the least ones. It is not yet time to kill Me. Too many people are in need of Me, and My apostles are not yet strong enough to take on their arms My off-spring: the World. Do not weep, Mother, forgive, good Mother, Your Son's need to tell those, who wish to or may deceive themselves, the truth that I know... I will be silent... But woe to those who cause God to be silent!... Mother, Marjiam, do not weep!... Please. Let no one weep.»

But in actual fact they are all weeping more or less bitterly.

Judas, as white as death in his striped red and yellow robe, dares still to speak, in a moaning ridiculous voice: «Believe me, Master, that I am amazed and grieved... I do not know what You mean... I know nothing... It is true that I have not seen anyone of the Temple. I have broken off contacts with everybody... But if You say so it must be true...»

«Judas!... You have not seen Sadoc either?»

Judas bends his head grumbling: «He is a friend. I met him as such, not as one of the Temple...»

[17] Jesus does not reply to him. He turns to Isaac and John of Endor, to whom He gives more advice concerning their work. 206.17

Meanwhile the women comfort Mary Who is weeping and the boy who is weeping seeing Mary weep.

Also Lazarus and the apostles are sad. But Jesus comes towards them. He is smiling kindly once again, and while embracing His Mother and caressing the child, He says: «And now I will say goodbye to you who are staying. Because we are leaving tomorrow at dawn. Goodbye, Lazarus. Goodbye, Maximinus. Joseph, I thank you for your kindness to My Mother and the women disciples, while waiting for Me. Thank you for everything. Lazarus, bless Martha once again in My name. I will come back soon. Come, Mother, to rest. And you, too, Mary and Salome, if you wish to come.»

«Of course we are coming!» say the two Maries.

«Well... to bed. Peace to everybody. God be with you.» He makes a gesture of blessing and goes out holding the boy by the hand embracing His Mother...

The stay in Bethany is over.

207. In the Grotto of Bethlehem, the Holy Mother Recalls Jesus' Birth.

3rd July 1945.

207.1 [1] Dawn has just begun to smile when Jesus leaves Bethany and turns His steps towards Bethlehem with His Mother, Mary of Alphaeus, Mary Salome, followed by the apostles and preceded by the boy, who finds reason to rejoice in everything he sees: the butterflies that awake, little birds that sing or peck on the path, flowers sparkling with dewy diamonds, a flock that comes into sight and in which there are many little bleating lambs. After crossing the torrent, which foams merrily amongst stones, south of Bethany, the group turns towards Bethlehem, along a road running between two ranges of hills, completely covered with green olive-trees and vineyards, and a few small fields in which the golden corn is almost ready for reaping. The valley is cool and the road quite comfortable.

Simon of Jonah comes forward, he reaches Jesus' group and asks: «Is this the road to Bethlehem? John says that the last time You took another road.»

«That is true» replies Jesus. «But that was because we were coming from Jerusalem. This one is shorter. At Rachel's sepulchre, which the women wish to see, we will part, as you decided some time ago. We will meet later at Bethzur, where My Mother wishes to stop.»

«Yes, we said so... But it would be so lovely if we were all there... particularly Your Mother... because, after all, She is the Queen of Bethlehem and of the Grotto, and She knows everything so well... If we heard the story from Her... it would be quite different, that's what I mean...»

Jesus smiles looking at Simon, who has kindly expressed his desire.

«Which grotto, father?» asks Marjiam.

«The Grotto where Jesus was born.»

«Oh! Lovely! I will come, too!...»

«It would be lovely indeed!» say Mary of Alphaeus and Salome.

«It would be beautiful!... It would mean going back to the time... when the world did not know You, that is true, but did not hate You yet... It would mean finding once again, the love of simple people who could but love and believe, with humility and faith.... And I would be able to lay aside this burden of bitterness which has been lying heavily on My heart since I learned that You are so hated, and I would lay it in Your manger... The kindness of Your eyes, of Your breath, of Your childish smile must still be there... and they would caress My heart... It is so grieved!...» Mary is speaking slowly, in a low voice expressing desire and sadness.

«Then, we shall go there, Mother. You will lead us. You are the Teacher today and I am the Little Boy Who is learning.»

«Oh! Son! No! You are always the Master...»

«No, Mother. Simon of Jonah is quite right. In the land of Bethlehem *You* are the Queen. It is Your first castle. Mary, of the house of David, lead this little group to Your abode.»

The Iscariot is on the point of speaking, but he remains silent. Jesus, Who has noticed and understands, says: «If anyone does not wish to come, because he is tired or for any other reason, he is free to proceed to Bethzur.» But no one replies.

[2] They proceed westwards, along the cool valley. The road then 207.2

bends lightly to the north along a protruding hill and they thus reach the road which takes from Jerusalem to Bethlehem, near a cube-shaped building surmounted with a small dome, which is Rachel's tomb. They all go near it and pray reverently.

«Joseph and I stopped here... Everything is exactly the same as then. Only the season is different. It was a cold day in the month of Chislev. It had rained and the roads were muddy, then an ice-cold wind began to blow and perhaps during the night there was frost. The roads had hardened, but furrowed by cart-wheels and crowded with people, they were like a sea crowded with boats and My little donkey had difficulty in proceeding...»

«And did You not, Mother?»

«Oh! I had You!...» and She looks at Him with a tender blissful face. She then resumes speaking: «It was getting dark and Joseph was very worried... a biting cold wind was blowing stronger and stronger... People were rushing towards Bethlehem, pushing one another and many took to abusing My little donkey because it was going so slowly in an effort to find suitable places for its hooves... It seemed to be aware that You were there... and that You were sleeping for the last time in the cradle of My bosom. It was cold... But I was warm. I could feel You coming... Coming? You could say: "Mother, I had been there nine months". Yes. But now it was as if You were coming from Heaven. Heaven was bending down over Me and I could see its brightness... I could see God inflamed with joy for Your oncoming birth and those flames pierced Me, burned Me, abstracted Me from everything... Cold... wind... crowds... it was all... nothing! I saw God... Now and again, with an effort, I would succeed in bringing My spirit back to the earth and I would smile at Joseph, who was afraid I might be cold and tired, and he led the little donkey lest it should stumble and he wrapped Me in a blanket lest I should get cold... But nothing could have happened to Me. I felt no jolts. I seemed to be moving along a starry path, among snow-white clouds, supported by angels... And I smiled... First at You... I looked at You, through the barrier of the flesh, while You were sleeping, with Your little fists closed, in Your cradle of living roses, My lily-bud... Then I smiled at My spouse, who was so distressed, to encourage him... And then at the people who were not aware that they were already breathing the air of the Saviour...

We stopped near Rachel's tomb to let the donkey rest for a moment and to eat a little bread and some olives, the provisions of
poor people. But I was not hungry. I could not be hungry... I was
nourished with My joy... [3]We took to the road again... Come. I 207.3
will show you where we met the shepherd... Do not worry, I cannot go wrong. I am living that hour again and I can find every
place because I see everything through a bright angelical light.
Perhaps the angelical group is here once again, invisible to our
bodies, but visible to our souls with its brightness, and everything is revealed and clear. They cannot be mistaken, and they
are leading Me... for My joy and yours. Here: Elias came from
that field into this one with his sheep, and Joseph asked him for
some milk for Me. And we stopped over there, in that field, while
he was drawing the warm nourishing milk and giving some advice to Joseph.

Come, come... Here is the path of the last little valley before
Bethlehem. We took it because the main road was a confusion
of people and horses, close to the town... [4]There is Bethlehem! 207.4
Oh! Dear land of My fathers, you gave Me the first kiss of My
Son! You opened your door, as good and fragrant as the bread of
* which you bear the name, to give the True Bread to the world dying of starvation! Like a mother, in whom there is still Rachel's
maternal love, you embraced Me, o holy land of David's Bethlehem, first temple of the Saviour, of the morning Star born of
Jacob to show Mankind the road to Heaven! Look how beautiful she is now in springtime! But she was also beautiful then, although fields and vineyards were bare! A thin veil of frost was
sparkling on the bare branches, which looked as if they were
covered with diamond dust, wrapped in a heavenly impalpable
veil. The chimney of every house was smoking while supper was
being prepared and the smoke, rising from terrace to terrace up
to this brow, made the town look veiled as well... Everything
was chaste, intimate, waiting... For You, Son! The earth perceived Your arrival... And also the people of Bethlehem would
have perceived You, because they are not bad, even if you do not
believe so. They could not give us hospitality... The good honest
homes in Bethlehem were crowded with insensitive proud peo-

* **the bread of which you bear the name**, as *Bethlehem* means *the house of bread*.

ple, who are always arrogant, and are so nowadays as well, and they could not perceive You... How many Pharisees, Sadducees, Herodians, scribes, Essenes there were! Oh! Their being dull *at present* is a consequence of their being hard-hearted *then*. They closed their hearts to love for their poor sister that night... and they remained and *still are* in darkness. They rejected God then, by rejecting love for their neighbour.

207.5 [5] Come. Let us go to the Grotto. It is useless to enter the town. The best friends of My Child are no longer there. Friendly Nature is quite sufficient to make a fire, with its stones, its stream, its wood. Nature perceived the coming of its Lord... There... come without hesitating... We go round here... There, over there are the ruins of David's Tower. Oh! it is dearer to Me than a royal palace! Blessed ruins! Blessed stream! Blessed tree because, as if by miracle, you allowed the wind to pull down so many of your branches so that we might find firewood and light a fire!»

Mary descends quickly towards the Grotto, She crosses the little stream on a board acting as a bridge, She runs in the open space before the ruins and falls on Her knees at the entrance of the Grotto, She bends and kisses the ground. All the others follow Her. They are touched... The boy, who has not left Her one moment, seems to be listening to a wonderful story and his little dark eyes drink in Mary's words and gestures without missing a single one.

Mary stands up and goes in saying: «Everything is exactly as then!... But then it was night... Joseph lit a lamp when I entered. Only then, dismounting from the little donkey I realised how tired and cold I was... An ox greeted us, I went near it, to feel its warmth and lean against the hay... Joseph laid the hay out here, where I am, to make a bed for Me, and he dried the hay for Me and for You, Son, at the fire he had lit in that corner... because he was as good as a father in his love of an angelical spouse... And holding each other's hand, like brother and sister lost in the darkness of night, we ate our bread and cheese, then he went over there to kindle the fire and he took off his mantle to close the entrance... In actual fact he put a veil before the glory of God descending from Heaven. You, My Jesus... and I lay on the hay, in the warmth of the two animals, wrapped in My mantle and covered with a woollen blanket... My dear spouse!... In

that hour of anxiety when I was all alone before the mystery of My first maternity, an hour full of uncertainty for every woman, and in My case, in My only maternity, it was also full of the mystery of what it would be to see the Son of God emerge from mortal flesh, he, Joseph, was like a mother, an angel to Me... he was My comfort then and always afterwards... [6]Then silence and 207.6
sleep wrapped the Just man... so that he might not see what for Me was God's daily kiss...

And with regards to Me, after the interval of human necessities, there came immeasurable waves of ecstasy from a heavenly sea and they raised Me higher and higher on their bright crests carrying Me up with them into an ocean of light, of joy, of peace, of love, until I was lost in the sea of God, of God's bosom... A voice from the earth whispered: "Are You sleeping, Mary?". Oh! it was so far away!... An echo, a remembrance of the earth!... And so faint it was that My soul did not stir, and I do not know how I replied, while I rose, I rose even higher into the depth of fire, of infinite beatitude of foreknowledge of God... up to Him... Oh! were You born of Me that night, or was I born of the Triune brightness? Did I give You or did You absorb Me to generate Me? I do not know... And then the descent, from choir to choir, from star to star, from cloud to cloud, a sweet, slow, blissful, placid descent, like a flower carried high in the sky by an eagle and then dropped, descending slowly, on the wings of the air, made more beautiful by a drop of rain, by a tiny piece of rainbow stolen in the sky... alights on its native soil... My diadem: You! You on My heart...

Sitting here, after adoring You on My knees, I loved You. At last I could love You without the barrier of the flesh, and I moved from here to take You to the love of him, who, like Me, was worthy of being one of the first to love You. And here, between these two rustic columns, I offered You to the Father. And here You rested for the first time on Joseph's heart... Then I swaddled You and together we laid You here... And I lulled You while Joseph was drying hay at the fire and when it was warm he placed it on Your chest and then we both adored You, bending over You, as I am doing now, to inhale Your breath, contemplating the humiliation to which love can lead and shedding tears which are certainly shed also in Heaven for the unexhausted joy of seeing God.»

207.7 [7] Mary, Who has been pacing to and fro while recalling the past, pointing out the places, panting with love, with bright tears shining in Her blue eyes and a smile of joy on Her lips, bends over Her Jesus, Who is sitting on a huge stone listening to Her recollection, and kisses His head, weeping, adoring as She did then...

«And then the shepherds... they were in here, adoring with their good souls and with the deep sigh of the earth which entered with them, with their scent of humanity, of herds and hay; and outside there were the angels, everywhere, who adored with their love, with their songs which no human creature can repeat, and with the love of Heaven, with the air of Heaven which came in with them, which they brought in, in all their brightness... Your birth, Blessed Son!...»

Mary has knelt down beside Her Son and weeps emotionally with Her head resting on His knees. No one dare speak for some time. More or less moved they all look around as if they expected to see the scene painted among the cobwebs and rough stones...

Mary collects Herself and says: «Now, I told you of the infinitely simple and infinitely great birth of My Son. With My woman's heart, not with the wisdom of a master. There is nothing else, because it was the greatest thing on the earth, concealed under very ordinary appearances.»

207.8 [8] «But the day after? And then later?» many ask, amongst them the two Maries.

«The following day? Oh! very simple! I was the mother who nurses her baby, washes him and swaddles him, as every mother does. I used to warm the water of the stream on a fire lit out there, so that the smoke would not hurt His little blue eyes, and then in the most sheltered corner in an old tub I washed My Child and put fresh swaddling clothes on Him. I washed His napkins in the stream and hung them out in the sun... and then — and it was My greatest joy — I suckled Him and He sucked and became rosier and happier... On the first day, at the warmest hour of the day, I sat out there to see Him properly. The light glimmers in here, it does not come in direct and the lamp and the flame of the fire made things look strange. I went out there, in the sun... and I looked at the Incarnate Word. The Mother then became acquainted with Her Son and the handmaid of God with Her Lord.

And I was a woman and a worshipper... Then Anna's house... the days near Your cradle, Your first steps, Your first word... But that happened later, in due course... And nothing, nothing was equal to the hour of Your birth... Only when I return to God I will find that fullness once again...»

«But... why set out at the last moment! How unwary of You! Why not wait? The decree provided for an extension for special cases such as birth or disease. Alphaeus said so...» says Mary of Alphaeus.

«Wait? Oh! no! That evening, when Joseph brought the news, You and I, Son, leapt for joy. It was the call... because You were * to be born here, and nowhere else, as the Prophets had foretold, and that sudden decree was as if merciful Heaven wanted Joseph to erase even the memory of his suspicion. It was what I was waiting for, for You, for him, for the Judaic world and for the future world, forever and ever. We decided. And we acted accordingly. Wait! Can the bride delay her nuptial dream? Why wait?»

«Well... anything might have happened...» says Mary of Alphaeus once again.

«I was not afraid of anything. I rested in God.»

«But did You know that everything would happen thus?»

«Nobody told Me. And I never thought of it, so much so that to encourage Joseph, I let him and you doubt that there was still time for the birth. But I knew, I really knew that the Light of the World was to be born during the feast of the Dedication.»

«And you, mother, why did you not go with Mary? And why did father not think of it? After all you were both going to come here! Did we not all come?» asks Judas Thaddeus sternly.

«Your father had decided to come after the Dedication and he told his brother. But Joseph would not wait.»

«But at least you...» insists Thaddeus.

«Do not reproach her, Judas. By mutual consent we decided it was just to lay a veil on the mystery of this birth.»

«Did Joseph know that it was to take place with those signs? If You did not know, how could he have known?»

«We knew nothing, except that He was to be born.»

«So?»

---

* **foretold** in *Micah 5:1-2*; the *decree* was the edict of the census, as seen in 27.2.

«So divine Wisdom guided us, as it was right that it should. Jesus' birth and His presence in the world were to appear devoid of uncommon features, which might arouse Satan... And you are aware that the present bitter hatred of Bethlehem people towards the Messiah is a consequence of Christ's first epiphany. Demoniacal hatred made use of the revelation to cause blood-
207.9 shed, and thereby intensify hatred. [9]Are you satisfied, Simon of Jonah, who are speechless and almost breathless?»

«Yes, so much... so much that I seem to be out of this world, in a holier place than if I were beyond the Velarium of the Temple... So much... that now that I have seen You in this place and in the light of that night, I am afraid that I did not behave with respect towards You, as if You were a great woman, but just a woman. Now... now I will not dare to call You: "Mary", as I did before. Before You were the Mother of My Master. Now I have seen You on the crests of those heavenly waves, I have seen You as a Queen, and I, a poor wretch, prostrate myself, because I am a slave» and he throws himself on the ground kissing Mary's feet.

Jesus speaks now: «Simon, stand up. Come here, close to Me» Peter goes to the left hand side of Jesus because Mary is on His right. «What are we now?» asks Jesus.

«We? Well, we are Jesus, Mary and Simon.»

«Very well. But how many are we?»

«Three, Master.»

«So we are a trinity. One day, in Heaven, the Divine Trinity had a thought: "It is now time that the Word should go to the world". And in a throb of love the Word came upon the earth. He parted therefore from the Father and the Holy Spirit. He came to work on the earth. The Two Who had remained in Heaven contemplated the deeds of the Word, remaining more united than ever to blend Thought and Love to assist the Word working on the earth. The day will come when an order will be issued from Heaven: "It is time for You to come back because everything has been accomplished", and then the Word will go back to Heaven, thus... (Jesus takes a step backwards leaving Mary and Peter where they were) and from the heights of Heaven, He will contemplate the deeds of the two who remained on the earth, who, by holy inspiration, will join together more than ever, to blend power and love to obtain the means of fulfilling the desire of the Word: "The redemption of the world through the perennial teaching of His Church". And the Father, the Son and the Holy Spirit will form a chain with Their beams to tie the two left on the earth more and more closely: My Mother, love; you, power. You will certainly have to treat Mary as a queen, but not as if you were a slave. Do you not think so?»

«I think everything You wish. I am overwhelmed! I... the power? Oh! If I am to be the power I must definitely lean on Her! Oh! Mother of my Lord, never abandon me, never, never...»

«Do not be afraid. I will always hold you by the hand, as I used to do with My Child until He could walk by Himself.»

«And after that?»

«And after I will support you with My prayers. Cheer up, Simon. Never doubt God's power. I did not doubt it, neither did Joseph. You must not doubt it either. God gives us His help hour
by hour, if we remain humble and faithful... [10]Come out here, 207.10
now, near the stream, in the shade of the good tree, which, if it were later in summer, would give you its apples in addition to its shade; come. We shall eat before going... Where, Son?»

«To Jala. It is near. And tomorrow we shall go to Bethzur.»

They sit in the shade of the apple-tree and Mary leans against its robust trunk.

Bartholomew watches Her, so young and still heavenly moved by the recollection She made, while She accepts from Her Son the food He has blessed and She smiles at Him with loving eyes, and he whispers: « "In His shade I am seated and His food is sweet to My taste".»

Judas Thaddeus replies to him: «It is true. She is sick with love. But we cannot say that She was awakened under an apple-tree.»

«Why not, brother? What do we know about the secrets of the King?» replies James of Alphaeus.

And Jesus smiling says: «The new Eve was conceived of the Thought at the foot of the paradisiacal apple-tree in order to put to flight the serpent and detoxicate the poisoned fruit by means of Her smile and Her tears. She became the tree of the redeeming fruit. Come, friends, and eat of it. Because to be nourished by its sweetness is to be nourished by the honey of God.»

«Master, please satisfy an old desire of mine for some clarification. Does the Song which we are reciting foresee Her?» asks * Bartholomew in a low voice while Mary is looking after the boy and speaking to the women.

«The Book speaks of her from its beginning and future books will speak of Her until the word of man changes into the everlasting hosanna of God's eternal City» and Jesus turns towards the women.

«You can hear that He descends from David! What wisdom, what poetry!» says the Zealot speaking to his companions.

207.11 [11] «Listen» the Iscariot who is still in the mood of the previous day and speaks very little, although he endeavours to emulate the freedom he had before, joins in the conversation «listen, I would like to understand why the Incarnation had to take place. Only God can speak in such a way as to defeat Satan. Only God can have the power of redeeming. And I do not doubt it. But I think that the Word might have lowered Himself less than He did by being born like every other man, submitting Himself to the miseries of childhood and so on. Could He not have appeared in human form already adult, in the appearance of an adult? And if He really wanted a mother, could He not have chosen one, an adoptive one as He did for a father? I think I asked Him once, but He did not reply at length, or I do not remember.»

«Ask Him! Since we are on the subject...» says Thomas.

«I won't. I upset Him and I feel as if I have not been forgiven yet. Ask Him on my behalf.»

«I beg your pardon! We accept everything without so many clarifications and you expect us to ask questions? It is not fair!» retorts James of Zebedee.

«What is not fair?» asks Jesus.

There is silence, then the Zealot speaks on behalf of everybody repeating Judas Iscariot's questions and the replies of the others.

«I do not bear a grudge. That is the first thing. I make the comments that I must make, I suffer and I forgive. That applies to him who is afraid, which is still the consequence of his perturbation. With regards to My *real* Incarnation I say: "It is just that it took place". In future many people will make mistakes

* **we are reciting** from *Song of Songs 2:3-5; 8:5.*

concerning My Incarnation, ascribing to Me the erroneous forms that Judas would like Me to have taken. A man seemingly solid in body, but in reality fluent like a lighting effect, so that I would and would not be flesh. And Mary's maternity would and would not be a real maternity. I am really flesh and Mary is really the Mother of the Word Incarnate. If the hour of My birth was but an ecstasy, that is because She is the new Eve without the burden of sin and without the heritage of punishment. But I did not lower Myself by resting in Her. Was the manna enclosed in the Tabernacle perhaps humiliated? No, on the contrary it was honoured by being in that abode. Others will say that I, since I was not real flesh, did not suffer and did not die during My stay on the earth. Of course, since they cannot deny that I was here, they will deny My real Incarnation or My true Divinity. No, I am really One with the Father *forever*, and I am united to God as Flesh, because as a matter of fact it is possible that Love reached what is unreachable because of His Perfection, by becoming Flesh to save flesh. A reply to all these errors is given by My whole life which shed blood from birth to death and was submitted to everything that is common to man, except sin. Yes, I was born of Her. For your welfare. You do not know how much Justice has been mitigated since the Woman has become its collaborator. Have I satisfied you, Judas?»

«Yes, Master.»

«Do likewise with Me.»

The Iscariot bends his head, is abashed and perhaps he is really touched by so much kindness.

The rest is protracted in the cool shade of the apple-tree. Some fall asleep, some doze. But Mary gets up and goes back into the Grotto and Jesus follows Her...

208. The Wrath of the Innocent Marjiam. Holy Mary with the Shepherd Elias. Going to Eliza's in Bethzur.

4th July 1945.

1 «We shall almost certainly find them if we go back on to the Hebron road for a little while. Please go in pairs looking for them 208.1
on the mountain paths. From here to Solomon's Pools and thence

to Bethzur. We will follow you. This is their pasture area» says the Lord to the Twelve and I understand that He is speaking of the shepherds.

The apostles are getting ready to go, each with his favourite companion and only the inseparable couple of John and Andrew do not get together because they both go to the Iscariot saying: «I will come with you» and Judas replies: «Yes, come, Andrew. It is better thus, John. You and I already know the shepherds. So it is better if you go with someone else.»

«Come with me, then, boy» says Peter leaving James of Zebedee, who without protesting goes with Thomas, while the Zealot joins Judas Thaddeus, James of Alphaeus goes with Matthew and the two inseparable Philip and Bartholomew remain together. The boy remains with Jesus and the Maries.

The road is cool and comfortable and runs among completely green mountains covered with forests and meadows. They meet herds going towards pastures in the faint light of dawn.

At the sound of every cattle-bell Jesus stops speaking and looks around, He then asks the shepherds whether Elias, the Bethlehemite shepherd, is in that area. I understand that by now Elias is called «the Bethlehemite». Even if other shepherds are from Bethlehem, he is by right or by mockery «the Bethlehemite». But no one knows where he is. They answer stopping their herds and ceasing to play their rustic flutes.

Almost every young man has one of those primeval cane flutes, which cause Marjiam to be thrown into ecstasies, until a good old man gives him his nephew's saying: «He will make himself another one», and Marjiam goes away happily with the instrument across his back, even if he does not know how to play it, at least for the time being.

208.2 2 «I would like so much to meet them!» exclaims Mary.

«We will certainly find them. In this season they are always near Hebron.»

The boy is interested in those shepherds who saw the Child Jesus and he asks Mary many questions and She explains everything patiently and kindly.

«But why did they punish them? They had done nothing but good!» asks the boy after hearing the story of their misfortunes.

«Because very often man makes mistakes, accusing innocent

people of evil deeds that in actual fact were done by someone else. But as they have been good and have forgiven, Jesus loves them so much. We must always be able to forgive.»

«But all the children who were slaughtered, how could they have forgiven Herod?»

«They are little Martyrs, Marjiam, and martyrs are saints. They not only forgive their executioners, but they love them, because they open Heaven to them.»

«But are they in Heaven?»

«No, not just now. But they are in Limbo where they are the joy of Patriarchs and of the just.»

«Why?»

«Because when they arrived with their souls purple with blood, they said: "Here we are, we are the heralds of Christ the Saviour. Rejoice, you who are waiting, because He is already on the earth". And everybody loves them because they are the bearers of these good tidings.»

«My father told me that also Jesus' Word is good tidings. So when my father goes to Limbo after repeating it on the earth, and I also go there, will we be loved as well?»

«You will not go to Limbo, My dear little one.»

«Why?»

«Because Jesus will have already gone back to Heaven and will have opened it and all good people will go straight to Heaven when they die.»

«I will be good, I promise. And Simon of Jonah? He too, eh? Because I do not want to become an orphan a second time.»

«He will be there as well, you may be sure, but there are no orphans in Heaven. We have God. And God is everything. We are not orphans here either. Because the Father is always with us.»

«But Jesus in that lovely prayer, which You teach me by day and my mother at night, says: "Our Father Who are in Heaven". We are not in Heaven yet. Therefore, how can we be with Him?»

«Because God is everywhere, son. He watches over the baby that is born and over the old man who is dying. The child who is born this moment, in the most remote part of the world, has God's love and eye with him and will have them until he dies.»

«Even if he is as bad as Doras?»

«Yes.»

«But can God, Who is so good, love Doras who is so bad and makes my old father weep?»

«He looks at him with disdain and sorrow. But if he should repent. He would say to him what the father of the parable said
208.3 to his repentant son. [3]You should pray that he may repent and...»

«Oh! no, Mother! I will pray that he may die!!!» says the child impetuously. Although his remark is not very... angelical, his impetuosity is so sincere that no one can help laughing.

Mary then resumes the sweet seriousness of a Teacher: «No, My dear. You must not do that to a sinner. God would not listen to you and would look sternly at you as well. We must wish our neighbour the greatest welfare, even if our neighbour is very bad. Life is a good thing because it gives man the possibility of gaining merits in the eyes of God.»

«But if one is bad, one gains sins.»

«We pray that he may become good.»

The boy is pensive... but he does not like this sublime lesson and he concludes: «Doras will not become good even if I pray for him. He is too bad. Even if all the baby martyrs of Bethlehem should pray with me, he would not become good. You do not know... You do not know that one day he struck my old father with an iron rod, because he found him sitting during working hours? He was not able to stand because he was not feeling well... and he beat him and left him half dead, and then kicked him on his face... I saw him because I was hiding behind a hedge... I had gone there because no one had brought me any bread for two days and I was hungry... I had to run away so that he might not hear me, because I was crying seeing my father like that, with blood on his beard, lying on the ground, as if he were dead... I was weeping when I went to beg some bread... but that bread is still lying here... and it tastes of the blood and tears of my father and mine, and of all those who are tortured and who cannot love those who torture them. I would like to strike Doras that he may feel what a blow is, and I would like to leave him without any bread, that he may learn what it is to be hungry, and I would make him work in the sun, in mud, under the threats of the overseer, without food, that he may know what he gives the poor... I cannot love him because... because he kills my holy father, and I... if I had not found you, to whom would I have belonged ?»

The child, in a fit of pain, shouts and cries, trembling, deranged, striking with his closed fists the air, as he cannot strike the slave-driver. The women are amazed and touched and they endeavour to calm him. But he is really in a fit of grief and does not hear anything. He shouts: «I cannot, I cannot love and forgive him. I hate him, I hate him on behalf of everybody, I hate
him, I hate him!...» He is in a pitiful and frightful state. [4]It is the 208.4
reaction of a creature who has suffered too much.

And Jesus says so: «That is Doras' gravest felony: to drive an innocent child to hate...» He then takes the child in His arms and speaks to him: «Listen, Marjiam. Do you want to go one day with your mummy, your daddy, your little brother and the old father?» «Yes...»

«Then you must not hate anybody. He who hates does not go to Heaven. You cannot pray for Doras just now? Well, do not pray, but do not hate. Do you know what you must do? You must never look back to think of the past...»

«But my father who suffers is not past...»

«That is true. But look, Marjiam, try and pray like this: "Our Father Who are in Heaven, please see to what is my wish...". You will see that the Father will listen to you in the best possible way. Even if you killed Doras, what would you do? You would lose the love of God, Heaven, the company of your father and mother and you would not relieve of his troubles the old man whom you love. You are too little to be able to do it. But God can. Tell Him. Say to Him: "You know how much I love my old father and how I love all those who are unhappy. Will You please see to this matter, because You can do everything". What? Do you not want to preach the Gospel? But the Gospel teaches love and forgiveness! How can you say to one: "Do not hate. Forgive" if you cannot love and forgive? Leave things to good God and you will see how well He can arrange matters. Will you do that?»

«Yes, I will, because I love You.»

Jesus kisses the boy and puts him down.

The incident is over as well as their journey. [5]There are three 208.5
large basins excavated in the rocky mountain, a really grand work, and the surface of the most limpid water sparkles as well as the waterfall that from the first basin falls into the second larger one and then into the third one, which is really a little

lake. Pipelines convey the water to distant towns. The whole mountain, from the spring to the basins and from the basins to the ground is most beautiful and fertile, thanks to the humidity of the soil in this area, and flowers more composite than wild ones, together with rare scented herbs, make the green sides of the mountain a most pleasant and brilliant sight. One would think that man has planted garden flowers here together with scented herbs, which, in the heat of the sun, diffuse in the air their aromas of cinnamon, camphor, clove, lavander and other pleasantly pungent, fragrant, strong, sweet smells, in a wonderful blend of the finest earthly perfumes. I would say that it is a harmonious conglomeration of smells because it is really a poem of herbs and flowers in hues and fragrance.

All the apostles are sitting in the shade of a tree covered with large white flowers, the name of which I do not know. They are huge pendulous bell-shaped flowers, of a white enamel hue, which dangle at the least breath of wind, diffusing their fragrance at each undulation. I do not know the name of this tree. Its flowers remind me of a shrub that grows in Calabria, which the locals call «bottaro», but the trunk is quite different, as this is a tall tree, with a robust trunk, and not a shrub. Jesus calls them and they hasten towards Him.

«We found Joseph almost at once, he was coming back from a market. They will all be at Bethzur this evening. We gathered together, by shouting to one another, and we remained here in the cool shade» explains Peter.

«What a lovely place! It looks like a garden! We were discussing whether it is natural or not, and some insist it is, some that it isn't» says Thomas.

«The land of Judaea has such marvels» states the Iscariot, who is inevitably inclined to grow proud by everything, also by flowers and herbs.

«Yes, but... I think that if Johanna's garden at Tiberias were abandoned and it became wild, also Galilee would have the marvel of wonderful roses among ruins» retorts James of Zebedee.

«You are not wrong. This is the area where Solomon's gardens were, and they were famous, like his palaces, throughout the world of those days. Perhaps it was here that he dreamt of the Song of Songs, and he ascribed to the Holy City all the beautiful flowers that he had grown here» says Jesus.

«So I was right!» exclaims Thaddeus.

«Yes, you were. Do You know, Master? He was quoting Ecclesiastes, joining the idea of the gardens to the idea of the basins and he concluded by saying: "But he realised that everything is vanity and nothing lasts under the sun, except the Word of My Jesus" » says James, the other brother.

«I thank you. But let us thank also Solomon, whether the orginal flowers are his or not. The basins that nourish herbs and men are certainly his. May he be blessed for them. Now let us go over to that big ruffled rose-bush, which has formed a flowery tunnel from tree to tree. We will stop there. We are almost half way...»

[6]... And they take to the road again about the ninth hour, when 208.6
every tree casts a long shadow in this area, which is very well cultivated in every part. One has the impression of walking through a botanic garden because all kinds of trees are represented: forest trees, fruit and ornamental ones. There are people working the land everywhere but they show no interest in the group passing by. On the other hand, it is not the only one. Other groups of Israelites are on their way back from the Passover celebration. The road is quite good although it is cut along the mountains, and the continuously varying landscape relieves travellers of the monotony of the journey. Streams and torrents form liquid silver commas and write words which they then sing their many intersecting meanderings, which flow through forests or hide under caves from which they come out more beautiful. They seem to be playing with plants and stones like happy children.

Also Marjiam, who is cheerful once again, plays and tries to make music with his instrument to imitate birds. But the sounds he produces are not songs, but dissonant laments, which appear to be most unwelcome to the more difficult members of the group, that is to Bartholomew, because of his age, and to Judas of Kerioth, for many reasons. But no one complains openly and the boy whistles frisking about. Only twice he points at a village nestling in the forests and asks: «Is it mine?» and turns pale. But Simon, who keeps him close to himself, replies: «Your village is very far

* **saying** as in *Qoelet 1:2-3.*

from here. Come, let us see if we can pick that beautiful flower and take it to Mary» and thus takes his mind off his worries.

208.7 [7] The sun is beginning to set when Bethzur appears on its hill and almost at the same time, on the secondary road they have taken to go there, they see the flocks of the shepherds and the shepherds who run to meet them. When Elias sees that Mary also is there, he lifts his arms in a gesture of surprise and remains thus, not believing his own eyes.

«Peace to you, Elias. It is I. We promised you, but it was not possible to meet in Jerusalem... Never mind, We are meeting now» says Mary kindly.

«Oh! Mother, Mother!...» Elias does not know what to say, At last he finds words: «Well, I am celebrating Passover now. It is just the same, or better still.»

«Of course, Elias. We sold well. We can kill a little lamb. Oh! Please be the guests of our poor table» beg Levi and Joseph.

«We are tired this evening, Tomorrow. Listen. Do you know a certain Eliza, the wife of Abraham of Samuel?»

«Yes. She lives in her house at Bethzur. But Abraham is dead and his sons died last year. The first one died of a disease in a few hours, and no one knows of what he died. The other died of a slow death and nothing stopped his decline. We gave her the milk of a young goat, because the doctors said it was good for him. He drank a lot of it, as all the shepherds took it to her, because the poor mother had sent people to look for whoever had a young goat giving milk for the first time in the herd. But it was of no avail. When we came back to the plain the young man would not take any food. When we came back in Adar, he had been dead two months.»

«My poor friend! She was so fond of Me in the Temple... and she was somehow related to Me through our ancestors... She was good... She left to marry Abraham, to whom she had been promised since her childhood, two years before Me and I remember when she came to offer her first-born to the Lord. She sent for Me, not only for Me, but later she wanted Me to be alone with her for some time... And now she is alone... Oh! I must make haste to comfort her! You stay here. I will go with Elias and I will enter by Myself. Sorrow demands respect...»

«Not even I, Mother?»

«Of course, always. But the others... Not even you, My little one. It would be painful for you. Come, Jesus!»

«Wait for us on the village square. Look for a shelter for the night. Goodbye» orders Jesus.

[8] And with only Elias for company, Jesus and Mary go as far as a large house, which is completely closed and silent. The shepherd knocks at the door with his stick. A maidservant looks out of a little window asking who it is. Mary moves forward saying: «Mary of Joachim and Her Son, from Nazareth. Tell your mistress.» 208.8

«It is useless. She does not want to see anybody. She is weeping her heart out.»

«Try.»

«No. I know how she drives me away if I try to take her mind off her worries. She does not want anyone, she will not see anyone or speak to anyone. She speaks only to the memory of her sons.»

«Go, woman. I order you to go. Say to her: "Little Mary of Nazareth is here, the one who was your daughter in the Temple...". You will see that she will be wanting Me.»

The woman goes away shaking her head. Mary explains to Her Son and to the shepherd: «Eliza was much older than I was. She was waiting in the Temple for her fiance to come back from Egypt where he had gone on inheritance matters and so she remained there up to an unusual age. She is almost ten years older than I am. The teachers used to entrust the little girls to the guidance of adult pupils... and she was My companion-teacher. She was good and... Here is the woman.»

In fact the servant thoroughly amazed rushes to open the door wide: «Come in, come in!» she says. And then in a low voice: «May You be blessed for getting her out of that room.»

Elias takes his leave and Mary enters with Her Son.

«But this man, really... For pity's sake! He is the same age as Levi...»

«Let Him come in. He is My Son and will comfort her better than I can.»

The woman shrugs her shoulders and precedes them through the long hall of a beautiful but sad house. Everything is clean, but everything seems dead...

[9] A tall woman, walking bowed in dark clothes, comes forward 208.9

in the dim light of the hall.

«Eliza! Dear! I am Mary!» says Mary running towards her and embracing her.

«Mary? You... I thought You were dead, too. I was told... when? I don't know... My head is empty... I was told that You died with many other mothers after the coming of the Magi. But who told me that You were the Mother of the Saviour?»

«The shepherds perhaps...»

«Oh! the shepherds!» The woman bursts into bitter tears. «Don't mention that name. It reminds me of the last hope for Levi's life... And yet... yes... a shepherd spoke to me of the Saviour and I killed my son taking him to the place where they said the Messiah was, near the Jordan. But there was nobody there... and my son arrived back in time to die... Fatigue, cold... I killed him... But I had no intention of being a murderer. I was told that He, the Messiah, cured diseases... and that is why I did it... Now my son accuses me of killing him...»

«No, Eliza. It is you that think so. Listen. I instead think that your son has taken Me by the hand saying: "Come to my dear mother. Take the Saviour to her. I am happier here than I would be on the earth. But she listens only to *her* weeping, and she cannot hear the words that I whisper to her with my kisses, poor mother, she is like a woman possessed by a demon who wants her to surrender to despair, because he wants us to be divided. If instead she resigns herself and believes that God does everything for a good purpose, we would be united for good, with our father and brother. Jesus can do it". And I came... with Him... Do you not wish to see Him?...» Mary has spoken holding the poor wretch in Her arms all the time, kissing her grey hair with unparalleled kindness.

«Oh! if it were true! But, why then did Daniel not come to You, to tell You to come sooner?... But who told me some time ago that You were dead? I don't remember... I don't remember... That is another reason why perhaps I waited too long to go to the Messiah. But they said that He, You, everybody had died at Bethlehem...»

208.10 «Never mind who said so. [10]Come here, look, My Son is here. Come to Him. Make your children and your Mary happy. Do you know that we suffer seeing you thus?» And She leads her towards Jesus Who is standing in a dark corner and only now comes forward, under a lamp that the maidservant has placed on top of a tall coffer.

The poor mother raises her head... and I now see that she is the Eliza who was also on Calvary with the pious women. Jesus stretches out His hands in a gesture of loving invitation. The poor wretch hesitates a moment, then she entrusts her own hands to His and finally, all of a sudden, she throws herself on to Jesus' chest, moaning: «Tell me, tell me that I am not guilty of Levi's death! Tell me that they are not lost forever! Tell me that I will soon be with them!...»

«Yes, I will. Listen. They are now exulting because you are in My arms. I will soon be going to them, and what shall I tell them? That you are not resigning yourself to the Lord? Shall I tell them that? The women of Israel, the women of David, so strong, so wise, are to be given the lie by you? No. You are suffering, because you suffered all alone. Your grief and you. You and your grief. One cannot endure it thus. Are you no longer bearing in mind the words* of hope for those whom death has taken away from us? "I mean to raise you from your graves and lead you back to the soil of Israel. And you will know that I am the Lord when I open your graves and raise you from your graves. When I put My spirit in you, you will live". The soil of Israel, for the just sleeping in the Lord, is the Kingdom of God. I will open it and give it to those who are waiting.»

«Also to my Daniel? And to my Levi?... He was so horrified at death!... He could not stand the idea of being far from his mother. That is why I wanted to die and be buried beside him...»

«But they were not there with their living parts. Only dead things were there and they could not hear you. They are in the place of expectation...»

«But does it really exist? Oh! Do not be scandalised at me. My memory has turned into tears! My head is full of the noise of the weeping and death-rattle of my sons. That death-rattle! That death-rattle. It has dissolved my brains. I have but that death-rattle in here...»

«And I will put the words of life there for you. I will sow the

* **words** in *Ezekiel 37:12-14*.

Life, because I am Life, where there is the din of death. Remember the great Judas Maccabee who wanted a sacrifice offered for the dead, rightly thinking that they are destined to rise again and that it is necessary to hasten their peace by means of suitable sacrifices. If Judas Maccabee had not been certain of their resurrection, would he have prayed and made people pray for the dead? As it is written, he thought that a great reward is set *
aside for those who die piously, as your sons certainly did... See, you are saying yes? So do not despair. But pray devoutly for your dead ones, that their sins may be expiated before I go to them. Then, without waiting for a moment, they will come to Heaven with Me. Because I am the Way, the Truth and the Life and I lead, and I speak the Truth and I give Life to those who believe in My Truth and follow Me. Tell Me. Did your sons believe in the coming of the Messiah?»

«Of course, my Lord. I taught them to believe that.»

«And did Levi believe that if I wanted I could cure him?»

«Yes, My Lord. We hoped in You... but it was of no avail... and he died disheartened after hoping so much...» The woman resumes weeping again more calmly but more desolately in her calm than when she was agitated.

«Do not say that it was of no avail. He who believes in Me,
208.11 even if he is dead, will live forever... [11]Night is falling, woman. I will join My apostles. I leave My Mother with you...»

«Oh! Will you please stay as well!... I am afraid that if You go away, my torture will begin again... The storm is just beginning to calm at the sound of Your words...»

«Do not be afraid! You have Mary with you. I will come again tomorrow. I have something to tell the shepherds. Can I tell them to approach your house?...»

«Oh! Yes. They used to come for my son last year too... Behind the house there is an orchard and a rustic yard. They can go there as they used to do then, to keep the flock together...»

«All right. I will come. Be good. Remember that Mary in the Temple was entrusted to You. I entrust Her to you as well tonight.»

«Yes, do not worry. I will look after Her... I will have to see

* **As it is written** in *2 Maccabees 12:43-46.*

Her supper, to Her rest... For how long I have never thought of these things! Mary, will You sleep in my room, as Levi did when he was ill? I in my son's bed, You in mine. And I will feel as if I heard his light breathing again... He always held me by the hand...»

«Yes, Eliza. But before we shall speak of *many* things.»

«No. You are tired. You must sleep.»

«You, too...»

«Oh! It is I who have not slept for months... I weep... and weep... I can do nothing else...»

«This evening, instead, we shall pray, and then we shall go to bed and you will sleep... We shall sleep holding each other's hand. You may go, Son, and pray for us...»

«I bless you. Peace to you and to this house!»

And Jesus goes away with the maidservant who is dumbfounded and keeps repeating: «What a miracle, my Lord! What a miracle! After so many months she has spoken, she has reasoned... Oh! what a wonderful thing!... They were saying that she would die insane... And I was sorry, because she is good.»

«Yes, she is good and that is why God will help her. Goodbye, woman. Peace to you too.»

Jesus goes out on to the almost dark street and it all ends.

209. Jesus in Eliza's House Speaks of Sorrow that Bears Fruit.

5th July 1945.

[1] The news that Eliza has convinced herself that she should get rid of her tragic melancholy must have spread through the village, so much so that when Jesus, followed by His apostles and disciples goes towards the house, crossing the village, many people watch Him carefully. They also ask the various shepherds questions about Him, why He came, about those who are with Him, about the boy, the women, the medicine He gave Eliza to relieve her of the darkness of insanity so quickly as soon as He arrived, about what He is going to do or say... And who wishes to ask more questions, may do so... 209.1

The last question is: «Could we not come as well?» to which

the shepherds reply: «That we do not know. You ought to ask the Master. Go and ask Him.»

«And if He should ill-treat us?»

«He does not ill-treat even sinners. Go. He will be pleased.»

209.2 [2] A group of people, mainly elderly men and women, of the same age as Eliza, consult one another and then move forward approaching Jesus Who is speaking to Peter and Bartholomew, and rather hesitantly they call Him: «Master...»

«What do you want?» asks Bartholomew.

«To speak to the Master, to ask...»

«May peace come to you. What questions do you wish to ask Me?»

They take heart seeing Jesus smile and say: «We are all friends of Eliza, and of her house. We heard that she has been cured. We would like to see her and hear You. Can we come?»

«You can come certainly to hear Me. To see her, no, My dear friends. Mortify your friendship and your curiosity too. Because it is also curiosity. Have respect for a deep grief which is not to be disturbed.»

«But has she not recovered?»

«She is turning towards the Light. But when night comes to an end, is it suddenly midday? And when you light a fire, is the flame bright at once? The same applies to Eliza. And if a sudden gust of wind blows on the little starting flame, does it not put it out? Use discretion therefore. The woman is one big sore. Also friendship might irritate her because she needs rest, silence, and solitude, not tragic as yesterday's, but a resigned solitude to find herself once again...»

«So, when shall we see her?»

«Sooner than you think. Because she is now on the path to health. But if you knew what it means to come out of *that* darkness! It is worse than death. And he who comes out of it, after all, is ashamed of having been there and that the world should know.»

«Are you a doctor?»

«I am the Master.»

They have reached the house. Jesus speaks to the shepherds: «Go into the yard. Those who wish to come with you, may do so. But no one must make any noise or go beyond the yard. And you watch as well» He says to the apostles, «that everybody complies. And you (He speaks to Salome and Mary of Alphaeus) watch that the boy does not make any noise. Goodbye.» And He knocks at the door while the others turn the corner along a narrow street and go where they were told.

[3] The maidservant opens the door. Jesus goes in while the servant repeatedly bows to Him. 209.3

«Where is your mistress?»

«With Your Mother... and, just imagine! she has come down into the garden! How wonderful! How wonderful! And yesterday evening she came into the dining room... She was weeping, but she came. I would have liked her to take some food, instead of the usual drop of milk, but I was not successful!»

«She will take it. Do not insist. Be also patient in your love for your mistress.»

«Yes, my Saviour. I will do everything You tell me.»

I think, in fact, that if Jesus told the woman to do the strangest things, she would do them without objecting, because she is so convinced that Jesus is Jesus and that everything He does is right. In the meantime she takes Him into a large kitchen garden, full of fruit-trees and of flowers. But if the fruit-trees have begun by themselves to come into leaf and blossom, to set the fruit and make them grow, the poor flower plants, neglected for over a whole year, have become a miniature forest, which is so entangled that the weaker and lower plants are suffocated beneath the weight of the stronger ones. Flower-beds and paths no longer exist as they have become one chaotic tangle. There is some order only at the end of the garden where the maidservant has sown salads and vegetables for her own use.

Mary is there with Eliza under a very ruffled pergola, the shoots and tendrils of which reach down to the ground. Jesus stops and looks at His young Mother, Who with most refined art awakes and directs Eliza's mind to things completely different from what up to yesterday were the thoughts of the afflicted woman.

The servant approaches her mistress and says: «The Saviour has come.»

The women turn around and come towards Him, one with Her sweet smile, the other looking tired and bewildered.

«Peace be with you. This garden is beautiful...»

«It was beautiful...» says Eliza.

«And the soil is fertile. Look how much beautiful fruit is about to ripen! And how many flowers on the rose bushes! And over there? Are they lilies?»

«Yes, they are, round a fountain where my children used to play so much.But then it was tidy... Now everything is ruined here. And it no longer seems the garden of my sons.»

«In a few days it will be as it was before. I will help you. Is that right, Jesus? You will leave Me here for a few days with Eliza. We have so much to do...» says Mary.

«What You want, I want.»

Eliza looks at Him and whispers: «Thank You.»

Jesus caresses her white hair and then takes His leave to go to the shepherds.

209.4 [4]The women remain in the garden, but shortly afterwards, when Jesus' voice greeting the people present is heard in the calm air, Eliza, as if she were attracted by an irresistible force, goes slowly up to a very tall hedge beyond which is the yard.

Jesus speaks first to the three shepherds. He is close to the hedge, and in front of Him there are the apostles and the citizens of Bethzur who followed Him. The Maries with the boy are sitting in a corner. Jesus says: «But are you bound by contract or can you free yourselves from your commitment any time?»

«Well, we are really free servants. But we do not think that it is right to leave him at once, now that the flocks demand so much attention and it is difficult to find shepherds.»

«No, it is not fair. But it is not necessary to do it at once. I am telling you in good time, so that you may provide in all fairness. I want you to be free. To join the disciples and help Me...»

«Oh! Master!... » The three men become ecstatic with joy. «But will we be able?» they ask.

«I have no doubt about it. So that is settled. As soon as you can do it, you will join Isaac.»

«Yes, Master.»

209.5 «You may go among the rest. [5]I will speak a few words to the people.»

And leaving the shepherds He addresses the crowd.

«Peace be with you. Yesterday I heard two unfortunate people speak. One at the dawn of life; the other at its decline: two souls bewailing their distress. And I wept in My heart with them, seeing how much sorrow there is on the earth, and how only God can relieve it. God! The exact knowledge of God, of His great infinite bounty, of His constant presence, of His promises. I saw how one man can be tortured by another one and how death can drive him to desolation, on which Satan works to increase his grief and cause ruin. I then said to Myself: "The children of God must not suffer such tortures. Let us grant the knowledge of God to those who ignore it, let us give it once again to those who have forgotten it in the storm of sorrow". But I also saw that I am no longer sufficient by Myself for the infinite needs of My brothers. And I have decided to call many, in greater and greater numbers, so that all those who need the comfort of the knowledge of God may have it.

These twelve apostles are the first. As My representatives they can lead to Me, and therefore to comfort, all those who are bent under too heavy a burden of sorrow. I solemnly tell you: Come to Me, all of you who are afflicted, disgusted, broken-hearted, tired, and I will share your grief with you and give you peace. Come, through My apostles, disciples and women disciples, who are increasing every day with new people full of goodwill. You will find comfort in your grief, company in your solitude, the love of your brothers to make you forget the hatred of the world, you will find, above all, the supreme comforter, the perfect companion, the love of God. You will no longer doubt anything. You will no longer say: "Everything has come to an end for me!". But you will say: "Everything begins for me in a supernatural world, which abolishes distances and cancels separations", so that orphans will be reunited with their parents who have risen to Abraham's bosom, and fathers and mothers, wives and widows will find their lost children and husbands.

[6] In this land of Judaea, still near Bethlehem of Naomi, I re- 209.6
mind you that love relieves pain and gives joy. Consider, you who
* are weeping, Naomi's desolation when her house was left with-
out men. Listen to the words of her down-hearted dismissal of Orpah and Ruth: "Go back, each of you, to her mother's house.

* **Noemi**: whose story, together with that of Ruth, is in the vey short book of *Ruth*.

May the Lord be kind to you as you have been to those who have died and to me...". Listen to her weary insistence. She who once had been the beautiful Naomi and now was the tragic Naomi, crushed by grief, did not hope for anything else in life. She only wished to go and die in the place where she had been happy in the days of her youth with the love of her husband and the kisses of her children. She said: "Go, go. It is useless to come with me... I am as good as dead... My life is no longer here, but there, in the next world, where *they* are. Do not sacrifice your lives any longer beside a dying thing. Because I really am 'a thing'. I am indifferent to everything. God has taken everything away from me... I am bitter grief. And I would grieve you... and that would weigh sorely on my heart. And the Lord would ask me to account for that, He Who has already struck me so hard, because it would be selfishness to keep you, alive, near me, dead. Go to your mothers...". But Ruth stayed to support the sorrowful old woman.

Ruth had understood that there are sorrows which are always greater than one's own and that her grief of a young widow was lighter than the woman's who had lost her husband and two sons; as the grief of an orphan boy, who is compelled to live begging, without caresses, without good advice, is by far greater than the deep sorrow of a mother bereft of her children; likewise the keen regret of him who, for a number of reasons, goes as far as to hate mankind and see in every man an enemy whom he must fear and against whom he must defend himself, is even greater than other sorrows, because it involves not only flesh, blood and mentality, but the soul with its supernatural duties and rights and drives it to perdition. How many childless mothers there are in the world for motherless children! How many childless widows there are who could be compassionate towards solitary old aged people! How many there are, who, having been deprived of every love so that they may devote themselves entirely to the unhappy, could fight hatred with their need to love and thus give love to unhappy Mankind, which suffers more and more because it hates more and more!

209.7 [7] Sorrow is a cross, but it is also a wing. Mourning divests to reclothe. Rise, you who are weeping! Open your eyes, get rid of nightmares, of darkness, of selfishness! Look... The world is the barren land where one weeps and dies. And the world shouts:

"help" through the mouths of orphans, of sick, lonely, doubtful people, through the mouths of those who are made prisoners of hatred by treason or cruelty. Go among those who are shouting. Forget yourselves among those who are forgotten! Recover your health among those who are sick! Be hopeful among those who are despairing! The world is open to those willing to serve God in their neighbour and to gain Heaven: to be united to God and to those whom we mourn. The gymnasium is here. The triumph there. Come. Imitate Ruth in all your sorrows. Say with her: "I will be with you until I die". And even if those misfortunes, which consider themselves incurable, should reply to you: "Do not call me Naomi, call me Mara, for God has marred me bitterly" you must persist. And I solemnly tell you that those misfortunes one day, because of your persisting, will exclaim: "Blessed be the Lord Who relieved me of my bitterness, desolation and solitude, by means of a creature who knew how to make his sorrow bear good fruit. May God bless him because he is my saviour".

Remember that Ruth's kindness to Naomi gave the Messiah to the world, because the Messiah descends from David, as David descended from Jesse, Jesse from Obed, Obed from Boaz, Boaz from Salmon, Salmon from Nahshon, Nahshon from Amminadab, Amminadab from Ram, Ram from Hezron, Hezron from Perez, and they populated the fields of Bethlehem preparing the ancestors of the Lord. Every good deed is the origin of great things, which you do not even imagine. And the effort man makes against his own selfishness can cause such a wave of love, capable of rising higher and higher, supporting in its limpidity him who caused it, until it lifts him to the feet of the altar, to the heart of God.

May God grant you peace.»

And Jesus, without going back into the garden through the door built in the hedge, watches that no one goes near the hedge, from the other side of which comes a long weeping... Only when all the people of Bethzur have gone away, He departs with His apostles without disturbing those beneficial tears...

210. Towards Hebron. The Ill-Disposed Judas Iscariot.

6th July 1945.

210.1 [1] «I do not suppose you wish to make a pilgrimage to all the known places in Israel» says the Iscariot ironically. He is discussing in a group where there are Mary of Alphaeus and Salome together with Andrew and Thomas.

«Why not? Who forbids us?» asks Mary of Clopas.

«I do. My mother has been waiting for me for such a long time...»

«Well go to your mother. We will reach you later» says Salome and she seems to be adding mentally: «No one will miss you.»

«Certainly not! I am going with the Master. Contrary to what had been arranged, Mary is not coming. And that should not have been done to me, because I was promised She would come.»

«She stopped at Bethzur for a good reason. That woman was really unhappy.»

«Jesus could have cured her at once, without making her recover gradually. I do not know why He is no longer fond of working outstanding miracles.»

«He must have holy reasons for doing what He did» states Andrew calmly.

210.2 [2] «Of course! And He thus loses proselytes. Our stay at Jerusalem, what a disappointment it was! The more there is need for high-flown things, the more He crouches in the dark. I intended so much to see, to fight...»

«Excuse my question... But what did you want to see and with whom did you intend to fight?» asks Thomas.

«What? Who? But I wanted to see His miracles and then make head against those who say that He is a false prophet or possessed. Because *that* is what they say, see? They say that if Beelzebub does not support Him, He is a poor wretch. And since Beelzebub's whimsical disposition is well known and we know that he delights in taking and leaving, as a leopard does with its prey, and that this mentality is justified by facts, I become impatient when I think that He does nothing. We are cutting a lovely figure! The apostles of a Master... Who does nothing but teach... that is undeniable, but nothing else.» Judas' abrupt pause after the word «Master» makes the others think he was about to say something nasty.

The women are horrified and Mary of Alphaeus, being a relative of Jesus', says frankly: «I am not surprised at that, but I am astonished that He puts up with you, boy!»

But Andrew, the ever meek Andrew, loses his temper and blushing, very much like his brother just this once, says furiously: «Go away! And you won't cut any more bad figures because of the Master! And who asked you to come? He called us. Not you. You had to insist several times to be accepted. You imposed yourself. I do not know who keeps me from reporting everything to the others...»

«One can never talk to you. They are right when they say you are quarrelsome and ignorant people...»

«Well, to tell you the truth, neither do I understand how you can say that the Master made a mistake. Neither did I know of the whimsical disposition of the Demon. Poor thing! He must certainly be odd. Had he been intelligent he would not have rebelled against God. But I will take note of that» teases Thomas to avert the approaching storm.

«Don't jest, because I am serious. Can you perhaps say that He attracted attention in Jerusalem? Also Lazarus said so...»

Thomas breaks into a hearty laugh. Then, still laughing, and his laughter has already disconcerted Judas, he says: «He has not done anything? Go and ask the lepers at Siloam and Hinnom. That is: You will not find anyone at Hinnom, because they were all cured. If you were not there, because you were in a hurry to go to... your friends, and consequently you do not know, that does not prevent the valleys of Jerusalem and many more places from resounding with the hosannas of the lepers cured» concludes Thomas seriously. [3]And he continues sternly: «You suf- 210.3
fer from bile trouble, my friend. And thus you taste bitter and see green everywhere. It must be a recurring disease with you. And believe me, it is not very pleasant to live with one like you. You must change. I will not tell anybody anything, and if these good women will listen to me, they will be quiet as well, and so will Andrew. But you must change. You must not think that you have been disappointed because there is no disappointment. Neither are you necessary because the Master knows what to do by Himself. Don't you try to be the Master's master. And if

for that poor woman of Eliza He acted thus, it means that that was the right thing to do. Let snakes hiss and spit as they like. Don't go to the trouble of acting as a broker between them and Him and above all do not think that you lower yourself by being with Him. Even if He did not cure a simple thing such as a cold in the future, He is always powerful. His word is a continuous miracle. And set your mind at rest. We have no archers behind us! Don't worry, we will succeed in convincing the world that Jesus is Jesus. And be quiet, if Mary promised to come to your mother's, She will come. In the meantime we will go round this beautiful part of the country, it is our work! And why not? Let us make the women disciples happy by going to visit Abraham's tomb, his tree and Jesse's sepulchre and... what else did you say?»

«They say that this is the place where Adam lived and where Abel was killed...»

«The usual useless tales!» grumbles Judas.

«In one hundred years' time they will also say that the Grotto
210.4 of Bethlehem and many other things were a tale! [4]But excuse me! You wanted to go to that stinking cave at Endor, which you must agree did not belong to a holy cycle; don't you think so? And they have come here where they say there is the blood and the ashes of saints. Endor brought us John and who knows...»

«What a handsome acquisition John is!» scoffs the Iscariot.

«His face isn't, no. But in his soul he may be better than we are.»

«What? With his past!»

«Be quiet. The Master said that we are not to remember it.»

«Lovely! If I did any such things, I wonder whether you would not remember them!» «Goodbye, Judas. You had better be by yourself. You are too cross. I wish I knew what is the matter with you!»

«What is the matter with me, Thomas? The trouble is that I see that we are being neglected to the advantage of strange newcomers. And I see that everybody is preferred to me. And I also notice how He waits until I am away to teach you how to pray. And do you expect me to be happy with such a situation?»

«No, I don't. But may I point out that if you had come with us for the Passover Supper you would have been on the Mount of

Olives as well with us, when the Master taught us the prayer. I do not see how we are neglected because of any strange newcomer. Are you referring to the poor innocent boy? Or because unhappy John is with us?»

«Because of both of them. Jesus hardly ever speaks to us now. Look at Him even now... He is loitering over there, talking and talking to the boy. He will have to wait a long time before He can put him among the disciples! And the other one will never be a disciple. He is too proud, too learned, too hardened, with bad tendencies. And yet: "John here, John there"...»

«Father Abraham, help me to bear this in patience!!! And in what do you think the Master prefers others to you?»

«Do you not see that even now? When it was time to leave Bethzur, after stopping to teach three shepherds who could have very well been taught by Isaac, whom does He leave with His mother? Me? you? No. He leaves Simon. An old man who can hardly speak!...»

«But the little he says is always said right» retorts Thomas, who is now alone because the women and Andrew have gone away and are walking fast in front of them as if they wished to get past a stretch of the road where the sun is very warm.

5 The two apostles have become so excited that they do not hear 210.5
Jesus coming, because the noise of His footsteps is completely muffled by the dust of the road. But if He makes no noise, the two are shouting as loud as ten people and Jesus can hear. Behind Him there are Peter, Matthew, the two cousins of the Lord, Philip and Bartholomew and the two sons of Zebedee with Marjiam between them.

Jesus says: «You are right, Thomas. Simon speaks little, but the little he says is always right. His mind is placid and his heart honest. And above all he has a great goodwill. That is why I left him with My Mother. He is a true reliable man and at the same time knows how to live, he has suffered and is old. Therefore — I am saying this because I suppose there is someone who thinks My choice was unfair — therefore he was the most suitable to remain. Judas, I could not allow My Mother to be left alone near a poor woman who is still ill. And it was just that I should leave Her. My Mother will complete the work that I started. But I could not leave Her with My brothers, or with Andrew, James or John, or with you. If you do not understand the reason, I do not know what to say...»

«Because She is Your Mother, She is young, beautiful, and people...»

«No! People will always have filth in their thoughts, on their lips and hands and particularly in their hearts, dishonest people who see their sentiments in everybody else; but I am not concerned with their mud. It falls off by itself, when it is dry. But I preferred Simon because he is old and he would not remind the desolate woman too much of her dead sons. You young men would have recalled them with your youth... Simon knows how to watch without being noticed, he never demands anything, he understands and can control himself. I could have taken Peter. Who would be better than he near My Mother? But he is still too impulsive. You know that I tell him openly, and he takes no offence. Peter is sincere, and he loves sincerity even to his own detriment. I could have taken Nathanael. But he has never been to Judaea before. Simon instead knows the country well and he will be valuable in bringing My Mother to Kerioth. He knows where your country house and the town house are and he will not...»

210.6 [6] «But... Master!... But is Your Mother really coming to mine?»

«We said so. And when you say something, you do it. We shall proceed slowly, stopping to evangelize these villages. Do you not want Me to evangelize Your Judaea?»

«Of course, Master!... But I believed... I thought... »

«Above all you were causing yourself a lot of trouble through your own imagination. By the second phase of the moon of Sivan we shall all be at your mother's. *We*, that is also My Mother and Simon. For the time being She is evangelizing Bethzur, a Judaean town, as Johanna is evangelizing Jerusalem with the assistance of a girl and a priest who was previously a leper, as Lazarus with Martha and old Ishmael are evangelizing Bethany, as Juttah is evangelized by Sarah and I am sure that your mother speaks of the Messiah at Kerioth, You cannot certainly say that I have left Judaea without voices. On the contrary, although it is more narrow-minded and stubborn than any other region, I have given it the sweetest voices, the voices of women, beside those of Isaac, a holy man, and of Lazarus, a friend of Mine. A woman knows how to use words with the subtle art of a woman, a mistress in leading souls to where she wants. Are you not speaking any more? Why are you almost weeping, you big moody boy? What is the use of poisoning yourself with shadows? Have you still any reason to be upset? Tell Me! Speak up...»

«I am bad... and You are so good. Your goodness always strikes me, because it is always so fresh and so new... I... I can never tell when I am going to find it on my way.»

«You are right. It is not possible for you to know. Because it is neither fresh nor new. It is eternal, Judas. It is omnipresent, Ju-
210.7 das... [7]Oh! We are near Hebron and Mary, Salome and Andrew are waving their hands to us. Let us go. They are speaking to some men. They must be asking where the historical places are. Your mother is becoming young again by this recollection, my dear brother!»

Judas Thaddeus smiles at his Cousin and Jesus smiles back.

«We are all becoming young!» says Peter. «I seem to be at school once again. But this is a lovely school! Much better than Elisha's, the grumbler. Do you remember him, Philip? What did we not do to him! Remember the story of the tribes? "Say the towns of the tribes!"; "You did not say them in chorus... Repeat them..."; "Simon, you look like a sleeping frog. You are left behind. Start all over again". O dear! My head was full of names of towns and villages of bygone days, and I knew nothing else. Instead here, one really learns! Do you know, Marjiam? One of these days your father will be going to sit his exams, now that he has learned...»

They all laugh while going towards Andrew and the women.

211. The Return to Hebron. Preaching and Miracles in the Garden of John the Baptist's House.

7th July 1945.

[1]They are all sitting in a circle in a thicket near Hebron and 211.1
they are eating while speaking to one another. Judas, who is now sure that Mary will go to his mother's, is in the best of spirits and endeavours to erase the memory of his bad humour with his companions and the women, by showering his attention on them. He must have gone to the village to do the shopping and he says that

he has found a great difference in it since last year. «The news of Jesus' preaching and miracles has reached this place. And the people have begun to ponder many things. Do You know, Master, that Doras has some property in this part of the country? Also Chuza's wife has some land on these mountains and a castle of her own, as a marriage settlement. Obviously the ground has been prepared both by her and by Doras' peasants, because some of his men from Esdraelon must be here. He... Doras told them to be quiet. But they!... I don't think they would be silent even if he tortured them. The death of the old Pharisee greatly surprised everybody, You know? And the very good health of Johanna, who came here before Passover. Ah! Also Aglae's lover has served You. You know that she ran away shortly after we came here. And he played havoc among many innocent people to avenge himself. So that the people concluded by thinking of You as an avenger of the oppressed and they are now expecting You. I mean the better ones...»

«Avenger of the oppressed! I really am. But in a supernatural way. None of those who see Me with sceptre and axe in My hands as king and executioner according to the spirit of the earth, is right. I certainly came to free people from oppression. From the oppression of sin, which is the most serious, of illness, of desolation; from ignorance and selfishness. Many will learn that it is not fair to oppress people, simply because one has been placed by fate in a high position, and that, on the contrary, a high position should be used to raise up those who are down at the bottom.»

«Lazarus does that, also Johanna. But they are only two against hundreds...» says Philip disconsolately.

«Rivers are not as wide at their sources as they are at their estuaries. A few drops, a trickle of water, but later... There are rivers that look like seas at their mouths.»

«The Nile, eh? Your Mother told me of the time You went to Egypt.She always said to me: "A sea, believe Me, a green-blue sea. To see it in flood is a dream!" and She told me of the plants that seem to spring from the water and of all the greenery that seemed to be left by the receding water...» says Mary of Alphaeus.

«Well, I tell you that, as the Nile at its source is a trickle of water and then becomes the giant it is, so the tiny trickle of great people who for the time being bend with love and out of love over the least of their brothers, will become a multitude later. For the time being Johanna, Lazarus, Martha, but how many, how many!» Jesus seems to be seeing those who will be merciful to their brothers and He smiles, enraptured in His vision.

[2]Judas confides that the head of the synagogue wanted to come with him, but he did not dare to make a decision by himself: «Do you remember, John, how he drove us away last year?»* 211.2

«I remember... But let us ask the Master.»

And when Jesus is questioned He says that they will go into Hebron. If the people want them, they will call them and they will stop; otherwise they will pass without pausing.

«So we shall also see the Baptist's house. To whom does it belong now?»

«To whoever wants it, I think. Shammai went away and never came back. He took away servants and furniture. The citizens to avenge themselves of his abuse of power, knocked the enclosure wall down, and the house now belongs to anybody. At least the garden does. They gather there to venerate their Baptist. They say that Shammai was murdered. I do not know why... apparently because of women...»

«Certainly some filthy plot at court!...» whispers Nathanael through his beard.

[3]They get up and go towards Hebron, towards the Baptist's house. When they are almost there, they see a serried group of citizens coming forward rather hesitatingly. They seem curious and embarrassed. But Jesus greets them smiling. They take heart, they open out and that severe person, the head of the synagogue, whom they had met in the previous year, emerges from the group. 211.3

«Peace to you!» greets Jesus instantly. «Will you allow us to stop in your town? I am here with all My favourite disciples and with some of their mothers.»

«Master, but do You not bear us, or me, a grudge?»

«Grudge? I do not know what it is, neither do I know why I should bear it.»

«Last year I offended You...»

---

* **drove us away**, in 77.8.

«You offended an Unknown man, thinking it was your right to do so. Later you understood and you were sorry you had done it. But that is past. And as repentance cancels sin, so the present deletes the past. Now I am no longer Unknown to you. So what are your sentiments towards Me?»

«Of respect. Lord. Of… desire…»

«Desire? What do you want from Me?»

«To know You better than I do at present.»

«How? In what way?»

«Through Your word and Your deeds. We have received news about You, Your doctrine, Your power, and we were told that You were involved in the liberation of the Baptist. So You did not hate him, You did not try to oust our John!… He himself admitted that it was through You that he saw the valley of the holy Jordan once again. We went to him and spoke to him of You and he said to us: "You do not know what you have rejected. I should curse you, but I forgive you because He taught me to forgive and to be meek. But if you do not wish to be anathematised by the Lord and by me, love the Messiah. And have no doubts. This is his evidence: spirit of peace, perfect love, greatest wisdom, heavenly doctrine, absolute meekness, power over everything, total humility, angelical chastity. You cannot be wrong. When you breathe peace near a man Who says He is the Messiah, when you drink the love emanating from Him, when you pass from your darkness into Light, when you see sinners being redeemed and flesh being cured, then say: 'This is truly the Lamb of God!' ". We know that Your deeds are those mentioned by John. Therefore forgive us, love us, give us what the world expects from You.»

«That is why I am here. I have come from far away to give to the town of John also what I give every place that accepts Me. Tell Me what you wish from Me.»

«We also have sick people, and we are ignorant. We are ignorant particularly with regards to what is love and goodness. John, in his total love for God, has an iron hand and a fiery word and he wants to bend everybody as a giant bends a blade of grass. Many give way to dejection, because man is more sinful than holy. It is difficult to be saints!… You… they say that You raise, You do not bend, You do not cauterise, You use balms, You do not crush, You caress. We know that You are paternal with sinners and You are powerful against diseases, whichever they may be, and above all the diseases of hearts. Our rabbis can no longer do that.»

[4] «Bring Me your sick people and then gather in this garden, which has been abandoned and was desecrated by sin, after it had been made a temple for the Grace that lived in it.» 211.4

The people of Hebron spread out in all directions as fast as swallows. Only the head of the synagogue remains and together with Jesus and the disciples he goes in beyond the enclosure of the garden, to the shade of a bower where entangled roses and vines have grown wild. The population is soon back. With them there is a paralytic in a stretcher, a blind young woman, a dumb boy and two sick people, whose trouble I do not know. The last two are walking supported by other people.

Jesus greets each sick person saying: «Peace to you.» Then He asks the kind question: «What do you want Me to do for you?» followed by the chorus of lamentations, as each one wishes to tell his own story.

Jesus, Who was sitting, stands up and goes to the dumb boy, whose lips He wets with His saliva and utters the great word: «Open.» And He repeats it wetting the sealed eyelids of the woman with His finger moistened with saliva. He then stretches out His hand to the paralytic and says to him: «Rise!», and finally He imposes His hands on the two sick people saying: «Be cured, in the name of the Lord!». And the boy who previously mumbled, says distinctly: «Mummy!», while the young woman winks at the light with her unsealed eyelids, and with her fingers protects her eyes from the unknown sun, weeping and laughing, and looks again, with half open eyes, not being accustomed to the light, at the leaves, the earth, the people and particularly at Jesus. The paralytic comes boldly off the stretcher and his compassionate bearers lift it, empty as it is, to make the people afar understand that the grace has been granted, while the two sick people cry for joy and kneel down to venerate their Saviour.

The crowds are frantically shouting hosanna, Thomas, who is near Judas, looks at him so intensely and with such a clear expression, that Judas declares to him: «I was foolish, forgive me.»

[5] When the shouting subsides, Jesus begins to speak. 211.5

«The Lord spoke to Joshua saying: "Speak to the children

of Israel and say to them: Choose the cities of refuge of which I spoke to you through Moses, where a man who has killed accidentally, unwittingly, may find sanctuary and may thus avoid the wrath of the next of kin, the avenger of blood". And Hebron was one of those towns. It is also written: "And the elders of the town will not hand the innocent man over to him who wants to kill him, but they will receive him and assign him a place in which to live and he will remain there until he appears for judgement and until the death of the high priest then in office; only then he may go back to his town and to his house".

That law already contemplates and prescribes merciful love towards our neighbour. God enacted that law because it is not legal to condemn without interrogating the accused, neither is it legal to kill in a fit of wrath. The same can be said with regards to moral crimes and accusations. It is not legal to accuse unless one knows, neither can one pass judgement without interrogating the accused. But nowadays a new series of sentences and accusations has been added to those already existing in respect of the usual sins or alleged offences: the ones moved against those who come in the name of God. In the past they were moved against the Prophets, now they are repeated against the Precursor of Christ and against Christ.

You are aware of it. Drawn by deception out of the land of Shechem, the Baptist is now awaiting death in Herod's prison, because he will never submit to falsehood or compromise, and his life may be crushed and his head cut off, but they will not be able to suppress his honesty or cut his soul off the Truth, which he has served faithfully in all its divine, supernatural and moral forms. And likewise Christ is persecuted with double and decuple fury, because He does not confine Himself to saying: "It is not lawful" to Herod, but He thunders the same "It is not lawful" wherever He finds sin or knows it is a sin, without excluding any class, in the name of God and for God's honour.

211.6 [6] How can that happen? Are there no more servants of God in Israel? Yes, there are, But they are "idols".

In Jeremiah's letter to the exiles, the following is written *
among many other things. And I am drawing your attention to it

* **Jeremiah's letter** in *Baruc 6.*

because every word of the Book is a lesson that, as the Spirit had it written for a current event, refers to an event that will take place in the future. So it is written: "... When you enter Babylon you will see gods made of gold, silver, stone, wood... Be on your guard, do not imitate the foreigners, do not have any fear of their gods... Say in your hearts: 'Lord, it is You only that we must worship'". And the letter describes the details of those idols whose tongues are made by a craftsman and they do not make use of them to reproach their false priests, who strip them of their gold to clothe prostitutes with it and later they remove the same gold, desecrated by the perspiration of prostitution, to reclothe the idol; idols can rust and woodworm can corrode and are clean and tidy only if man washes their faces and clothes them, whereas they can do nothing by themselves, although they have sceptre and axe in their hands. And the Prophet concludes: "Therefore be not afraid of them". And he continues: "Those gods are as useless as broken pots. Their eyes are full of the dust raised by the feet of those who enter the temple, and they close them tight, as in a sepulchre or like a man who has offended the king, because anyone can steal their precious robes. They cannot see the light of the lamps, so they are like temple beams, and the lamps serve only to blacken them with smoke, while owls, swallows and other birds fly over their heads and soil them with excrement, and cats nestle among their clothes and tear them. So you must not be afraid of them, *they are dead things*. Neither is their gold of any use to them, it is only a display, and if it is not polished, the idols do not shine, as they did not feel anything when they were made. *Fire did not awake them*. They were bought at fabulous prices. They are carried wherever man wants to take them because they are shamefully powerless... So why are they called gods? Because they are worshipped with offerings and a show of false ceremonies, which are not felt by those who perform them, nor believed by those who see them. Whether they are treated badly or well, they are incapable of paying back either treatment, as they are incapable of electing or overthrowing a king, they can give neither wealth nor evil, they cannot save a man from death or deliver a weak man from an overbearing one. They feel no pity for widows and orphans. They are like the stones of the mountains"... This is more or less what the letter says.

211.7 [7] Now, we also have idols, no more saints, in the ranks of the Lord. That is why Evil can rise against Good. The evil that soils with excrement the intellects and hearts of those who are no longer saints, and nestles among the false robes of goodness.

They can no longer speak the words of God. Of course! Their tongue is made by man and they speak the words of man, when they do not speak Satan's. And they can only foolishly reproach the innocent and the poor, but they are silent where they see the corruption of powerful people. Because they are all corrupt and they cannot accuse one another of the same crimes. They are greedy, not for the Lord, but for Mammon, and they work accepting the gold of lust and crime, bartering it, stealing it, seized with immoderate desire exceeding every limit and imagination. They are covered with dust, which rots on them and if they show clean faces, God sees their filthy hearts. They are corroded by the rust of hatred and the worm of sin and they cannot react to save themselves. They brandish maledictions as if they were sceptres and axes, but they do not know that they are cursed. Isolated in their thoughts and their hatred, like corpses in a sepulchre or prisoners in jail, they remain there, clinging to the bars lest somebody might take them away from there, because those dead people are still something: *mummies, nothing else but mummies* looking like human beings, while their bodies have turned into dry wood, and outside they would be old-fashioned articles in a world seeking Life, in need of Life as a child needs a mother's breast, a world that wants one who can give it Life and not the stench of death.

They do live in the Temple and the smoke of the lamps, that is of honours, blackens them, but no light descends upon them; and all passions nestle in them like birds and cats, while the fire of their mission does not give them the mystical torture of being burnt by the fire of God. They are refractory to Love. The fire of Charity does not inflame them, as Charity does not clothe them with its golden brightness. The dual Charity in shape and source: charity of God and of neighbour, the form; charity from God and from man, the source. Because God withdraws from a man who does not love, and thus the former source ceases; and man withdraws from a wicked man, and also the latter source ceases. Charity deprives a loveless man of everything. They allow themselves to be bought at a cursed price, and to be led where it suits profit and power.

No. It is not right! *No money can buy a conscience,* particularly the conscience of a priest or a teacher. It is not right to acquiesce in the mighty things of the earth when they induce acts contrary to God's commandments. That is spiritual inability and
* it states: "A eunuch is not to be admitted to the assembly of the Lord". Thus, if a man, impotent by nature, cannot belong to the people of God, can a spiritually impotent man be His minister? Because I solemnly tell you that many priests and masters are suffering from guilty spiritual barrenness, as they lack spiritual virility. Many. Too many!

[8] Meditate. Observe. Compare. You will see that we have many 211.8
idols, but few ministers of the Good, which is God. That is why the sanctuary towns are no longer a sanctuary. Nothing is now respected in Israel and saints die because those who are not saints hate them.

But I invite you: "Come!". I call you in the name of your John who is languishing because he is a saint, who was struck because he precedes Me and because he endeavoured to remove the filth from the paths of the Lamb. Come to serve God. The time is near. Do not be unprepared for Redemption. Let the rain fall on the sown ground. Otherwise it will fall in vain. You people of Hebron must be the leaders! You lived here with Zacharias and Eliza: the holy people who deserved John from Heaven; and here John spread the scent of Grace by means of his true childish innocence and from the desert he sent you the anti-corrupting incense of his Grace, which has become a wonder of penance. Do not disappoint your John. He raised the love for our neighbour to an almost divine level, whereby he loves the last dweller on the desert, as he loves you, his fellow-citizens, and he certainly implores Salvation for you. And Salvation means to follow the Voice of the Lord and believe in His Word. And from this sacerdotal town come in a body to the service of God. I am passing and I call you. Do not be inferior to prostitutes, for whom one word of mercy is sufficient to persuade them to abandon their previous life and come on to the way of Good.

---

* **is states** in *Deuteronomy 23:2.*

I was asked upon My arrival: "But do You not bear us a grudge?" Grudge? No, I have love for you! And I hope to see you in the multitude of My people, whom I lead to God, in the new exodus towards the *true* Promised Land: the Kingdom of God, beyond the Red Sea of sensuality and the deserts of sin, free from all kinds of slavery, to the eternal Land, which abounds in delight and is saturated with peace... Come! This is Love passing by. Whoever wishes can follow Him, because only goodwill is required to be accepted by Him.»

211.9 [9]Jesus has finished and there is wonder-struck silence. It seems that many are weighing, testing, enjoying and comparing the words they have heard.

While that is happening and Jesus, Who is tired and hot, sits down and speaks to John and Judas, a loud noise is heard coming from the other side of the garden enclosure. The shouts, at first confused, become clearer: «Is the Messiah there? Is He there?» and when they receive an affirmative reply, they bring forward a cripple who is so deformed that he looks like an S.

«Oh! it is Mashal!»

«But he is too crippled! What does he expect?»

«There is his mother, poor woman!»

«Master, her husband left her because of that freak of nature, her son, and she lives here of charity. But she is old and will not live very long...»

The freak of nature, he really is, is now before Jesus. It is not possible to see his face as he is so bent and twisted. He looks like the caricature of a man-chimpanzee, or of a humanised camel. His mother, a poor old wretch, does not even speak, she only moans: «Lord, Lord... I believe...»

Jesus lays His hands on the crooked shoulders of the man, who hardly reaches up to His waist, looks up to Heaven and thunders: «Rise and walk in the ways of the Lord» and the man gives a start and then springs up as straight as the most perfect man. His movement is so rapid that one would think that the springs, holding him in that abnormal position, had suddenly broken. He now reaches up to Jesus' shoulders, he looks at Him, then falls on his knees, with his mother, kissing the feet of his Saviour.

What happens in the crowd is indescribable... And against His will, Jesus is compelled to stay in Hebron, because the people are ready to make barriers at the gates to prevent Him from going out.

He thus enters the house of the elderly head of the synagogue, who has changed so much since last year...

212. At Juttah. A Wave of Love for Jesus Who Speaks in the House of Isaac.

8th July 1945.

[1] The whole population of Juttah has run to meet Jesus with the 212.1
wild flowers picked on the mountain sides and the early fruits they cultivate, besides the smiles of the children and the blessings of the citizens. And before Jesus can set foot in the village, He is surrounded by the good people who, warned by Judas of Kerioth and by John, sent ahead as messengers, have rushed with what they found best to honour the Saviour, and above all with their love.

Jesus blesses with gestures and words both adults and young people who press against Him kissing His tunic and hands, and lay sucklings on His arms so that He may bless them with a kiss. The first to do so is Sarah, who places against His heart the beautiful ten month old baby, whose name is Jesai.

Their love is so impetuous that it prevents progress. And yet it is like a rising wave. I think that Jesus proceeds carried more by that wave than by His own feet, and His heart is certainly carried very high, into the clear sky, by the joy of such love. His face shines with the brightness of the moments of greatest joy of Man-God. It is not the powerful magnetic looking face of the moments when He works miracles, nor the majestic face as when He discloses His continuous union with the Father, nor the severe one as when He condemns sin. They all sparkle with different lights, but the present one is the light of the hours of relaxation of His whole *ego,* assailed from so many sides, compelled to be always vigilant of every slightest gesture or word, both of His own or of others, surrounded by all the traps of the world that, like a malefic cobweb, throw their satanic threads around the Divine Butterfly of the Man-God, hoping to paralyze His flight and imprison His spirit, so that He may not save the world; to gag His word, so that He may not instruct the supreme guilty ignorance of the earth; to tie His hands, the hands of the Eternal Priest, so that they may not sanctify men, depraved by demon and flesh; to dim His eyes, so that the perfection of His look may not attract hearts to Himself, His look in fact is a magnet, forgiveness, love, charm overwhelming every resistance that is not the resistance of a perfect satan.

212.2 [2] Oh! Is the work of the enemies of the Christ still not always the same against the Christ? Science and Heresy, Hatred and Envy, the enemies of Mankind, who sprang from Mankind itself like poisoned branches from a good tree, do they not do all that, so that Mankind may die, as they hate it more than they hate the Christ, because they hate it in an active way, unchristianising it in order to deprive it of its joy, whereas they can bereave Jesus of nothing, as He is God, whilst they are dust? Yes, they do that.

But the Christ takes shelter in faithful hearts, whence He looks, speaks and blesses Mankind and then... and then He gives Himself to those hearts and they... and they touch Heaven with its blessedness, still remaining here, but burning their senses and organs, in their feelings and thoughts and in their souls, to the extent of being delightfully tortured in their whole being... Tears and smiles, groans and songs, exhaustion and dire urgency for life are our companions, more than companions they are our very being, because as bones are in the flesh and veins and nerves are under our skin and they all make one man, thus, likewise, all these burning things originating from the fact that Jesus gave Himself to us, are within us, in our poor humanity. And what are we in those moments which could not last forever, because if they lasted a few moments longer, we would die burnt and broken? We are no longer men. We are no longer the animals gifted with reason living on the earth. We are, we are, oh! Lord! Let me say it once, not out of pride, but to sing Your glories because Your glance burns me and makes me rave... We are then seraphim. And I am surprised that we do not emit flames and fierce heat perceptible by people and matter, as it happens in the apparitions of damned souls. Because if it is true that the fire of Hell is such that even the reflection emitted by a damned soul can set a piece of wood on fire and melt metals, what is *Your* fire like, o God, in Whom everything is infinite and perfect?

One does not die of fever, one does not burn because of it, one is not consumed by the fever of bodily diseases. You are our fever, Love! And by it we are burnt, we die, we are consumed and the fibres of our hearts, which cannot resist so much, are torn apart by it and for it. But I expressed myself badly, because love is delirium, love is a waterfall that shatters dams and descends knocking down everything that is not love, love is the thronging in the mind of sensations, which are all true and present, but no hand can write them down, as the mind is so fast in translating the feelings of the heart into thoughts. It is not true that one dies. One *lives*. Life is decupled. One lives a double life: as a man and as a blessed soul: the life of the earth, and that of Heaven. Oh! I am sure of it: one achieves and exceeds the life without faults, without restrictions and limitations, that You, Father, Son and Holy Spirit, You, God Creator, One and Triune, had given to Adam a prelude to the Life, after ascending to You, to be enjoyed in Heaven, following a placid transition from the Earthly Paradise to the Heavenly one, a transfer made in the loving arms of angels, like the sweet sleep and assumption of Mary into Heaven, to come to You!

One lives the true Life. Then one finds oneself here, and as I am doing now, one is amazed and ashamed of going so far and one says: «Lord, I am not worthy of so much. Forgive me, Lord» and one beats one's breast, because we are terrified at having been proud and a thicker veil is lowered over the splendour, because if it does not continue to blaze with overwhelming ardour, out of pity for our limitation, it gathers in the centre of our hearts, ready to blaze once again in a mighty way for another moment of blessedness wanted by God. The veil is lowered on the sanctuary where the fire, the light and love of God are burning... and exhausted and yet regenerated we carry on like... people inebriated with a strong sweet wine that does not dim reason but prevents us from having eyes and thoughts for what is not the Lord, You, my Jesus, ring linking our misery to divinity, means of redemption for our sin, creator of blessedness for our souls. You, Son, Who with Your wounded hands put our hands in the spiritual ones of the Father and of the Spirit, that we may be in You, now and forever. Amen.

[3]But where have I been while Jesus inflames me, inflaming 212.3

the people of Juttah with His loving glance? You may have noticed that I no longer speak of myself or I do so only seldom. How many things I could say. But the tiredness and physical weakness, which oppress me immediately after dictations, and spiritual modesty, which grows stronger and stronger the more I proceed, convince me and *compel* me to be silent. But today... I went too high and, we know, the air of the stratosphere makes one lose one's control... I went *much* higher than the stratosphere... and I could not control myself anymore... And I think that if we always kept quiet — we who are caught in these vortices of love — we would end up by deflagrating like projectiles, or rather, like overheated or closed boilers. Forgive me, Father. And now let us go on.

212.4 [4]Jesus enters Juttah and is led to the market square and then to the poor little house where Isaac languished for thirty years. They say to Him: «We come here to speak of You and to pray, as in a synagogue, the most true one. Because it is here that we became acquainted with You and here the prayers of a saint have asked You to come to us. Come in and see how we have arranged the place...»

The little house, which the previous year consisted only of three tiny rooms — the first one where Isaac, a sick man, begged, the second, a lumber room and the third, a kitchenette which opened onto the yard — is now one room only with benches in it for those who meet there. The few household implements of Isaac have been placed, like so many relics, in a little hut in the yard and the respectful people of Juttah have made the yard less dreary looking, as they have planted there some climbing plants, which now cover the rustic stockade with their flowers and form an incipient pergola, growing on a network of rope stretched out over the yard, at the height of the low roof.

Jesus praises them and says: «We can stop here. I only beg you to give hospitality to the women and the boy.»

«Oh! Master! That will never be needed! We will come here with You and You will speak to us, but You and Your friends are our guest. Grant us the blessing of giving You and the servants of God hospitality. We only regret that they are not as many as the houses...»

Jesus agrees and leaves the little house going towards that of

Sarah who will not give up her right to anybody to entertain Jesus and His friends at a meal...

[5]... Jesus is speaking in Isaac's house. The people crowd the 212.5
room and the yard and throng also the square, and Jesus, in order to be heard by everybody, stands in the middle of the room, so that His voice will carry both through the yard and through the square.

He must be dealing with a subject brought on by a question * or an event. He says: «... But have no doubt. As Jeremiah says, they will find out at the test how sorrowful and bitter it is to abandondon the Lord. Neither potash nor lye can remove the stains of certain crimes, My friends. Not even the fire of Hell can corrode that stain. It is indelible.

Also here we must acknowledge the justice of Jeremiah's words. Our great ones in Israel really look like the wild she-asses mentioned by the Prophet. They are accustomed to the desert of their hearts, because, believe Me, as long as one is with God, even if one is as poor as Job, even if one is alone, even if one is naked, one is never alone, poor or naked, one is never a desert, but they have rejected God in their hearts and thus they are an arid desert. Like wild she-asses they sniff in the air the smell of males, which in our case, because of their lust, are named power, money, as well as true and proper lechery, and they follow that smell, as far as crime. Yes. They follow it and will follow it even more so in future. They do not know *that their hearts,* not their feet, *are exposed* to the darts of God Who will avenge their crime. How confused kings, princes, priests and scribes will be, because they really said and still say to what is nothing, or worse, is sin: "You are my father. You have begotten me"!

I solemnly tell you that Moses in a fit of anger broke the Tables * of the Law when he saw the people in idolatry. Later he climbed the mountain, prayed, adored and obtained grace. That happened centuries ago. But idolatry has not yet died in the hearts of men, and will never rest, on the contrary it will rise, like yeast in flour. Almost every man now has his own golden calf. The earth is a forest of idols, because every heart is an altar, but hardly ever there is God upon it. He who is not a slave of one evil pas-

---

* **He says** in *Jeremiah 2*, referring to Israel's apostasy.

* **broke the Tables of the Law**: *Exodus 32-34*.

sion, is slave of another and he who has not one wicked desire, has another with a different name. He who has no greed for gold, has a greed for positions, he who has no lust for the flesh, is an utter egoist. How many *egos* are worshipped in hearts like golden calves! The day, therefore, will come when they are struck and they will call the Lord and will hear Him reply: "Go to your gods. I do not know you". I do not know you! A dreadful word when uttered by God to man. God created the race of Men and He knows each individual. If He therefore says: "I do not know you" it means that by the power of His will He has erased that man from His memory. I do not know you! Is God too severe because of that verdict? No. Man cried to Heaven: "I do not know you", as faithfully as an echo...

212.6 [6] Consider: man is obliged to acknowledge God out of gratitude and out of respect for his own intelligence.

Out of gratitude. God created man and granted him the ineffable gift of life and provided him with the super-ineffable gift of Grace. When man lost Grace through his own fault, he heard a great promise being made to him: "I will give Grace back to you". It is God, the offended party, Who says so to the offender, as if He, God, were guilty and obliged to make amends. And God keeps His promise. Behold, I am here to give Grace to man. God has not confined Himself to giving only what is supernatural, but He has lowered His Spiritual Essence to provide for the coarse necessities of man's flesh and blood, and He gives the heat of the sun, the relief of water, corn, vines, all kinds of trees and all races of animals. Thus man received from God *all* the means of life. He is the Benefactor. Man must be grateful and show his gratitude by endeavouring to know Him.

Out of respect for one's own reason. A madman and an idiot are not grateful to those who cure them, because they do not understand the true value of the cure. And they hate those who wash them and feed them, who accompany them and put them to bed, who watch that they do not get hurt, because beastly as they are on account of their illness, they mistake cures for tortures. *The man who fails in his duties towards God disgraces himself, a being gifted with reason*. Only a fool or an idiot cannot tell his father from a stranger, a benefactor from an enemy. But an intelligent man knows his father and his benefactor and takes pleasure in knowing him better and better, also with regards to things of which he is unaware, as they happened before he was born or before he was helped by his father or benefactor. That is what you must do with the Lord to show that you are intelligent and not brutes.

But too many people in Israel are like those fools who do not know their father or their benefactor. Jeremiah asks: "Can a girl forget her ornaments and a bride her sash?" Oh! yes. Israel is made of such foolish girls, of such wanton brides who forget honest ornaments and sashes to put on tinsels of prostitutes; and this is found to happen more and more frequently, the more one climbs the classes that should be the teachers of the people. And God's reproach, with His wrath and regret, is addressed to them: "Why do you endeavour to prove that your behaviour is good to obtain love, whereas you teach the wickedness of your ways of living, and the blood of poor and innocent people was found on the hems of your garments?".

[7] My friends, distance is good and evil. To be very far from the 212.7
places where I am likely to speak is an evil, because it prevents you from hearing the words of Life. And you regret it. That is true. But it is good inasmuch that it keeps you away from the places where sin ferments, corruption boils and snares hiss to act against Me, hampering Me in My work, and against the hearts of people, by insinuating doubts and falsehood with regards to Me. But I prefer you to be far away rather than corrupted. I will see to your formation. You know that God had provided before we were acquainted with one another, so that we might love one another. I was known before we met. Isaac was your announcer. I will send many Isaacs to speak My words to you. However, you must know that God can speak everywhere and privately to the spirit of man and instruct him in His doctrine.

Do not be afraid that by being alone you may be led into error. No. If you do not want, you will not be unfaithful to the Lord and to His Christ. On the other hand, he who just cannot stay away from the Messiah should know that the Messiah opens His heart and stretches out His arms to him and says: "Come". Come, whoever wishes to come. Stay here, whoever wishes to stay. But both the former and the latter should preach Christ by means of an honest life. Preach Him against the dishonesty that nestles in too many hearts. Preach Him against the levity of the numerous people who do not know how to persevere faithfully and forget their ornaments and sashes of souls called to the wedding with Christ. You said to Me in your happiness: "Since You came here, we have had neither sick nor dead people. Your blessing has protected us". Yes, health is a great thing. But make sure that My present coming makes you all wholesome spiritually, always and in everything. To that effect I bless you and I give My peace to you, to your children, to your fields, crops, homes, herds and orchards. Make a holy use of them, do not live for them, but by them, giving what is superfluous to those in need, and you will thus obtain an overflowing measure of the Father's blessings and a place in Heaven. You may go. I will stay here to pray...»

9th July.

212.8 [8] I am reading again what I wrote yesterday, rewriting some incomprehensible words, out of pity for your eyes, Father. It is distressing to read it... it is so inferior to what I felt while describing my mood! And yet, to be helped to say what the Lord made me feel, lest I should describe it in the wrong way and also for my own relief — because it is also painful, you know? — I invoked my St. John. I said to him: «You know these things very well. You experienced them. Help me.» And I was comforted by his presence, by his smile of an eternal good simple-minded man and by his caress. But now I feel that my poor word is so inferior to the feelings I experienced... All human things are straw, only the supernatural is gold. And a human being cannot even describe it.

213. At Kerioth, Jesus Gives a Prophetic Speech in the Synagogue. The Beginning of the Apostolic Preaching.

[9th July 1945.]

213.1 [1] The inside of the synagogue of Kerioth, the very spot where on the ground they laid Saul, who died after seeing the future glory of Christ. In this place, in a crowd of people from which Jesus and Judas emerge — they are the tallest and both their faces *

---

* **they laid Saul**, in 78.8.

are shining, one out of love, the other for the joy of seeing that his town is always faithful to the Lord and is distinguishing itself by bestowing solemn honours upon the Master — there are the notables of Kerioth and a little farther away from Jesus the citizens, packed like seeds in a sack. The synagogue is so full that it is difficult to breathe, although the doors are open. And in order to pay homage to the Master and hear Him, they end up by making such confusion and so much noise that it is impossible to hear anything.

Jesus puts up with the situation and is silent. But the others become impatient, they gesticulate and shout: «Silence!» But their voices are lost in the hubbub, like a cry on a stormy beach.

Judas wastes no time. He climbs onto a tall bench and strikes the lamps, which are hanging in a cluster, one against the other. The hollow metal resounds and the chains rattle against one another, like musical instruments. The people turn silent and at last it is possible to hear Jesus speak.

He says to the head of the synagogue: «Give Me the tenth roll from that shelf.» And once He has it, He opens it and hands it back to the head of the synagogue saying: «Read the fourth chapter of the story, the second Book of Maccabees.»

The head of the synagogue obeys and begins to read. And Onias' vicissitudes, Jason's errors and Menelaus' betrayals and thefts are presented for the consideration of those present. The chapter is over. The head of the synagogue looks at Jesus Who has been listening carefully.

[2] Jesus nods that it is enough and then turns to the people: «In 213.2
the town of My dearest disciple I will not speak the usual words to teach you. We shall be staying here for a few days and I want him to say them to you, because it is from here that I want to begin the direct contact, the *continuous* contact between apostles and people. That was decided in upper Galilee where it had a first bright success. But the humility of My disciples caused them to withdraw into the background, because they are afraid that they are not capable and that they would be usurping My place. No. They must do it, they will do well and help their Master. The true apostolic preaching is therefore to begin here, joining in one love only the Galilean Phoenician borders to the lands of Judah, the southern ones, bordering on the countries of the

sun and sands. Because the Master is no longer sufficient for the needs of the crowds. And also because it is right that the eaglets should leave their nests and make their first flights while the Sun is still with them and His strong wing can support them.

Therefore, during these days, I will be your friend and your comfort. They will be the word and will spread the seed that I gave them. Therefore I will not teach the public, but I will give you a privileged thing: a prophecy. I ask you to remember it for the future when the most dreadful event of Mankind will darken the sun and in the darkness your hearts may be led to judge erroneously. I do not want you to be led into error, because from the first moment you have been good to Me. I do not want the world to be in a position to say: "Kerioth was the enemy of Christ". I am just and cannot allow criticism, whether spiteful against Me or fond of Me, to be able to accuse you of faults against Me, spurred by its feelings. As it is not possible to expect equal holiness in the children of a large family, so it is not possible to expect it in a large town. But it would be strongly against charity to say: "The whole family or the whole town is anathema" because of one wicked son or one bad citizen.

Listen therefore, then remember, be always faithful, and as I love you so much as to wish to defend you from an unfair accusation, so you must love those who are innocent. Always. Whoever they may be. Whatever their kindred may be with the guilty ones.

213.3 [3] Now listen. The time will come when in Israel there will be informers of the treasury and of the country, who in the hope of making friends with foreigners, will speak ill of the true High Priest, accusing him of alliance with the enemies of Israel and of wicked deeds against the sons of God. And to achieve their objective they are capable of committing crimes, laying the responsibility on the Innocent One. And the time will come, still in Israel, even more than at the times of Onias, when an infamous man, intriguing to become the Pontiff, will go to the mighty ones in Israel and will corrupt them with the gold of false words, which is even more infamous, and will twist the truth of facts, and he will not speak against crimes, on the contrary, pursuing his shameful object, he will do his best to corrupt customs to have a firmer grip on the souls deprived of God's friendship: everything to reach his aim. And he will succeed. Of course! Because if in the very abode on Mount Moriah there are no gymnasia of the impious Jason, in actual fact they are in the hearts of the inhabitants of the mountain, who for the sake of exemptions are willing to sell what is worth much more than a piece of ground, that is, their very conscience. The fruits of the old error can still be seen, and he who has eyes to see, can see what is happening over there, where there should be charity, purity, justice, goodness and deep holy religion. But if those fruits are already the cause of tremor, the fruits of their seeds will cause not only tremor, but God's malediction.

And here is the true prophecy. I solemnly tell you that he who slyly achieved a position and reliance, by means of long underhand tricks, will give into the hands of His enemies, in exchange for money the High Priest, the True High Priest. Deceived by protestations of love and pointed out to His executioners with an act of love, He, the True High Priest, will be killed without any regard for justice. What charges will be made against Christ, because I am speaking of Myself, to justify the right to kill Him? Which fate will be reserved for those who do that? A fate of immediate dreadful justice. Not an individual fate, but a collective one for the accomplices of the traitor. A more remote and even more dreadful fate than the destiny of the man whom remorse will drive to crown his demoniac soul by committing a final crime against himself. Because that one will end in a moment. This last punishment will be a long and frightful one. You will find it in the sentence: "... and His indignation was aroused and he ordered Andronicus to be stripped of the purple and to be killed on the very spot where he had laid impious hands on Onias". Yes, the sacerdotal race will be struck in its sons as well as in the executioners. And you can read the destiny of the evil associated mass of people in the following words: "The voice of this blood cries to Me from the earth. Therefore you shall be accursed..." And they will be said by God to the whole people who did not guard the gift of Heaven. Because if it is true that I have come to redeem, woe to those who will be murderers and will not be redeemed, amongst this people whose first redemption is My Word.

I have told you. Remember that. And when you hear them say

that I am an evil-doer, say: "No. He warned us. And this is the sign, which is being fulfilled and He is the Victim killed for the sins of the world".»

213.4 [4]The people leave the synagogue and gesticulating they all speak of the prophecy and of the esteem that Jesus has of Judas. The people of Kerioth are elated at the honour conferred on them by the Messiah by choosing the town of an apostle, and precisely of the apostle of Kerioth to begin the apostolic teaching as well as at the gift of the prophecy. Although it is a sad one, it is a great honour to have received it with the loving words preceding it...

Jesus and the group of the apostles are the only ones to be left in the synagogue; they then go into the little garden between the synagogue and the house of the head of the synagogue. Judas has sat down and is weeping.

«Why are you weeping? I do not see any reason...» says the other Judas.

«Well. I almost feel like doing the same myself. Did you hear Him? We are to speak now...» says Peter.

«We have already done a little of that up on the mountain. And we will improve all the time. You and John did it successfully at once» says James of Zebedee to encourage them.

«I am the worst... but God will help me. Is that right, Master?» asks Andrew.

Jesus, Who was looking through some parchment rolls He had brought with Him, turns around and says: «What were you saying?»

«That God will help me when I have to speak. I will try and repeat Your words as best I can. My brother is afraid and Judas is weeping.»

«Are you weeping? Why?» asks Jesus.

«Because I have really sinned. Andrew and Thomas can tell You. I have been running You down and You benefit me by calling me "dearest disciple" and asking me to teach here... How much love!...»

«But did you not know that I loved you?»

«Yes. But... Thank You, Master. I will never grumble again; I am really darkness and You are the Light.»

The head of the synagogue comes back and invites them to

his house, and while going there he says: «I am thinking of Your words. If I have understood You properly, as in Kerioth You found a favourite disciple, our Judas of Simon, so You prophesy You will find an unworthy one. I am sorry for that. Fortunately our Judas will make up for the other...»

«With my whole being» says Judas, who has collected himself.

Jesus does not speak, but He looks at His interlocutors and makes a gesture opening out His arms as if He wanted to say: «It is so.»

214. The Blessed Virgin at Kerioth in Judas' House. Afflictions of a Mother Disclosed to Holy Mary.

10th July 1945.

[1] Jesus is about to sit down at the table with all His friends in Judas' beautiful house. And He says to Judas' mother, who has come from her country house to give proper hospitality to the Master: «No, mother, you must stay with us as well. We are like a family here. This is not the cold formal banquet for casual guests. I took your son, and I want you to take Me as a son, as I take you as a mother, because you are really worth it. Is that right, My friends, that thus we shall be happier and feel at home?» 214.1

The apostles and the two Maries nod wholeheartedly. And Judas' mother, her eyes bright with tears, sits between her son and the Master, in front of Whom there are the two Maries with Marjiam between them. The maidservant brings the food, which Jesus offers, blesses and then hands out, because Judas' mother is strict on that point. And He always hands out starting with her, which moves the woman more and more and makes Judas proud and pensive at the same time.

They talk about various subjects in which Jesus endeavours to get Judas' mother interested and He strives as well to make her become familiar with the two women disciples. [2] Marjiam is 214.2
helpful in this respect as he states that he is very fond also of Judas' mother: «Because her name is Mary like all good women.»

«And will you not love the one who is waiting for us on the lake, you little rascal?» asks Peter half-seriously.

«Oh! very much, if she is good.»

«You can be sure of that. Everybody says so, and I must say so as well, because if she has always been kind to her mother and to me, she must be really good. But her name is not Mary, son. She has an odd name, because her father called her after the thing that had brought him wealth and he called her Porphirea. Purple is beautiful and precious. My wife is not beautiful, but she is precious on account of her goodness. And I have been very fond of her because she is so peaceful, chaste and quiet. Three virtues... eh! not easily found! I eyed her carefully since she was a girl. When I came to Capernaum with fish I used to see her mending the nets, or at the fountain, or working silently in the kitchen garden and she wasn't an absent-minded butterfly fluttering here and there, neither was she a thoughtless little hen looking around at every crow of a cock. She never raised her head when she heard the voice of a man, and when I, in love with her goodness and her wonderful plaits, her only beauties, and... well, also moved to pity because she was treated like a slave at home... when I began to say hello to her — she was then sixteen years old — she hardly replied to me, she pulled her veil over her face and remained more indoors. Eh! It took a very long time to find out whether she considered me an ogre or not and before I could send my bestman to her!... But I do not regret it. I could have travelled all over the world, but I would not have found another one like her. Am I right, Master, that she is good?»

«Yes, she is very good. And I am sure that Marjiam will love her even if her name is not Mary. Will you not, Marjiam?»

«Yes. Her name is "mummy" and mummies are good and are loved.»

214.3 [3] Judas then says what he did during the day. I understand that he went to inform his mother of their visit, and then he began to speak in the country near Kerioth together with Andrew. He then says: «But tomorrow I would like everybody to come. I do not want to be the only one to be noticed. As far as possible, we should go in twos, a Judaean with a Galilean. For instance, John and I, Simon and Thomas. I wish the other Simon came! But you two (he points at Alphaeus' sons) can go together. I told everybody, also those who did not want to know, that you are the Master's cousins. And you two (he points at Philip and Bartholomew) can also go together. I told them that Nathanael is a rabbi who came to follow the Master. That impresses people very favourably. And... you three will stay here. But as soon as the Zealot comes, we can form another couple. And then we will change around, because I want the people to meet everybody...» Judas is sprightly. «I spoke about the decalogue, Master, endeavouring especially to clarify those parts in which this area is more lacking...»

«Do not let your hand be too heavy, Judas, please. Always bear in mind that one achieves more by means of kindness than by intolerance and that you are a man as well. So examine yourself and consider how easy it is also for you to fall and how you become upset when you are reproached too frankly» says Jesus while Judas' mother bends her head blushing.

«Do not worry, Master. I am striving to imitate You in everything. But in the village, which we can also see through that door (the doors are open while they are eating and a beautiful view can be seen from this room which is upstairs) there is a sick man who would like to be cured. But he cannot be carried here. Could You come with me?»

«Tomorrow, Judas, tomorrow morning, definitely. And if there are more sick people tell Me or bring them here.»

«You really want to benefit my fatherland, Master?»

«Yes. So that no one may say that I have been unfair to those who did no harm to Me. I help also wicked people! So why not the good ones of Kerioth? I wish to leave an indelible memory of Me...»

«What? Are we not coming back here?»

«We will come back again, but...»

4 «Here is the Mother, the Mother with Simon!» trills the boy 214.4
who sees Mary and Simon climbing the staircase leading up to the terrace where the room is.

They all stand up and go towards the two who have just arrived. There is the noise of exclamations, of greetings, of seats moved about. But nothing diverts Mary from greeting first Jesus and then Judas' mother, who has bowed down deeply, and whom Mary raises again embracing her as if she were a dear friend met after a long absence.

They go back into the room and Mary of Judas tells the maidservant to bring in fresh food for the new guests.

«Here, Son, Eliza's greetings» says Mary, handing a small parchment roll to Jesus Who unfolds it and reads it, then says: «I knew. I was sure. Thank You, Mother. On My behalf and on Eliza's. You really are the health of the sick!»

«I? You, Son. Not I.»

«You; and You are My greatest help.» He then turns to the apostles and women disciples and says: «Eliza writes: "Come back, my Peace. I want not only to love You, but to serve You". So we have relieved a creature of her anguish and melancholy, and we have gained a disciple. Yes, we will go back.»

«She wishes to meet also the women disciples. She is recovering slowy, but without relapsing. Poor Eliza! She still undergoes moments of frightful bewilderment. Does she not, Simon? One day she wanted to try to come out with Me, but she saw a friend of Daniel's... and we had great difficulty in calming her weeping. But Simon is so clever! And since Eliza expressed the desire to return to the world, but the world of Bethzur is too full of memories for her, Simon suggested we should call Johanna. And he went to call her. After the feast she went back to Bether, to her magnificent rose-garden in Judaea. Simon says that he seemed to be dreaming, while crossing the hills covered with rose-bushes, that he was already in Paradise. She came at once. She is in a position to understand and pity a mother mourning her sons! Eliza has become very fond of her and I came away. Johanna wants to persuade her to leave Bethzur and go to her castle. And she will succeed because she is as sweet as a dove but as firm as a rock in her decisions.»

«We shall go to Bethzur on our way back and then we shall part. You women disciples will stay with Eliza and Johanna for some time. We will go through Judaea and we shall meet in Jerusalem for Pentecost»...

214.5 [5] The Most Holy Virgin Mary and Mary, Judas' mother, are together. They are not in the town house, but in the country one. They are alone. The apostles are outside with Jesus, the women disciples and the boy are in the magnificent apple-orchard and their voices can be heard together with the noise of clothes beaten on washboards. They are perhaps doing the washing while the boy is playing.

Judas' mother, sitting in a dim-lit room beside Mary, is speaking to Her: «These peaceful days will be like a dream to me. Too short! Yes, too short! I know that we must not be selfish and that it is fair that You should go to that poor woman and to so many other unhappy people. But I wish I could!... I wish I could spare the time, or come with You!... But I cannot. I have no relatives apart from my son and I must look after the property of the family...»

«I understand... It is painful to part from one's son. We mothers would always like to be with our children. But we are giving them for a great cause, and we will not lose them. Not even death can take our sons away from us, if they and we are in grace in the eyes of God. But ours are still on the earth, even if by the will of God they are torn from our bosoms to be given to the world for its good. We can always join them and even the echo of their deeds is like a caress to our hearts, because their deeds are the scent of their souls.»

6 «What is Your Son to You, Woman?» asks Mary of Judas in a 214.6
low voice.

And the Most Holy Mary replies promptly: «He is My joy.»

«Your joy!!!...» and then Judas' mother bursts into tears and lowers her head to hide them. She bows so low as to almost touch her knees with her forehead.

«Why are you weeping, my poor friend? Why? Tell Me. I am happy in My maternity, but I can also understand those mothers who are not happy...»

«Yes. Not happy! And I am one of them. Your Son is Your joy... Mine is my grief. At least he has been so. Now, since he has been with Your Son, I am not so worried. Oh! of all those who pray for Your holy Son, for His welfare and triumph, there is no one, after You, Blessed Woman, who prays so much as this unhappy mother who is speaking to You... Tell me the truth: what do You think of my son? We are two mothers, one facing the other, between us there is God. And we are speaking of our sons. It can be but easy for You to speak of Yours. I... I have to strive against myself to speak of mine. And yet, how much good, or how much grief, can come to me from this conversation! And even if it is grief, it will always be a relief to speak about it... That woman of Bethzur became almost insane when her sons died, did she not? But I swear it to You, sometimes I have thought and still think, looking at my Judas who is handsome, healthy, intelligent, but he is not good, not virtuous, not righteous in his soul, not sound in his feeling, I often think that I would prefer to mourn him dead rather than know that he is disliked by God. But tell me, what do You think of my son? Be frank. This question has been tormenting my heart for over a year. But whom could I ask? The citizens? They did not yet know that the Messiah existed and that Judas wanted to go with Him. I knew. He told me when he came here after Passover, elated, violent, as usual, when he has a sudden fancy, and as usual, scornful of his mother's advice. His friends in Jerusalem? A holy prudence and a pious hope prevented me. I did not want to say: "Judas is following the Messiah" to those whom I cannot love because they are everything but saints. And I hoped that his fancy notion would vanish, like many others, like all of them, even at the cost of tears and desolation, as happened in the case of more than one girl whom he charmed here and elsewhere, but never married. Do you know that there are places where he will no longer go because he may receive a fair punishment? Also his being of the Temple was a whim. He does not know what he wants. Never. His father, may God forgive him, spoiled him. I never had any authority on the two men in my house. I could but weep and make amends with all kinds of humiliation... When Johanna died — and although no one told me, I know that she died of a broken heart when Judas told her that he did not want to get married, after she had been waiting for all her youth, whereas everybody knew that in Jerusalem he had sent friends to a very rich woman who owned stores as far as Cyprus to enquire about her daughter — I had to shed many bitter tears, because of the reproaches of the dead girl's mother, as if I were an accomplice of my son. No. I am not. I have no authority over him. Last year, when the Master came here, I realised that He had understood... and I was about to speak. But it is painful, very painful for a mother to have to say: "Be careful of my son. He is greedy, hard-hearted, vicious, proud and inconstant". And that is what he is. I am praying that Your Son, Who works so many miracles, may work one for my Judas... But tell me, please tell me, what do You think of him?»

214.7 [7] Mary, Who has been silent all the time, with an expression of pitiful sorrow while listening to that maternal lament of which Her righteous soul cannot disapprove, says in a low voice: «Poor mother!... What do I think? Yes, your son is not the limpid soul of John, nor the meek Andrew, not the firm Matthew who wanted to change and did change... He is... inconsistent, yes, he is. But we shall pray so hard for him, both you and I. Do not weep. Perhaps your motherly love, which would like to be proud of your son, makes you see him more perverted than he is...»

«No! No! I see right and I am so afraid.» The room is full of the weeping of Judas' mother and in the half-light Mary's white face has become even paler because of the maternal confession that sharpens all the suspicions of the Lord's Mother. But She controls Herself. She draws the unhappy mother to herself and caresses her while she, abandoning all reservedness, painfully and confusedly informs Mary of all the harshness, pretensions and violence of Judas and concludes: «I blush for him when I see I am the object of the loving attention of Your Son! I have not asked Him. But I am sure that besides doing it out of kindness, He wants to say to Judas by means of His loving attention: "Remember that this is how a mother is to be treated". Now, for the time being he appears to be good... Oh! If it were only true! Help me, help me with Your prayers, You Who are holy, so that my son may not be unworthy of the grace that God granted him! If he does not want to love me, if he cannot be grateful to me, who gave birth to him and brought him up, it does not matter. But let him really love Jesus; let him serve Him loyally and gratefully. But if that cannot be then... then may God take his life. I would rather have him in a sepulchre... at last I *would have* him because since he reached the age of reason he was hardly ever mine. Better dead than a bad apostle. Can I pray for that? What do You say?»

«Pray the Lord that He may do what is best. Do not weep any more. I have seen prostitutes and Gentiles at the feet of My Son, and publicans and sinners with them. They all became lambs through His Grace. Hope, Mary, hope. The grief of mothers saves their sons, do you not know that?...»

And everything ends on that pitiful question.

215. Philip and Andrew Preach at Bethginna. Healing of the Lunatic Daughter of the Innkeeper.

11th July 1945.

215.1 [1]I do not see the return to Bethzur nor the rose-gardens of Bether, which I was so anxious to see. Jesus is alone with the apostles. Marjiam is not there either, as he has obviously been left with Our Lady and the woman-disciples. It is a very mountainous area, but also very rich in vegetation, with forests of conifers, or rather of pine-trees, and the balsamic invigorating scent of resin spreads everywhere. And Jesus is walking across those green mountains, with His disciples, facing westwards.

I hear them talking about Eliza who seems to have changed considerably and has been convinced to follow Johanna to her estate in Bether, and they are speaking of Johanna's kindness too. They are also discussing the tour they are about to make, towards the fertile plains before the sea. And the names of past glories come to light again, giving rise to stories, questions, explanations and friendly discussions.

«When we reach the top of this mountain, I will show you all the areas in which you are interested. They may suggest you thoughts for your sermons to the crowds.»

«But how can we do that, my Lord? I am not capable» moans Andrew, and Peter and James join him. «We are the most unlucky ones.»

«Oh! In that case I am no better. If it was gold or silver, I could talk about it, but about these things...» says Thomas.

«And what about me? What was I?» asks Matthew.

«But you are not afraid of the public, you are debating» replies Andrew.

«Yes, but on different matters...» retorts Matthew.

«Of course!... But... Well, you already know what I would like to say, so just imagine that I have already told you. The fact is that you are worth more than we are» says Peter.

«Listen, My dear. There is no need to be sublime. Simply say what you think, with your firm belief. Believe Me, when one is convinced, one can always persuade others» says Jesus.

But Judas of Kerioth implores: «Give us some hints. An idea put forth properly may be useful in many ways. I think these places have been left without one word about You. Because no one seems to know You.»

«The reason is that there is still a strong wind blowing from the Moriah... It makes sterile...» replies Peter.

«It is because it has not been sown. But we will sow» retorts the Iscariot, who is sure of himself and happy after his first success.

[2] They reach the top of the mountain. A wide panorama stretch- 215.2
es out from there and it is beautiful to look at it standing in the shade of the thick trees which crown the top, so varied and sunny: overlapping chains stretching in every direction like petrified billows of an ocean lashed by opposite gales and then, as if in a calm gulf, everything subsides into an endless brightness showing a vast plain in which a little mountain rises, as solitary as a lighthouse at the entrance of a harbour.

«Look. That village spread along the crest, as if it wanted to enjoy all the sunshine, and where we will be stopping, is like
* the centre of a crown of historical places. Come here. There is (to the north) Jarmuth. Do you remember Joshua? The defeat of the kings who wanted to attack the camp of Israel, which was strengthened by the alliance with the Gibeonites. And near it there is Bethshemesh, the sacerdotal town in Judah where the Ark was returned by the Philistines with the gold votive offerings prescribed by the diviners and priests to the people to be freed from the calamities that had struck the guilty Philistines. And over there is Zorah, lying completely in the sun, Samson's fatherland, and a little to the east Timnath where he got married and where he performed many brave deeds and did so many foolish things. And there are Azekah and Shochoh, formerly Philistine camps. Further down is Zanoah, one of the towns in Judah. Now turn around, here is the Valley of the Terebinth, where David fought Goliath. And over there is Makkedah, where Joshua defeated the Amorites. Turn around again. Can you see that solitary mountain in the middle of the plain, which once belonged to the Philistines? Gath is there, Goliath's fatherland and the place where David took refuge with Achish to escape from the mad

---

* **historical places**: where the events narrated in *Joshua 10*; *Judges 13-16*; *1Samuel 4-6; 17; 18; 27* took place.

rage of Saul, and where the wise king pretended he was mad because the world defends fools from wise people. Where the horizon opens out, there are the plains of the very fertile land of the Philistines. We will go through there, as far as Ramlé. And now let us enter Bethginna. You, precisely you, Philip, who are looking at Me so imploringly, will go around the village, with Andrew. While you are walking about, we shall stop near the fountain or in the village square.»

«Oh! Lord! Don't send us alone. Please, come with us!» they beg.

«Go, I said. Obedience will be of more help to you than My mute presence.»

215.3 [3] ... And so Philip and Andrew go, at random, through the village, until they find a small hotel, an inn, rather than a hotel, and inside there are some brokers bargaining for lambs with some shepherds. They go in and stop disconcertedly in the middle of the yard, which is surrounded by very rustic porches.

The hotel-keeper rushes towards them: «What do you want? Lodgings?»

They consult looking at each other, and they appear to be utterly dismayed. Probably they cannot remember even one word of what they had decided to say. Andrew is the first to regain control of himself and he replies: «Yes, lodgings for us and for the Rabbi Israel.»

«Which rabbi? There are many of them! But they are wealthy gentlemen. They do not come to the villages of poor people to bring their wisdom to the poor. The poor have to go to them and we are lucky if they allow us to go near them!»

«There is only one Rabbi of Israel. And He has come to bring the Gospel to the poor, and the poorer and more sinful they are, the more He looks for them and approaches them» replies Andrew kindly.

«In that case He will not make much money!»

«He does not seek wealth. He is poor and good. When He can save a soul it is a full day for Him» replies once again Andrew.

«Oh! It is the first time that I hear that a rabbi is good and poor. The Baptist is poor but severe. All the others are severe and rich, as greedy as leeches. You over there, have you heard? Come here, you who travel around the world. These men say that there is a poor but good Master Who comes looking for poor people and sinners.»

«Ah! It must be the one who wears a white robe like an Essene. I saw him some time ago at Jericho» says one of the brokers.

«No. That one is by himself. It must be the one of whom Thomas told us, because he happened to speak about him with some shepherds on the Lebanon» replies a tall brawny shepherd.

«Indeed! And he would come as far as here, if he was on the Lebanon! For the sake of your eyes of a cat!» exclaims another one.

While the innkeeper is speaking and listening to his customers, the two apostles have remained standing in the middle of the yard like two poles.

[4] At last one of the men says to them: «Ehi! You! Come here! 215.4
Who is He? Where does that man you spoke of come from?»

«He is Jesus of Joseph, from Nazareth» says Philip seriously and he looks as if he were expecting to be laughed at.

But Andrew adds: «He is the Messiah foretold. I implore you, for your own good, listen to Him. You have mentioned the Baptist. Well, I was with him, and he pointed to us Jesus Who was passing and said: "There is the Lamb of God, Who takes away the sins of the world". When Jesus descended into the Jordan to be baptised, the Heavens opened and a Voice cried out: "This is My beloved Son, My favour rests on Him" and the Love of God descended like a dove, shining over His head.»

«See? It is the Nazarene! But tell me, since you say you are His friends...»

«No, not His friends: we are His apostles, His disciples and we have been sent to announce that He is coming, so that those who are in need of salvation may go to Him» clarifies Andrew.

«All right. But tell me. Is He really as some say, that is, a holy man, holier than the Baptist, or is He a demon as others describe Him? You are always with Him, because if you are His disciples, you must be with Him, tell us frankly. Is it true that He is lewd and a guzzler? That He loves prostitutes and publicans. That He is a necromancer and He evokes spirits at night to find out the secrets of hearts?»

«Why do you ask these men such questions? Ask them instead whether it is true that He is good. They will take it amiss and they will go and tell the Master our evil reasoning and we will be cursed. One never knows!... Whether He is God or a demon, it is better to treat Him well.»

It is Philip who speaks now: «We can reply to you quite frankly because there is nothing wicked to be concealed. He, our Master, is the Saint of all saints. He spends His days teaching. He goes tirelessly from place to place seeking the hearts of men. He spends the night praying for us. He does not disdain the pleasures of the table and friendship, but not for His own advantage, but only to approach those who otherwise would be unapproachable. He does not repel publicans and prostitutes but only because He wants to redeem them. His way is traced out with miracles of redemption and miracles over diseases. Winds and seas obey Him. But He does not need anybody to work His prodigies, neither does He have to evoke spirits to know hearts.»

«How can He?... You said that winds and seas obey Him... But they are not endowed with reason. How can He give them orders?» asks the innkeeper.

«Tell me, man: according to you is it more difficult to give an order to the wind or the sea or to death?»

«By Jehovah! You cannot give orders to death! You can throw oil on the sea, you can hoist sails over it, or, more wisely, you can avoid going to sea. You can lock doors against the wind. But you cannot give an order to death. There is no oil capable of calming it. There is no sail which, hoisted on our little boat, can make it sail so fast as to leave death behind. And there are no locks for it. It comes in when it wants to, even if the doors have been locked. Oh! No one gives orders to that queen!»

«And yet our Master commands it. Not only when it is near. But also after it has come. A young man of Nain was about to be put into the dreadful mouth of his sepulchre, and He said to him: "I tell you: rise!" and the young man came back to life. Nain is not in the country of the hyperboreans. You can go and see.»

«Just like that? In the presence of everybody?»

«On the road. In the presence of the whole of Nain.»

215.5 [5] The innkeeper and his customers look at one another in silence. Then the innkeeper says: «But He will do that only for His friends.»

«No, man. For all those who believe in Him and not for them

only. He is Mercy on the earth, believe me. No one turns to Him in vain. Listen. Is there anyone amongst you who suffers from or weeps because of diseases in the family, doubts, remorse, temptations, ignorance? Go to Jesus, the Messiah of the Gospel. He is here today. He will be elsewhere tomorrow. The Grace of the Lord Who is passing should not be let it pass in vain» says Philip who has become more and more sure of himself.

The innkeeper ruffles his hair, opens and closes his mouth, tortures the fringes of his belt... at last he exclaims: «I will try! I have a daughter. Up to last summer she was all right. Then she became a lunatic. She remains like a mute animal in a corner, she never moves from it and only with difficulty her mother can dress her and feed her. The doctors say that her brain has been burnt by too much sunshine, others say that it is due to an ill-starred love. The people say she is possessed. How can that be, as she has never been away from here?! Where would she have got that demon? What does your Master say? That a demon can take also an innocent person?»

Philip replies without hesitation: «Yes, to torture the relatives and drive them to despair.»

«And... Can He cure lunatics? Should I hope?»

«You must believe» says Andrews promptly. And he tells them of the miracle of the Gerasenes and concludes: «If those who were a legion in the hearts of sinners fled thus, why should the one who forced his way into the heart of a young person not flee? I tell you, man: for those who hope in Him also what is impossible becomes as easy as breathing. I have seen the works of my Lord and I am a witness of His power.»

«Oh! in that case which of you is going to call Him?»

«I will go myself, man. I will soon be back.» And Andrew runs away while Philip remains speaking to them.

6 When Andrew sees Jesus standing in a lobby out of the mer- 215.6
ciless sun shining in every part of the square, he runs towards Him saying: «Come, Master. The daughter of the innkeeper is lunatic. Her father implores You to cure her.»

«Did he know Me?»

«No, Master. We have tried to make You known to him...»

«And you have succeeded. When one reaches the point of believing that I can cure an incurable disease, one is already well advanced in faith. And you were afraid that you did not know how to do it. What did you tell him?»

«I don't think I could tell You. We told him what we thought of You and of Your deeds. Above all we told him that You are Love and Mercy. The world has such wrong knowledge of You!!!»

«But you know Me well. And that is enough.»

215.7 [7] They arrive at the small inn. All the customers are standing at the door, full of curiosity, and in the middle there is Philip with the innkeeper who keeps talking to himself.

When he sees Jesus, he runs to meet Him: «Master, Lord, Jesus... I... I believe so firmly that You are You, that You know everything, You see everything, You can do everything, I believe it so firmly that I say to You: Have mercy on my daughter although I have so many sins in my heart. Do not punish my daughter because I have been dishonest in my trade. I will no longer be grasping, I swear it. You can see my heart with its past and with its present thought. Forgive and have mercy on us, Master, and I will speak of You to everybody who comes here, to my house...» The man is on his knees.

Jesus says to him: «Stand up and persevere in your present sentiments. Take Me to your daughter.»

«She is in a stable, my Lord. The sultry weather makes her feel worse. And she will not come out.»

«It does not matter. I will go to her. It is not the sultry weather. It is the demon who perceives My coming.»

They go into the yard and then into a dark stable, followed by all the rest.

The girl, unkempt and lean, becomes agitated in the darkest corner and as soon as she sees Jesus, she shouts: «Back, go back! Do not disturb me. You are the Christ of the Lord, I am one struck by You. Leave me alone. Why do You always follow me?»

«Go out of this girl. Go. I want it. Give your prey back to God and be quiet!»

There is a heart-rending shout, a jerk, her body becomes flabby and collapses onto the straw... then she calmly, sadly asks questions expressing her amazement: «Where am I? Why am I here? Who are they?» and she invokes: «Mummy». The young girl becomes shy when she realises that she is without veil and with a torn dress in the presence of many strangers.

«Oh! Eternal Lord! But she is cured...» and strange to be seen the innkeeper weeps like a child and tears stream down his ruddy cheeks... He is happy and he weeps and does not know what to do, except kiss Jesus' hands, while the mother of the girl also weeps, surrounded by her amazed little ones, and kisses her first-born now free from the demon.

All the people present shout in amazement and many more rush to see the miracle. The yard is full.

«Remain with us. Lord. It is getting dark. Rest under my roof.»

«Man, we are thirteen.»

«Even if you were three hundred it would not matter. I know what You mean. But the greedy dishonest Samuel is dead, Lord. Also my demon has fled. Now there is a new Samuel. And he will still be the innkeeper. But a holy one. Come, come with me, that I may pay you homage as a king, a god. Such as You are. Oh! blessed be the sun that brought You here today...»

216. In the Plain Towards Askelon. The Disciples' Wavering Allegiance Predicted with the Parable of the Dandelion.

12th July 1945.

[1] The sun is blazing down on the countryside and is scorching 216.1
the ripe corn drawing a scent from it, which reminds one of the smell of bread. There is a vague smell in the air, the smell of sunshine, of laundry, of crops, of summer.

Because every season, I could say every month, and even every hour of the day has its smell, as each place has its own, if one has sharp senses and a keen spirit of observation. The smell of a winter day with a biting cold wind is quite different from the mellow smell of a foggy winter day, or of a snowy one. And how different is the smell of springtime that comes and announces itself by means of a scent, which is not a scent, and is very different from the smell of winter. One gets up in the morning and the air has a different smell: the first breath of springtime. And so forth for the smell of orchards in blossom, of gardens, of corn, down to the warm smell of vintage and then, in the middle, the smell of earth after a storm...

And what about the hours? It would be foolish to say that the smell of dawn is like that of noon, or that the latter is like that of the evening or night. The first is fresh and virginal, the second is pleasant and jolly, the third is tired and saturated with all the smells exhaled by everything during the day; the last one, the night one, is calm and cosy, as if the Earth were a huge cradle taking in its little ones to rest.

And what about places? Oh! the smell of a seashore is so different at dawn and in the evening, at noon and at night, when the sea is stormy or calm, if the beach is pebbly or sandy! And the smell of seaweed, which appears after tides, and the sea seems to have opened its bowels to let us breathe the stench of its depths. That smell is so different from that of inland plains, which differs from that of hilly places, which is different from the smell of high mountains.

Such is the infinity of the Creator Who impressed a sign of light, or colour, or scent, or sound, or shape, or height on each of the infinite things that He created. O infinite beauty of the Universe, I now only see you through the visions and the remembrance of what I saw, loving God and praying Him through His works and the joy I felt watching them, how vast, mighty, inexhaustible and ever fresh you are. You are never tired and never tire anyone. On the contrary, man is renewed watching you, o Universe of my Lord, he becomes better and purer, he is elevated and he forgets... Oh! I wish I could always contemplate you and forget the inferior part of men, loving in and for their souls and leading them to God! And so, following Jesus, Who is going with His apostles across this plain full of crops, I digress once again allowing myself to be carried away by the joy of speaking of my God through His magnificent works. That is love, too, because one praises what one loves in a person or simply praises the person one loves. The same applies to creature and Creator. He who loves Him, praises Him, and the more one loves Him the more one praises Him for Himself and for His works. But I will now order my heart to be silent and I will follow Jesus, not as a worshipper, but as a faithful chronicler.

216.2 [2] Jesus is walking through the fields. It is a hot day. The place is desert. There is not a soul in the fields. There are only ripe ears of corn and a few trees here and there. Sunshine, corn, birds, lizards, green tufts of grass, which is still in the calm of the air, are the only things to be seen around Jesus. On one side of the main road along which Jesus is walking — a dusty dazzling ribbon between the fields undulating with corn — there is a little village, on the other side a farm. Nothing else.

Everybody is hot and proceeds in silence. They have taken off their mantles but as they are wearing woollen tunics, however light they may be, they suffer the heat just the same. Only Jesus, His two cousins and the Iscariot are wearing linen or hempen clothes. Jesus' and the Iscariot's garments are of white linen, whereas those of Alphaeus' sons look thicker and heavier than linen and they are also dyed in a darker ivory shade, exactly the shade of unbleached hemp. The others are wearing their usual robes and are drying their perspiration with the linen cloth which covers their heads.

They reach a thicket of trees at a crossroads. They stop in the healthy shade and drink avidly out of their flasks.

«It is as warm as if it had been on the fire» grumbles Peter.

«I wish there was a little stream here! But there is absolutely nothing!» sighs Bartholomew. «I will have none left before long.»

«I think I would say that it is better to walk on the mountains» moans James of Zebedee, who is flushed with heat.

«A boat is the best of all. It is cool, restful, clean, ah!» Peter's heart flies back to his lake and his boat.

«You are right. But there are sinners on the mountains as well as on the plains. If they had not driven us away from the Clear Water and had not persecuted us so closely, I would have come here between Tebeth and Shebat. But we shall soon be on the seaside. The air is cooled there by the open sea wind» says Jesus comforting them.

«Eh! We need it! We are like dying pikes here. But how can the corn be so beautiful when there is no water?» asks Peter.

«There is underground moisture which keeps the soil damp» explains Jesus.

«It would be better if it was above ground instead of under. What am I going to do with it, if it is down there? I have no roots!» says Peter impulsively and they all laugh.

Judas Thaddeus becomes serious and says: «The soil is as selfish as some souls, and it is equally arid. If they had allowed us to stop in that village and spend the Sabbath there, we would have enjoyed shade, water and rest. But they drove us away...»

«And we would have had food as well. Now we have not even that. And I am hungry. I wish there was some fruit! The fruit trees are all close to the houses. And who is going to pick it? If the people here are in the same mood as those over there...» says Thomas, pointing at the village they left behind, to the east.

«Take my portion of food. I am not very hungry» says the Zealot.

«You may take also Mine» says Jesus. «Those who feel more hungry, should eat.»

But when the food portions of Jesus, of the Zealot and of Nathanael are put together, they look very scanty, as one can tell from the dismayed looks of Thomas and the younger ones. But they nibble silently at their tiny portions.

The patient Zealot goes towards a spot where a row of green plants on the parched soil suggests the presence of moisture. There is in fact a trickle of water in the bottom of a ditch, just a trickle, which is bound to disappear before long. He shouts to his distant companions to come and refresh themselves, and they all rush there, and following the intermittent shade of a row of plants on the bank of the half dry brook, they are able to refresh their dusty feet, and wash their perspired faces. But first of all they fill their empty flasks and leave them in the water, in the shade, to keep them cool. They sit down at the foot of a tree and being tired they doze off.

216.3 [3] Jesus looks at them lovingly and sympathetically and shakes His head. The Zealot, who has gone to drink once again, notices His gesture and asks Him: «What is the matter, Master?»

Jesus stands up, He goes towards the Zealot and clasping him with one arm He takes him towards another tree saying: «What is the matter? I grieve at your fatigue. If I were not sure of what I am doing to you, I could never set My mind at peace while causing you so much trouble.»

«Trouble? No, Master! It is a joy to us. Everything vanishes following You. We are all happy, believe me. There is no regret, there is no...»

«Be quiet, Simon. Humanity remonstrates also in good people. And from a human point of view, you are not wrong in remonstrating. I have taken you away from your homes, from your families, from your business and you came thinking that it was going to be quite different to follow Me... But your present remonstration, your internal protest will calm down one day, and you will then realise that it was good to go through fog and mud, through dust and dog-days, persecuted, thirsty, without food, following a persecuted, hated, slandered Master... and worse still. Everything will seem beautiful to you then. Because your minds will be different, and you will see everything in a different light. And you will bless Me for leading you along My difficult way...»

«You are sad, Master. And the world justifies Your sadness, but we are no part of it. We are all happy...»

«All? Are you sure?»

«Are You of a different opinion?»

«Yes, Simon, I am. *You* are always happy. You have understood. Many others have not. See those who are sleeping? Do you know how many thoughts they are turning over in their minds even while sleeping? And all those among the disciples? Do you think they will be faithful until everything is accomplished? Look: let us play this old game that you certainly played when a boy (and Jesus picks a round fully ripe dandelion growing among the stones. He raises it gently to His mouth, blows and the dandelion dissolves into tiny umbrellas, which wander in the air with their *little* tufts on top of the tiny handles). See? Look... How many have fallen on My lap as if they were in love with Me? Count them... They are twenty-three. They were at least three times as many. And the others? Look. Some are still wandering, some have fallen because of their weight, some, which are proud of their silvery plume, are haughtily rising higher, some are falling into the mud that we made with our flasks. Only... Look, look... Of the twenty-three that were on My lap, seven more have gone. That hornet flying by was enough to blow them away!... What were they afraid of? Or by what were they allured? Were they afraid of its sting? Or were they allured by its beautiful black and gold hues, or by its graceful appearance, its iridescent wings?... They have gone... Following a deceitful beauty. Simon, the same will happen to My disciples. Some will go because

of their restlessness, some because of their inconsistency, their pride, their dullness, their frivolity, their lust for filth, some for fear, some because of their foolishness. Do you think that in the crucial hour of My mission I shall have beside Me all those who now say to Me: "I will come with You"? The tiny tufts of the dandelion, which My Father created, were more than seventy... and now there are only seven left on My lap, because some more have been blown away by this puff of wind that has caused the thinner stems to flutter away... It will be like that. And I am think-
216.4 ing of how much you have to struggle to be loyal to Me... [4]Come, Simon. Let us go and look at those dragonflies dancing over the water. Unless you prefer to have a rest.»

«No, Master. Your words have grieved me. But I hope that the cured leper, the persecuted man whom You have rehabilitated, the solitary whom You have gifted with company, the nostalgic man longing for love to whom You have opened Heaven and the world may find and give love, I hope that that man will not abandon You... Master... what do You think of Judas? Last year You wept with me because of him. Then... I do not know... Master, never mind those two dragonflies, look at me, listen to me. I would not say this to anybody. I would not tell my companions, my friends. But I will tell You. I am not successful in loving Judas. I must admit it. He rejects my desire to love him. He does not hold me in contempt, on the contrary he is even too courtly with the old Zealeat who he realises is more skilful than the others in knowing men. But it is the way he behaves. Do you think he is sincere? Tell me.»

Jesus is silent for a few moments as if He were enchanted by the two dragonflies that resting on the surface of the water form a tiny rainbow with their iridescent elytra, a precious rainbow as it attracts a curious midge, which is swallowed by one of the voracious insects, which, in turn, is immediately snatched and devoured together with the midge, by a toad or frog, lying in wait. Jesus stands up, as He had almost lain down to see the little tragedies of nature and says: «It is just like that. A dragonfly has strong jaws to feed on herbs and strong wings to catch gnats, and a frog has a large mouth to swallow dragonflies. Each has his own and makes use of it. Let us go, Simon. The others are waking up.»

«But You have not replied to me, Master. You did not want to.»

«I did! My old wise man, meditate and you will find...» And Jesus goes from the ditch towards His disciples who are waking up looking for Him.

217. The Ears of Corn Picked on the Sabbath. "The Son of Man is Lord of the Sabbath".

13th July 1945.

1 We are still in the same place, but the setting sun is more bearable. 217.1

«We must go and reach that house» says Jesus.

They set out and reach it. They ask for bread and refreshment. But the farmer drives them away rudely.

«Race of Philistines! Vipers! They are always the same! They were born of that stock and bear poisonous fruit» grumble the tired and hungry disciples. «May you be given tit for tat.»

«Why do you lack charity? The time of the law of retaliation is over. Come forward. It is not yet night and you are not dying of hunger. Offer this little sacrifice so that these souls may become hungry for Me» says Jesus exhorting them.

But the disciples go into a field and begin to pick the ears of corn, they rub them on the palms of their hands and eat them. I think they do it more out of spite than to satisfy their hunger.

«They are good, Master» shouts Peter. «Are You not having any? And they have a double flavour... I would like to eat up the whole field.»

«You are right! So they would repent for not giving us any bread» say the others while walking through the corn and eating with relish.

Jesus is walking alone on the dusty road. The Zealot and Bartholomew are five or six yards behind Him, speaking to each other.

2 There is another crossroads, where a secondary road crosses the main one, and a group of sulky Pharisees is standing there. 217.2
They must be coming back from the Sabbath celebration in the village that can be seen at the end of the secondary road, a large

flat town, which looks like a huge animal lying in its den.

Jesus sees the Pharisees, looks at them and smiling kindly greets them: «Peace be with you.»

Instead of replying to His greetings, one of the them asks arrogantly: «Who are You?»

«Jesus of Nazareth.»

«See, I told you it was Him» says another.

In the meantime Nathanael and Simon have come close to the Master, whereas the other apostles are coming towards the road, walking along the furrows. They are still chewing and have some corn in their hands.

The Pharisee who had spoken first, probably because he is the most important one, carries on speaking to Jesus, Who has stopped waiting to hear what they have to say: «Ah! So You are the famous Jesus of Nazareth? Why have You come so far?»

«Because there are souls to be saved here also.»

«We are quite sufficient for that. We know how to save our souls and those of our subjects.»

«If it is so, you are doing the right thing. But I have been sent to evengelize and save.»

«Sent! Sent! Who can prove it to us? Not Your deeds certainly!»

«Why do you say that? Are you not interested in your Life?»

«Of course! You are the one who administers death to those who do not adore You. So You want to kill the whole sacerdotal and Pharisaic classes, and the class of scribes and many more, because they do not worship You and they never will. Never, do You understand? We, the chosen ones in Israel, will never worship You. Neither shall we love You.»

«I do not compel you to love Me and I say to you: "Worship God"because...»

«That is, You, because You are God, are You not? But we are not the horrible people of Galilee nor the foolish people of Judah who follow You forgetting our rabbis...»

«Do not be upset, man. I am not asking for anything. I am fulfilling My mission, I teach people to love God and I repeat the Decalogue to them, because it has been forgotten, and what is worse, it is badly applied. I want to give Life. Eternal Life. I do not wish anybody a bodily death and much less a spiritual one.

The Life in which I asked you whether you were interested, is the life of your soul, because I love your soul, even if your soul does not love Me. And it grieves Me to see that you are killing it by offending the Lord and despising His Messiah.»

The Pharisee becomes so excited that he seems to have fallen into a fit of convulsions: he disarranges his clothes, he tears his fringes, he takes off his headgear, he ruffles his hair and shouts: «Listen! Listen! Hear what He says to me, to Jonathan of Uziel, a direct descendant of Simon the Just. That I offend the Lord! I don't know who keeps me from cursing You, but...»

«It is fear that keeps you. But you may do it. You will not be burnt to ashes just the same. But you will be in due course, and then you will invoke Me. But between you and Me, there will *then* be a red stream: My Blood.»

«All right. [3]But in the meantime, since You say that You are a 217.3
saint, why do You allow certain things? Since You say that You are a Master, why do You not teach Your apostles before anybody else? Look at them, behind You!... They still have in their hands the instrument of their sin! Can You see them? They have picked corn and this is the Sabbath. They have picked ears of corn, which do not belong to them. They have infringed the Sabbath and they have stolen.»

«They were hungry. In the village where we arrived yesterday evening, we asked for bread and lodgings. They drove us away. Only an old woman gave us some of her bread and a handful of olives. May God give her one hundredfold, because she gave us everything she had, and she only asked for a blessing. We walked for a mile and then we stopped, complying with the law, and we drank the water of a stream. Then, at sunset, we went to that house... They rejected us. You can see that we were willing to obey the Law», Peter replies.

«But you did not. It is not legal to do manual work on Sabbaths and it is never legal to take what belongs to other people. My friends and I are scandalised.»

* «But I am not. Have you not read how David at Nob took the consecrated bread of the Proposition for himself and his companions? The sacred loaves belonged to God, in His house, and

---

* **read** in: *1Samuel 21:1-7.*

by a perpetual order were to be kept for the priests. It is written: *
"They will belong to Aaron and his sons, who shall eat them in a holy place, because they are a most holy thing". And yet David took them for himself and his companions, because he was hungry. If, therefore, the holy king entered the house of God and ate the bread of the Proposition on a Sabbath, although it was not legal for him to eat it, and yet it was not imputed to him as a sin, because also after that event God continued to love him, how can you say that we have sinned it we pick on the soil of God the ears of corn that have grown and ripened through His will, the ears that belong also to birds, and you deny that men, the sons of the Father, may eat?»

«They asked for those loaves, they did not take them without asking. And that makes the difference. In any case it is not true that God did not impute that sin to David. God struck him very hard!»

«Not because of that. It was because of his lewdness, of the census, not because...»

«Oh! That's enough. It is not legal, and that is all. You have no
217.4 right to do it and you shall not do it. [4]Go away. We do not want you on our land. We do not need you. We do not know what to do with you.»

«We shall go.»

«And forever, remember that. Let Jonathan of Uziel never find you again in his presence. Go!»

«Yes, we will go. But we will meet again. And then it will be Jonathan who wants to see Me to repeat his judgement, and to rid the world of Me forever. But then it will be Heaven that will say to you: "It is not legal for you to do it", and that "it is not legal" will resound in your heart like the sound of a bugle-horn throughout your life and beyond. As on Sabbaths the priests in the Temple infringe the Sabbath rest but do not commit sin, so we, servants of the Lord, can attain love and help from the Most Holy Father, without thus committing sin, since man denies us his love. There is One here Who is by far greater than the Temple and can take anything He wants of what exists in creation, because God has made everything a footstool for the Word. And

---

* **written** in *Leviticus 24:9*. Real sins of David were: *Leudness* (already in 94.7) and the *census* (in *2Samuel 24:1-17*; *1Chronicles 21:1-17*).

I take and give. And that applies both to the ears of corn of the Father, laid on the immense table of the Earth, and to the Word. I take and give. Both to the good and to the wicked. Because I am Mercy. But you do not know what is Mercy. If you knew what My being Mercy means, you would also know that I want nothing but mercy. If you knew what Mercy is, you would not have condemned innocent people. But you do not know. You do not even know that I do not condemn you, you do not know that I will forgive you and, more than that, I will ask the Father to forgive you. Because I want mercy and not punishment. But you do not know. You do not want to know. And that is a greater sin than the one you impute to Me, it is greater than the one you say these innocent men have committed. You must know that the Sabbath was made for man and not man for the Sabbath and that the Son of man is also master of the Sabbath. Goodbye...»

He turns to His disciples: «Come. Let us go and look for a place where to lie down among the sands that are now near. The stars will keep us company and dew will refresh us. God, Who sent manna to Israel, will provide nourishment also for us, His poor faithful servants.» And Jesus leaves the rancorous group and goes away with His disciples, while night is falling with its first violet shadows...

They find at last a hedge of Indian figs, on the top leaves of which, bristling with thorns, is some fruit which is beginning to ripen. Anything is good when one is hungry. And stinging themselves, they pick the ripest ones and proceed thus until the fields become sandy dunes. The noise of the sea can be heard in the distance.

«Let us rest here. The sand is soft and warm. Tomorrow we will go to Ashkelon» says Jesus and tired as they are, they all lie down at the foot of a high dune.

218. Near Ashkelon, the Philistine Ananiah. Healing of Little Dinah's Mother.

14th July 1945.

[1] The fresh dawn breath wakes the sleeping apostles. They rise 218.1
from their sand beds, where they slept close to a dune strewn

with small tufts of dry grass, and they climb to the top. A large sandy coast appears before them, whereas a little farther away and a little closer to them there are beautiful well cultivated fields. The white stones of a dry torrent are conspicuous against the golden sand and their whiteness — the whiteness of dry bones — stretches as far as the sea, the surface of which glitters in the distance, rippled by the morning tide and a light mistral. They walk on the edge of the dune as far as the dry torrent, which they cross, and they carry on walking across the dunes, which crumble under their feet and are so undulated that they seem a solid continuation of sea.

They reach the shore-line, where they can walk faster, and while John is hypnotised by the boundless ocean beginning to shine in the rising sun, and he seems to be drinking in its beauty as his eyes become bluer and bluer, Peter who is more practical, takes his sandals off, pulls up his tunic and paddles in the shallow water looking for little crabs or shells to suck. A beautiful sea town is about two miles away, stretched along the coast above a semilunar rocky barrier beyond which sands have been carried by storms and blown by winds. And the rocks of the barrier, now that the water recedes at low tide, appear here as well, compelling thus the apostles to walk on the dry sand in order not to cut their bare feet on the sharp rocks.

«Where is the entrance to the town, my Lord? I can only see a very solid wall from here. It is not possible to enter by sea. The town is in the inner most spot of the gulf» says Philip.

«Come. I know where the entrance is.»

«Have You already been here?»

«Once, when I was a child, but I would not remember. But I know where to go.»

«How strange! I have noticed that many a time... You never take the wrong road. Sometimes we make You go wrong. One would think that You have already been to the places we go to» remarks James of Zebedee.

218.2 Jesus smiles but does not reply. [2]He walks confidently as far as a little rural suburb where market gardeners grow vegetables for the town. The fields and market gardens are tidy and well looked after and men and women are working in them, pouring water in the furrows, after drawing it laboriously from wells by hand, or in the old squeaky method by means of buckets pulled up by a poor blindfolded donkey walking around the well. But they do not say anything. Jesus greets them. «Peace be with you.» But if they are not hostile, they are certainly indifferent.

«My Lord, we are running the risk of dying of hunger here. They do not understand Your greetings. I will try now» says Thomas. And he starts a conversation with the first market gardener he sees: «Are your vegetables expensive?»

«Not more than other market gardeners'. Dear or not dear, according to how thick a purse is.»

«Well said. But, as you can see, I am not dying of starvation. I am fat and rosy even without your vegetables. Which means that my purse is well stocked. Listen: we are thirteen and we have money to spend. What can you sell us?»

«Eggs, vegetables, early almonds, apples flabby by age, olives... Whatever you want.»

«Give me some eggs, apples and bread for everybody.»

«I have no bread. You will find it in town.»

«I am hungry now, not in an hour's time. I don't believe that you have no bread.»

«I have not got any. The women are making it. See that old man over there? He always has plenty, because as he is closer to the road, pilgrims often ask him for it. Go to Ananiah and ask him. I will bring you the eggs now. But, mind you, they cost a coin a pair.»

«What a thief you are! Do your hens perhaps lay golden eggs?»

«No. But it is not pleasant to be in the middle of the stench of poultry, and one does not do it for nothing. In any case, you are Jews, are you not? So pay!»

«You can keep your eggs. And that's you paid!» and Thomas turns his back to him.

«Ehi! man! Come here. I will give you them for less. Three for a coin.»

«Not even four. You can eat them yourself and may they choke you.»

«Come here. Listen. How much are you prepared to give me?» The market gardener chases Thomas.

«Nothing. I don't want them anymore. I wanted to have a snack before going to town. But it is better so. I will not lose my voice or my appetite before singing the king's stories and I will have a good meal at the hotel.»

«I will give you them for a didrachma a pair.»

«Ugh! You are worse than a horse-fly. Give me your eggs. And make sure they are new laid ones. Otherwise I will bring them back and I will make your snout yellower than it already is.» And Thomas comes away with at least two dozen eggs in the fold of his mantle. «See? From now on I will do the shopping in this land of thieves. I know how to deal with them. They are lousy with money when they come to purchase our goods for their women and our bracelets are never heavy enough and they haggle over prices
218.3 for days. I will avenge myself. [3]Now let us go and see that other nasty piece of work. Come, Peter. Here, John, take the eggs.»

They go to the old man whose market garden is near the main road, which from the north leads to the town running near the houses of the suburb. It is a fine well paved road, certainly Roman work. The eastern town gate is now quite near and beyond it one can see that the road proceeds straight and becomes really artistic, with a shady porch on each side, supported by marble columns, in the cool shade of which people walk leaving the middle of the road to donkeys, camels, dogs and horses.

«Hail! Will you sell us some bread?» asks Thomas.

The old man either does not hear or does not want to hear. In actual fact the squeaking of the water-wheel is such that it can cause confusion.

Peter loses his temper and shouts: «Stop your Samson! At least it will be able to catch its breath and not die under my eyes. And listen to us!»

The man stops the donkey and casts a side glance at his interlocuter, but Peter disarms him saying: «Eh! Is it not right to give the name of Samson to a donkey? If you are a Philistine, you *
should like it because it is an insult to Samson. If instead you come from Israel, you should like it because it reminds you of a defeat of the Philistines. So you can see...»

«I am a Philistine and am proud of it.»

«You are right. And I will be proud of you if you give us some bread.»

---

* **Samson**: his feats are narrated in *Judges 14-16*. While accounts of the conflicts between Jews and Philistines constitute most of the book First Samuel.

«But are you not a Judaean?»

«I am a Christian.»

«What place is that?»

«It is not a place. It is a person. I belong to that person.»

«Are you His slave?»

«I am more free than any other man because he who belongs to that person does not depend on anybody, except God.»

«Are you speaking the truth? Not even on Caesar?»

«Phew! What is Caesar as compared to Him Whom I follow, and to Whom I belong, and in Whose name I ask you to give me some bread?»

«But where is that powerful man?»

«That man over there, the One looking here and smiling. He is the Christ, the Messiah. Have you never heard of Him?»

«Yes, the king of Israel. Will He defeat Rome?»

«Rome? The whole world, also Hell.»

«And you are His generals? Dressed like that? Perhaps to evade the persecutions of the wicked Jews.»

«Well... it is, and it isn't. But give me some bread and while eating I will explain the situation to you.»

«Bread? But I will also give you water, and wine, and seats in the shade, for you and for your companion and for your Messiah. Call Him.»

And Peter rushes towards Jesus. «Come, come. He will give us what we want... that old Philistine. But I think he will assail You with questions... I told him Who You are... I more or less told him... But he is favourably disposed.»

[4] They all go to the market garden where the man has already arranged benches round a coarse table under a thick vine pergola. 218.4

«Peace to you, Ananiah. May your ground be fertile because of your charity and may it bear you rich fruit.»

«Thank You. Peace to You. Sit down. Anibe! Nubi! Bring bread, wine and water at once» the old man orders two women who are certainly African, because one is absolutely black with thick lips and frizzly hair and the other is very dark but more of a European type.

And the old man explains: «They are the daughters of my wife's slaves. She is dead and the slaves who came with her are also dead. But the daughters are here. They come from the High and Low Nile. My wife came from there. It's forbidden, eh? But I don't care. I am not an Israelite and the women of inferior race are meek.»

«Are you not from Israel?»

«I am by force, because Israel oppresses us like a yoke. But... You are an Israelite and You will feel insulted at what I say?...»

«No. I am not offended. I would only like you to listen to the voice of God.»

«It does not speak to us.»

«That is what you say. I am speaking to you, and that is His voice.»

«But You are the King of Israel.»

The women who are arriving with bread, water and wine when they hear «king» being mentioned, stop dumbfounded looking at the smiling dignified young man, whom their master calls «King», and they are about to withdraw, almost creeping out of respect.

«Thank you, women. Peace to you, too.» Then, addressing the old man: «They are young... You may go on with your work.»

«No. The soil is wet and can wait. Speak to us a little. Anibe, unharness the donkey and take it to the stable. And you, Nubi, pour the last buckets of water and then... Are you stopping here, Lord?»

«Do not go to any further trouble. I only want to take some food and then I will go to Ashkelon.»

«It is no trouble. Go to town, but come back here in the evening. We will share our bread and salt. You two, hurry up. You see to the bread, you call Jetheo, tell him to kill a kid and prepare it for this evening. Go.» And the two women go away without speaking.

218.5 [5]«So You are a king. But Your army? Herod is cruel in every possible way. He rebuilt Ashkelon. But for his own glory. And now!... But You know the disgraceful things of Israel better than I do. What will You do?»

«I have but the weapon that comes from God.»

«David's sword?»

«The sword of My word.»

«Oh! You have some hopes! It will become blunt against

bronze hearts.»

«Do you think so? I am not aiming at a kingdom in this world. I am aiming at the Kingdom of Heaven on behalf of all of you.»

«Us all? Me, as well, a Philistine? And my slaves?»

«For everybody. You and them. And for the most uncivilised man in the centre of African forests.»

«Do You want to establish such a wide kingdom? Why do You call it of Heaven? You could call it: Kingdom of the Earth.»

«No, do not misunderstand me. My Kingdom is the Kingdom of the True God. God is in Heaven. So it is the Kingdom of Heaven. Every man is a soul clad with a body and a soul can live but in Heaven. I want to cure your souls, remove their errors and hatred and lead them to God through goodness and love.»

«I like that very much. I do not go to Jerusalem, but I know that no one in Israel has spoken like that for ages. So You do not hate us?»

«I do not hate anyone.»

The old man is pensive... then he asks: «And have the two slaves got a soul the same as you people of Israel?»

«Of course they have. They are not captured wild beasts. They are unhappy creatures. They deserve love. Do you love them?»

«I do not ill-treat them. I want them to obey, but I never use a lash and I feed them well. They say that an ill-fed animal will not work. But also an ill-fed man is bad business. And they were born in the house. I saw them when they were babies. They are the only ones who will be left, because I am very old, You know? Almost eighty. They and Jetheo are what is left of my old household. I am fond of them as I am of my property. They will close my eyes...»

«And then?»

«And then... Who knows! I don't know. They will go and work as maidservants and the house will fall to pieces. I am sorry. I made it wealthy by my work. This ground will be covered with sand again and become sterile... This vineyard... My wife and I planted it. And that rosery... It's Egyptian, Lord. I smell the perfume of my wife in it... It seems my son... the only son who is buried under it and is now dust... Sorrows... It is better to die young and not see all that and death which is approaching...»

«Your son is not dead, neither is your wife, their souls survive.

Their flesh is dead. Death must not frighten you. *Death is life for those who hope in the Lord and live righteously*. Think about it... I am going to town. I will come back this evening and I will ask you to allow Me to sleep under that porch with My disciples.»

«No, my Lord. I have many empty rooms. I offer them to You.»

Judas puts some coins on the table.

«No. I don't want them. They are of this country that is hateful to you. But perhaps they are better than those who rule over us. Goodbye, my Lord.»

«Peace to you, Ananiah.»

The two slaves together with Jetheo, a brawny elderly peasant, have come to see Him leave. «Peace to you as well. Be good. Goodbye» and Jesus touches lightly Nubi's frizzy hair and the shiny straight hair of Anibe, He smiles at the man and departs.

218.6 [6]Shortly afterwards they enter Ashkelon along the road of the double porch, which goes straight to the centre of the town. The town is an imitation of Rome, with fountains and basins, squares in the style of the Forum, towers along the wall and Herod's name everywhere, which he obviously had placed to praise himself since the population of Ashkelon do not applaud him. The town is busy and becomes more so as the time passes and one approaches its centre, which is spacious and airy, with the sea as a bright background like a turquoise enclosed in the pink coral tongues of the houses spread in the deep arc of the coast. Rather than a gulf it is indeed a true arc, a section of a circle made very pale pink by the sunshine.

«Let us divide into four groups. I will go, or rather I will let you go. Then I will make My choice. Go. After the ninth hour we will meet at the gate where we came in. Be wise and patient.»

And Jesus looks at them going away and remains alone with Judas Iscariot who has stated that he will give nothing to the people here because they are worse than heathens. But when Judas hears that Jesus wishes to wander about in silence, he changes his mind and says: «Do You mind being alone? I would go with Matthew, James and Andrew as they are the least capable ones...»

«You may go. Goodbye.»

And Jesus all alone, wanders far and wide in the town, a seeming non-entity amongst busy people who pay no attention to Him. Only two or three children look at Him curiously and a woman provokingly dressed comes resolutely towards Him smiling alluringly. But Jesus looks at her so severely that she becomes purple, lowers her eyes and goes away. At the corner she turns around again, and as a man who watched the scene jeers at her bitingly, laughing at her defeat, she wraps herself in her mantle and runs away.

The children, instead, walk around Jesus, looking at Him and smiling in response to His smiles. One more daring than the others asks: «Who are You?»

«Jesus» He replies caressing him.

«What are You doing?»

«I am waiting for some friends.»

«From Ashkelon?»

«No, from My country and from Judaea.»

«Are You rich? I am. My father has a beautiful house and he makes carpets in it. Come and see. It is not far.»

And Jesus goes with the boy and they enter a long archway, which is a kind of covered road. At the other end they catch a glimpse of the sea, which is very bright in the sunshine and looks even more lively in the dim light of the archway.

[7] They meet a haggard little girl who is weeping. «That is Di- 218.7
nah. She is poor, You know? My mother gives her food. Her mother cannot work any more. Her father died, at sea. In a storm while going from Gaza to the harbour of the Great River to take goods there and to collect some. And as the goods belonged to my father and Dinah's father was one of our sailors, my mother now sees to them. But there are so many of them who have been left fatherless thus... What do You say? It must be dreadful to be orphans and poor. Here is my house. Don't tell my mother that I was in the street. I should have been at school. But I was expelled because I was making my companions laugh with this...» and he pulls out from his clothes a puppet carved in wood, set in a thin piece of wood, which is really very comical, with its slipper chin and its very queer nose.

Jesus' lips tremble as if He were on the point of smiling, but He controls Himself and says: «That is not your school teacher, is it? Or a relative? It is not right.»

«No. It's the head of the synagogue of the Jews. He is old and ugly and we always make fun of him.»

«That is not right either. He is certainly much older than you are and...»

«Oh! He is very old, he is almost humpbacked and blind, but he is so ugly looking!... It's no fault of mine, if he is so ugly!»

«No. But you are wrong in making fun of an old man. You will be ugly too, when you are old, because you will be bent with age; you will be bald, almost blind, you will need a stick to walk, your face will be like that one. So? Will you be happy if an ill-mannered boy makes fun of you? And why should you worry your master and disturb your companions? It is not right. If your father knew, he would punish you and your mother would be upset. I will not tell them anything. But you will give Me two things immediately: your promise that you will no longer commit such offences and that puppet. Who made it?»

«I did, Lord...» says the humiliated boy, who is now conscious of the seriousness of his... misdeeds... And he goes on: «I like to carve wood very much! Sometimes I carve the flowers or the animals which are on the carpets. You know?... dragons, Sphynxes and other animals...»

«You may do that. There are so many beautiful things on the earth! So are you going to promise and will you give me that puppet? Otherwise we are no longer friends. I will keep it as a souvenir and I will pray for you. What is your name?»

«Alexander. And what will You give me?»

Jesus is embarrassed. He always has so little! But He remembers that He has a beautiful buckle on the collar of one of his tunics. He looks for it in His bag, finds it, takes it off and gives it to the boy. «And now let us go. But, mind you, even if I go away, I will know everything just the same. And if I know that you are a bad boy, I will come back here and tell your mother everything.» The agreement is made.

218.8 [8] They enter the house. Beyond the hall there is a large yard on three sides of which there are large rooms with the looms.

The maidservant who opened the door is amazed seeing the boy with a stranger and informs the landlady, a tall kind looking woman who comes immediately asking: «But has my son not been well?»

«No, woman. He brought Me here to see your looms. I am a stranger.»

«Do You wish to make some purchases?»

«No. I have no money. But I have friends who love beautiful things and have money.»

The woman looks curiously at the man who so candidly admits that he is poor and she says: «I thought You were a rich man. Your manners and aspect are those of a lord.»

«Instead I am only a Galilean rabbi: Jesus, the Nazarene.»

«We are in business and we are unprejudiced. Come and see.»

And she takes Him to see her looms where young women are working under her guidance. The rugs are really valuable both in terms of design and shade: they are deep, soft and look like flower beds in bloom or kaleidoscopes of gems. On others there are allegorical figures, such as hyppogryphs, mermaids, dragons or heraldic gryphons like ours, intermingled with flowers.

Jesus admires them. «You are very clever. I am glad I have seen all this. And I am glad that you are a good woman.»

«How do you know?»

«It is written on your face and the boy told Me about Dinah. May God reward you for it. Even if you do not believe it, you are very close to the Truth, because there is charity in you.»

«Which truth?»

«The Most High Lord. He who loves his neighbour and practices charity both towards his family and his subjects, and extends it to unhappy people, has already Religion in himself.
[9]That is Dinah, is it not?» 218.9

«Yes. Her mother is dying. Later, I will take her, but not for the looms. She is too young and too delicate. Dinah, come to this gentleman.»

The little girl, with the sad look of unhappy children, approaches Jesus shyly.

Jesus caresses her and says: «Will you take Me to your mother? You would like her to be cured, would you not? Well, then, take Me to her. Goodbye, woman. And goodbye, Alexander. And be good.»

He goes out holding the girl's hand. «Are you alone?» He asks her.

«I have three little brothers. The last one never knew his father.»

«Do not weep. Can you believe that God can cure your mother? You know, do you not, that there is only one God Who loves the men that He created and especially good children? And that He can do everything?»

«Yes, I know, Lord, My brother Tolme used to go to school and at school he was mixed with Jewish boys. That is why we know many things. I know that God exists and His name is Jehovah and that He punished us because the Philistines were bad to Him. The Jewish children always reproach us for that. But I was not there then, neither was my mother or my father. So why...» tears choke her words.

«Do not weep. God loves you, too, and He brought Me here, for you and for your mother. Do you know that the Israelites are expecting the Messiah Who is to come to establish the Kingdom of Heaven? The Kingdom of Jesus, the Redeemer and Saviour of the world?»

«I know, my Lord. And they threaten us saying: "Then there will be trouble for you".»

«And do you know what the Messiah will do?»

«He will make Israel a great country and will treat us very badly.»

«No. He will redeem the world, He will remove sin, He will teach people not to sin, He will love the poor, the sick, the afflicted, He will go to them, and He will teach the rich, the healthy, the happy to love them and He will tell everybody to be good to reach the blissful eternal life in Heaven. That is what He will do. And He will not oppress anybody.»

«And how will people know Him?»

«Because He will love everybody and will cure the sick people that believe in Him, He will redeem sinners and teach love.»

«Oh! I wish He came before my mother dies! How I would believe in Him! How I would pray Him! I would go and look for Him until I found Him and I would say to Him: "I am a poor girl without father and my mother is dying, I hope in You" and I am sure that, although I am a Philistine, He would hear me.» Her voice throbs with simple deep faith.

Jesus smiles looking at the poor girl walking beside Him. She cannot see His bright smile as she is looking ahead, towards the house which is now close at hand...

218.10 [10]They arrive at a poor little house, at the end of a blind alley.

«It's here, my Lord. Come in...» A small miserable room, a straw mattress with a worn out body on top of it, three little ones between three and ten years of age, sitting near the mattress. Misery and starvation are portrayed everywhere.

«Peace to you, woman. Do not get excited. Do not trouble yourself. I found your daughter and I know that you are not well. I have come. Would you like to be cured?»

In a small voice the woman replies: «Oh! My Lord!... It's the end for me!...» and she weeps.

«Your daughter believes that the Messiah could cure you. And what about you?»

«Oh! I believe that, too. But where is the Messiah?»

«It is I, Who am speaking to you.» And Jesus, Who was bending over the mattress whispering His word to the poor woman, stands up and shouts: «I want it. Be cured.»

The children are almost afraid of His majesty, and the three amazed faces remain around their mother's pallet. Dinah presses her hands against her little breast. A light of hope, of beatitude shines on her face. She is so touched, that she is almost panting. Her mouth is open to utter a word which her heart is already whispering and when she sees that her mother, so far wan and exhausted, sits up, as if she were supported by a strength infused into her, and then stands up, with her eyes staring all the time at the Saviour, Dinah utters a cry of joy: «Mummy!». The word filling her heart has been spoken!... And then another one: «Jesus!» And embracing her mother she compels her to kneel down saying: «Adore Him, adore Him! It is He, the prophesied Saviour of Whom Tolme's teacher spoke.»

«Worship the True God, be good, remember Me. Goodbye.» And He goes out quickly while the two happy women are still prostrated on the floor...

219. At Ashkelon, the Apostles Learn that Preaching with Different Approaches Produces Different Effects.

15th July 1945.

[1] The apostles arrive at the town gate in successive little groups, 219.1
according to the directions of Jesus. The Master is not yet there.

But He arrives soon, emerging from a little street running along the walls.

«The Master must have had good fortune» says Matthew. «Look how He is smiling.»

They meet and then all together go out of the gate and take to the main road again, a road lined with suburb market gardens.

Jesus asks them: «Well? How did it go with you? How did you do?»

«Very badly» the Iscariot and Bartholomew reply together.

«Why? What happened?»

«They almost stoned us. We had to run away. Let us go away from this place of barbarians. Let us go back to where people love us. I will not speak again here. Actually I had no intention of speaking. Then I allowed myself to be convinced and You did not stop me. And yet You know how things are...» The Iscariot is angry.

219.2 [2] «But what happened to you?»

«Eh! I had joined Matthew, James and Andrew. We went to Judgement Square, because it is the meeting place of refined people who have plenty of time to listen to those who speak. We decided that Matthew should speak, being the most suitable one to talk to publicans and their clients. And he began by speaking to two men who were quarrelling over the ownership of a field involved in an intricate inheritance: "Do not hate each other for what is perishable and for what you cannot take with you in the next life. But love each other so that you may enjoy the eternal good which you can achieve by controlling your evil passions, without any other struggle, and thus win and possess Good". That is what you were saying, is that right? And when two or three people approached us, he continued: "Listen to the Truth that is teaching the world, so that the world may have peace. You can see that the world suffers because it entertains an excessive attachment for things that perish. The earth is not everything. There is also Heaven, and in Heaven there is God, as on the earth there is now His Messiah, Who sent us to inform you that the time of Mercy has come and that no sinner can say: 'I shall not be heard', because he who is really repentant is forgiven, heard, loved and invited to the Kingdom of God". Many people had already gathered together and some were listening respectfully, while some were asking questions, thus disturbing Matthew. I never reply to anybody, to avoid interrupting the speech. I speak and then I reply to any question at the end. Let them bear in mind what we want to tell them and be silent. But Matthew wanted to reply at once!... And they were asking us questions as well. But there were also some who sneered saying: "There is another madman! He certainly comes from that den of Israel. They are like weeds those Jews, they spread everywhere! They talk everlasting nonsense! They have God as their companion. Listen to them! God is on their sword edge and on their sharp tongues. Listen, listen. Now they are calling in question His Messiah. Some other raving lunatic who will torture us as always happened in the past. Let the plague catch Him and His race!". Then I lost my temper. I pulled Matthew back, as he was going on speaking, smiling as if they were paying homage to him, and I began to speak, taking * Jeremiah as my starting point: "See how the waters rise from the North and become an overflowing torrent...". "Upon hearing the noise of the water, you will lose your strength; your pride, your hearts, your arms, your feelings, everything will collapse. Because the punishment of God for you, mischievous race, will have the roar of a waterfall, whereas it will be earthly armies and heavenly warriors to punish your stubbornness, attacking you by order of the Heads of the People of God. And you, the remains of the island of sin and door of Hell, will be exterminated! You have become arrogant because Herod has rebuilt your homes? But you will be shaved until you become hopelessly bald and you will be struck by all sorts of punishments in your towns and villages, in your valleys and plains. The prophecy is not yet dead..." and I wanted to continue, but they rushed upon us and only because a heaven-sent caravan was passing along one of the streets, we managed to take shelter, as stones were already flying. They hit the camels and their drivers; there was an uproar and we made off. Afterwards we remained quietly in a little suburb yard. Ah! I will never come back here again...»

[3] «I beg your pardon, but you offended them! It's your fault! 219.3
Now we understand why they were so hostile when they came

* **Jeremiah** 47. In his oracle against Philistines.

to drive us away!» exclaims Nathanael. And he continues: «Listen, Master. We, that is Simon of Jonah, Philip and I had gone towards the tower overlooking the sea. There were some sailors and ship owners there, loading goods for Cyprus, Greece and other more distant places. And they were cursing the sun, the dust and their hard work, their Philistine destiny that implied that they were slaves of overbearing people, whereas they could have been kings. And they cursed the Prophets, the Temple and all of us. I wanted to go away, but Simon objected saying: "No, on the contrary, we must approach these sinners. The Master would do that, and we must do it as well". "Then, you can speak to them" said Philip and I. "And if I do not know what to say?" said Simon. "Then we will help you" we replied. Simon then, smiling, went towards two men who had sat down perspiring on a huge bale they could not lift onto the boat, and he said: "It's heavy, isn't it?". "It's not so much its weight, as the fact that we are tired. And we have to complete the loading, because that's what the owner wants. He wants to sail when the sea is calm, because this evening the sea will be rough and he must be beyond the rocks to be out of danger". "Rocks in the sea?". "Yes, over there, where the water foams, a nasty spot". "Currents, eh? Of course! The south wind blows around the promontory and collides with the current there...". "Are you a sailor?". "A fisherman, a fresh water fisherman. But water is always water and wind always wind. I have finished up in the water more than once myself and my catch went back into the lake. Our trade is a good one but can also be unpleasant. There is no place entirely bad and no race entirely cruel. With a little goodwill it is always possible to come to some agreement and one finds out that there are good people everywhere. Come on! I want to give you a hand" and Simon called Philip saying: "Come on, you will catch the load there, I will catch it here and these good people will lead us over there, to the boat, and down to the holds". The Philistines were rather unwilling, but then they allowed them to help. After putting the bale in its place, and others, which were on the bridge as well, Simon began to praise the boat, as he only knows how, and he praised the sea, the town that was so beautiful as seen from off shore and he took an interest in navigation and in foreign towns. And they were all around him, thanking him and praising him...

Until one asked him: "But where are you from? From the Nile area?". "No, from the sea of Galilee. But as you can see I am not a tiger". "That is true. Are you looking for a job?". "Yes". "I will take you on, if you wish. I can see that you are a clever sailor" said the owner. "I instead will take you". "Me? But did you not tell me that you want a job?". "That is true. My work is to take men to the Messiah of God. You are a man. So you are work for me". "But I am a Philistine!". "And what does that mean?". "It means that you hate us, that you have persecuted us from time immemorial. Your chiefs have always said so...". "The Prophets, eh? But now the Prophets are voices that no longer shout. Now there is only the great holy Jesus, He does not shout, but calls people with a friendly voice. He does not curse, He blesses. He does not cause misfortunes, but removes them. He does not hate and does not want anyone to hate. On the contrary He loves everybody and He wants us to love also our enemies. In His Kingdom there will no longer be winners and losers, free men and slaves, friends and enemies. There will no longer be such distinctions which hurt, which are the consequence of human wickedness; but there will be only *His* followers, that is people who live in love, in freedom, in the victory over everything which is burdensome or sorrowful. I beg you. Please believe my words and desire Him. The prophecies were written. But He is greater than the Prophets and prophecies are obliterated for those who love Him. See this beautiful town of yours? You would find it much more beautiful in Heaven, if You went so far as to love our Lord Jesus, the Christ of God". That is what Simon was saying and he was simple and inspired at the same time and everybody listened to him diligently and respectfully. Then some citizens came out of a street shouting, and they were armed with clubs and stones and they saw us and they knew from our clothes that we were foreigners, and now I understand, they realised that we were of your race, Judas, and they thought that we were all of your kind. If those of the boat had not protected us we would have been in trouble! They lowered a lifeboat and took us away by sea and they let us ashore near the garden where we were at midday and from there we came here together with the people who cultivate
flowers for the rich of the country. [4]But, Judas, you have ruined 219.4
everything! Is that the way to abuse people?»

«It is the truth.»

«But it is to be used discreetly. Peter did not tell lies, but he knew what to say» retorts Nathanael.

«Oh! me! I tried to put myself in the place of the Master, and I thought: "He would be so kind. And I as well..."» says Peter simply.

«I like strong attitudes. They are more regal.»

«Your usual idea! You are wrong, Judas. The Master has been endeavouring to correct that idea of yours for a year. But you will not yield to corrections. You are as obstinate in your error as those Philistines upon whom you rushed» says Simon the reproachfully.

«When did He ever correct me for that? In any case everybody has his own ways and makes use of them.»

The Zealot starts at those words and looks at Jesus, Who is silent and Who responds with a light smile of understanding to Simon's remindful glance.

«That is not a good reason» says James of Alphaeus calmly and continues: «We are here to correct ourselves before correcting others. The Master has been first our Master. And He would not have been our Master if He had not wanted us to change our habits and minds.»

«He was Master in wisdom...»

«He was? He is» says Thaddeus seriously.

«How much cavilling! All right, He is.»

«And He is our Master in everything else, not only in wisdom. His teaching applies to everything there is in us. He is perfect, we are imperfect. Let us endeavour therefore to become perfect» advises James of Alphaeus kindly.

«I don't think I committed a fault. The fault lies with that cursed race. They are all wicked.»

219.5 «No. You cannot say that» bursts out Thomas. [5]«John went among the lowest class: the fishermen who were taking their catch to the market. And look at this damp sack. It is full of choice fish. They gave up their profit to give it to us. They were afraid that morning catch might not be fresh by evening, so they went back to sea and they wanted us to go with them. We seemed to be on the lake of Galilee and I can assure you that if the place reminded us of it, if also the boats full of keen faces reminded us,

John reminded us much more. He seemed another Jesus. Words flowed from his smiling lips as sweet as honey and his face shone like another sun. How he resembled You, Master! I was moved. We were at sea for three hours, waiting for the nets, stretched out between floats, to become full of fish and they were three hours of utter happiness. Then they wanted to see You. But John said: "We will meet at Capernaum" as if he was saying: "We will meet in the square of your village". And yet they promised to come and they took due note. And we had to argue not to be laden with too much fish. They gave us the best ones. Let us go and cook them. We shall have a feast this evening, to make up for yesterday's fasting.»

«But what did you say to them» asks the Iscariot who is disconcerted.

«Nothing special. I spoke of Jesus» replies John.

«But the way you can speak of Him! Also John quoted the Prophets. But he turned them upside down» explains Thomas.

«Upside down?» asks the Iscariot surprised.

«Yes. You extracted harshness from the Prophets, he extracted sweetness. Because, after all, their severity is love, exclusive violent love, if you wish so, but it is still love for souls that they would like to be faithful to the Lord. I do not know whether you have ever considered that, as you were educated among the scribes. I have, although I am a goldsmith. Also gold is hammered and melted in a crucible, to make it more beautiful. Not out of hatred: but for love. That is how the Prophets dealt with souls. I understand it, probably because I am a goldsmith. He
* quoted Zechariah's prophecy concerning Hadrach and Damascus and when he came to the sentence: "Seeing this Ashkelon will be terrified, and Gaza will be seized with trembling, so will Ekron, at the ruin of her prospects. The king will vanish from Gaza", he began to explain how all that happened because man had abandoned God, and speaking of the coming of the Messiah, Who is loving forgiveness, he promised that from a poor royalty, such as the sons of the earth wish for their countries, the men who follow the Doctrine of the Messiah will succeed in attaining an eternal infinite royalty in Heaven. To say that, is nothing, but

* **prophecy** in *Zechariah 9:1-8.*

to hear it! I thought I was listening to music and that I was being carried away by angels. And thus the Prophets, who gave you a cudgelling, gave us delicious fish.»

Judas is disconcerted and remains silent.

219.6 [6] «And what about you?» the Master asks His cousins and the Zealot.

«We went towards the shipyards, where the caulkers work. We also preferred to go amongst the poor people. But there were also some wealthy Philistines watching their boats being built. We did not know which of us should speak so we drew lots, as children do. Judas held up seven fingers, Simon two and I four. So it was for Judas to speak. And he did» explains James of Alphaeus.

«What did you say» they all ask.

«I openly made myself known for what I am, saying that I was asking them in their hospitality to be kind enough to listen to the word of a pilgrim who considered them as brothers, having the same origin and same end, and the hope, which although not common was full of love, to take them to the house of the Father and call them "brothers" forever, in the great joy of Heaven. Then I said: "Zephaniah, our Prophet said: 'The region of the sea will be a place for shepherds... they will lead flocks there to pasture; among the house of Ashkelon they will rest at evening'" and I clarified my idea saying: "The Supreme Shepherd has come amongst you. He is not armed with arrows, but with love. He stretches out His arms towards you and points out His holy pastures. He remembers the past only to pity men for the great harm they do and have done to themselves through hatred, like foolish children, while they could have relieved so much sorrow by loving one another, since they are brothers. This land" I said "will be the place of holy shepherds, the servants of the Supreme Shepherd who are already aware that they will have their richest pastures here and their best flocks; and their hearts, in their declining years, will be able to rest thinking of your hearts and the hearts of your children, more intimate than friendly homes, because Jesus Our Lord, will be their Master". They understood me. They asked me questions, or rather, they asked *us all* questions. And Simon told them of his cure, my brother spoke to them

* **said** in *Zephaniah 2:4-7*.

of Your goodness towards the poor. And here is the proof. This fat purse for the poor we shall find on our way. The Prophets did not harm us either...»

Judas does not utter a single word.

7 «Well» says Jesus comfortingly, «Judas will do better next 219.7
time. He thought he was doing the right thing by doing what he did. And as he acted for an honest purpose, he committed no sin. And I am equally satisfied with him. It is not easy to be an apostle. But one learns. I regret one thing only. That I did not have this money before and that I did not meet you. I needed it for a miserable family.»

«We can go back. It is still early... But, excuse me. Master. How did You come across it. What did You do? Just nothing? Did you not evangelize?»

«I? I walked. By means of My silence I said to a prostitute: "Abandon your sinful life". I met a boy, somewhat of a little rogue, and I evangelized him and we exchanged gifts. I gave him the buckle which Mary Salome had put on my tunic at Bethany, and he gave Me this work of his» and Jesus takes out from His tunic the caricatural puppet. They all look at it and laugh. «Then I went to see some beautiful carpets which a man makes in Ashkelon to sell them in Egypt and elsewhere... and I comforted a little fatherless girl and I cured her mother. And that is all.»

«And You think that is little?»

«Yes. Because there was also the need of some money, but I had none.»

«But let us go back... we did not upset anyone» says Thomas.

«And what about your fish?» says James of Zebedee jokingly.

«The fish? Well. You who are... anathematised, go to the old man who is giving us hospitality and start preparing. We will go to town.»

«Yes» says Jesus. «But I will show you the house from a distance. There will be many people. I will not come, because they would keep Me. I do not wish to offend our host who is waiting for us, by declining his invitation. Rudeness is always against charity.»

The Iscariot lowers his head even more and becomes purple, such is the change of his colour, remembering how often he has committed that fault.

Jesus resumes: «You will go into the house and look for the little girl, she is the only girl there, so you cannot be mistaken. You will give her this purse and say to her: "God sends you this because you believed. It is for you, your mummy and your little brothers". Nothing else. And come back at once. Let us go.»

And the group breaks up as Jesus goes to town with John, Thomas and His cousins, whereas the others go towards the house of the Philistine market gardener.

220. The Heathens of Magdalgad. Jesus Incinerates a Pagan Idol and Saves a Woman in Childbirth.

16th July 1945.

220.1 [1] Ashkelon and its market gardens are already but a memory. In the cool hours of a wonderful morning, Jesus and His disciples, turning their backs to the sea, direct their steps towards the low but beautiful green hills rising from the fertile plain. His apostles, who are both well rested and satisfied, are all in good fettle and speak of Ananiah, of his slaves, of Ashkelon, of the tumult in town when they went back to take the money to Dinah.

«It was my fate that I should be in straits because of the Philistines. After all, hatred and love have the same manifestations. And I, who had never suffered at the hands of Philistine hatred, was almost wounded by their love. They were on the point of capturing us to compel us to tell them the whereabouts of the Master, so elated were they because of the miracle. And how they shouted! Didn't they, John? The town was boiling like a pot. Those who were upset would not listen to reason and they were looking for the Jews to thrash them, those who had been benefited, or their friends, were endeavouring to persuade the former that a god had passed by. What a turmoil! They can talk it over for months. The trouble is that they talk with clubs rather than with their tongues. Well... it is up to them. They can do as they like» says Thomas.

«But... they are not bad...» remarks John.

«No. They are only blinded by so many things» replies the Zealot.

Jesus does not speak along a good stretch of the road. He then says: «Here, I will now go up to that village on the mountain, while you go on to Ashdod. Be careful. Be gentle, kind and patient. Even if they laugh at you, bear it in peace, as Matthew did yesterday, and God will help you. At sunset leave the town and go to the pond near Ashdod. We shall meet there.»

«But, my Lord, I will not let You go all alone!» exclaims the Iscariot. «These people are violent... It is not wise.»

«Do not be afraid for Me. Go, Judas, and be prudent yourself Goodbye. Peace be with you.»

The Twelve go away but they are not very enthusiastic. Jesus looks at them depart and He takes the cool shady path up the hill. The hill is covered with olive, walnut and fig-trees and with well cultivated vineyards that are already promising good crops. On the plains there are little fields of cereals, while white-haired goats are grazing on the green grassy slopes.

[2]Jesus arrives at the first houses of the village. He is about 220.2
to enter when He meets a strange procession. There are women shouting, men howling an alternate lament and they are performing a kind of dance around a blindfolded billygoat, which they beat while proceeding. The knees of the animal are already bleeding after stumbling and falling on the stones of the path. Another group of people, who are also shouting and howling, are moving around a carved simulacrum, which is really very ugly and they hold up pans full of embers, which they keep alive by spraying resins and salt over them, at least I think that is what is happening, as the former smell of turpentine and the latter crackles like salt. Another group is gathered around a wizard, before whom they continuously bow, shouting:

«By your strength!» (men)

«You only can!» (women)

«Implore the god!» (men)

«Remove the witchcraft!» (women)

«Order the matrix!»

«Save the woman!»

And then all together, with a hellish howl, shout:

«Death to the sorceress!»

And they start all over again, with a variant:

«By your strength!»

«You only can!»

«Command the god!»
«To let us see!»
«Order the billygoat!»
«To show us the sorceress!»
And with another hellish cry:
«Who hates the house of Phara!»

220.3 [3]Jesus stops a man in the last group and kindly asks him: «What is happening? I am a foreigner...»

The procession has stopped for a moment to beat the billygoat, spray resins on the embers and take breath, and the man explains: «The wife of Phara, the great man of Magdalgad is dying in childbirth. Someone who hates her, has cast a spell on her. Her womb has become strangulated and the child cannot come into the world. We are looking for the sorceress to kill her. Only that way Phara's wife can be saved, and if we do not find the sorceress we will sacrifice the billygoat to implore supreme mercy from goddess Matrix (I now realise that the monstruous puppet is a goddess)...»

«Stop. I can cure the woman and save her son. Tell the priest» says Jesus to the man and to two more who have approached Him.

«Are You a doctor?»

«More than a doctor.»

The three men elbow their way through the crowd and go to the idolatrous priest. They speak to him. The rumour spreads. The procession, which had set out again, stops.

The priest, imposing in his many coloured rags, nods to Jesus and orders: «Young man, come here!» And when Jesus is near him: «Is what You say true? Mind you, if what You say does not happen, we will infer that the spirit of the sorceress is embodied in You and we will kill You instead of her.»

«What I said is true. Take Me to the woman at once and in the meantime give Me the billygoat. I need it. Remove the bandage from its head and bring it here.»

They do so. The poor stunned staggering bleeding animal is brought to Jesus Who caresses its thick black coat.

«Now you must obey Me in everything. Will you do that?»

«Yes!» shout the crowd.

«Let us go. Do not shout anymore and stop burning resins. It is an order.»

[4] They enter the village and along the main street they go to a house situated in the centre of an orchard. Shouting and crying can be heard through the wide open doors, and above all, the lugubrious dreadful laments of the woman who cannot give birth to her child. 220.4

They run to tell Phara, who looking wan and with ruffled hair comes forward together with two weeping women and some useless wizards who are burning incense and leaves on copper pans.

«Save my wife!»

«Save my daughter!»

«Save her, save her!» shout in turn the husband, an old woman and the crowd.

«I will save her and her boy as well, because it is a boy, a very healthy one, with two sweet eyes the hue of a ripe olive and dark hair on his head like this fleece.»

«How do You know? What? Can You see also inside a womb?»

«I see and penetrate everywhere. I know everything and I can do everything. I am God.»

If He had thrown a thunderbolt, the effect would not have been the same. They all throw themselves on the ground, as if they were dead.

«Stand up. Listen. I am the powerful God and I cannot bear other gods before Me. Light a fire and throw that statue on to it.»

The crowds rebel. They begin to doubt the mysterious «god» who orders the goddess to be burned. The priests are most indignant.

But Phara and his mother-in-law, who are interested in the woman's life, oppose the hostile crowd and since Phara is the great man in the village, the crowd checks its anger. But the man asks Him: «How can I believe that You are a god? Give me a sign and I will order them to do what You want.»

«Look. See the wounds of this billygoat? They are open, are they not? They are bleeding, are they not? And the animal is almost dead. Well, I do not want that... Now, look.»

The man bends, looks... and shouts: «There are no wounds!» and he throws himself on the ground begging: «My wife, my wife!»

But the priest of the procession threatens: «Watch, Phara! We do not know who He is! Dread the revenge of the gods!»

The man is seized with double fear: the gods, his wife... He asks: «Who are You?»

«I am He Who I am, in Heaven, on the earth. All power is subject to Me, every thought is known to Me. The dwellers of Heaven adore Me, those in Hell fear Me. And those who believe in Me will see all wonders being performed.»

«I believe! I believe... Your Name!»

«Jesus Christ, the Incarnate Lord. Burn that idol! I cannot bear gods in My presence. Put out those thuribles. Only My Fire is powerful and willing. Obey, or I will incinerate that vain idol, and I will go away without saving anyone.»

Jesus is awesome in His linen robe, from the shoulders of which hangs His blue mantle behind Him, His arm raised in a gesture of command, His face gleaming... They are afraid of Him, no one speaks... In the silence, the heart-rending exhausting cries of the suffering woman are distinctly heard. But they are still reluctant to obey. Jesus' face is becoming more and more awesome to human eyes. It is really a fire burning both matter and souls. And the copper pans are the first to suffer. The men holding them are compelled to throw them away as they can no longer stand their heat. And yet the coal seems to be out... Then the idol-bearers are forced to lay on the ground the litter which they were carrying shoulder-high as the shafts are becoming carbonised, as if a mysterious flame burned them, and as soon as the litter is on the ground, the idol catches fire.

The crowds are terrorised and run away...

220.5 [5] Jesus turns to Phara: «Can you really believe in My power?»

«I do believe. You are God. The God Jesus.»

«No. I am the Word of the Father, of Jehovah of Israel, and I have come in Flesh, Blood, Soul and Divinity to redeem the world and give men faith in the True God, the One, Triune God Who is in the Most High Heavens. I have come to give help and mercy to men, so that they may abandon Error and come to the Truth, which is the Only God of Moses and of the Prophets. Can you still believe?»

«Yes, I do.»

«I have come to bring the Way, Truth and Life to men, to demolish idols, to teach wisdom. Through Me the world will be redeemed, because I will die for love of the world and for the eternal salvation of men. Can you still believe?»

«Yes, I believe.»

«I have come to tell men, that if they believe in the True God, they will have eternal life in Heaven, near the Most High, Who is the Creator of every man, animal, plant and planet. Can you still believe?»

«Yes, I do believe.»

Jesus does not even enter the house. He only stretches out His arms towards the poor woman's room, with His hands open as in the resurrection of Lazarus, and He shouts: «Come out to the light to know the Divine Light and by order of the Light which is God!» A thundering order, echoed after a moment, by a cry of triumph having in its sound both wail and joy, and then the feeble weeping of a new-born baby, feeble but clear and growing more and more in strength.

«Your son is crying to greet the earth. Go to him and tell him, both now and later, that not the earth, but Heaven is his fatherland. Bring him up for Heaven, and that applies to you as well. That is the Truth speaking to you. Those things (and He points at the copper pans, crumpled up on the ground like dry leaves, and now completely useless, and at the ashes marking the place of the idol's litter) are Falsehood that neither helps nor saves. Goodbye.» And He is about to go away.

[6] But a woman rushes forth with a lively baby wrapped in linen 220.6
swaddling clothes and she shouts: «It's a boy, Phara. He is beautiful and strong, His eyes are as dark as a ripe olive and his hair is darker and thinner than the hair of a little sacred goat. And your wife is resting blissfully. She no longer suffers, as if nothing had happened. It was all so sudden, when she was already dying... and after those words...»

Jesus smiles and as the man presents the baby to Him, He touches its head with the tips of His fingers. The people — with the exception of the priests who go away indignantly when they see Phara's defection — gather around them to see the baby and look at Jesus.

Phara would like to give Him gifts and money for the miracle. But Jesus kindly but resolutely says: «Nothing. A miracle can only be paid for by loyalty to God Who granted it. I will retain this billygoat as a memory of your town.» And He goes away with the billygoat, which trots along beside Him, as if Jesus were his owner, and now that it is cured, it looks happy and bleats for joy of being with one who does not strike it…

They go down the slopes of the hill and take the main road which leads to Ashdod…

220.7 [7] When in the evening, near the shady pond, Jesus sees the apostles coming, their amazement is mutual, as they see Jesus with the ram and He sees them with the disappointed faces of those who have not done any business.

«A disaster, Master! They did not hit us, but they drove us out of town. We have been wandering about the country and we got some food but we had to pay highly for it. And yet we were kind…» they say desolately.

«It does not matter. We were driven away also at Hebron last year, but this time they honoured us. You must not lose heart.»

«And what about You, Master? And that goat?»

«I went to Magdalgad. I incinerated an idol and its thuribles, I made a baby boy come into the world, I preached the True God by means of miracles and I took this goat, destined to an idolatrous rite, as My reward. Poor thing, it was covered with wounds.»

«But now it is all right! It's a wonderful animal.»

«It is a sacred animal, destined to the idol… Yes, it is now sound. The first miracle I worked to convince them that I am the Powerful One, and not their piece of wood.»

«And what are You going to do with it?»

«I am taking it to Marjiam. A puppet yesterday, a goat today. It will make him happy.»

«Are You going to take it with You all the way to Bether?»

«Of course. I see nothing horrible about it. If I am the Shepherd, I can certainly have a ram. We will give it to the women. And they will go to Galilee with it. We will find a little she-goat. Simon, you will become the shepherd of little goats. It would be better if they were sheep… But there are more goats than lambs in the world… It is a symbol, My dear Peter. Remember that… By means of your sacrifice you will make many lambs of rams. Come. Let us go to that village among the orchards. We shall find lodgings either in the houses or on the sheaves which are already tied up in the fields. And tomorrow we will go to Jabneel.»

The apostles are surprised, grieved, disheartened. They are surprised at the miracles, grieved because they were not there, disheartened because of their inability, whereas Jesus can do everything.

He, instead, is so happy!... And He is successful in convincing them: «Nothing is useless. Not even defeat, because it serves to make you humble, whereas speech serves to make a name, Mine, resound and leave a remembrance in hearts.» And He is so persuasive and bright with joy that they also cheer up.

221. Going to Jabneel. A Lesson on Prejudices Against Pagans: the Parable of the Deformed Son.

17th July 1945.

[1] «Shall we go to Ekron from Jabneel?» ask some of the apostles while walking across a very fertile country, in which the corn is taking its final sleep in the bright sunshine that has ripened it. The reaped fields resemble immense sad death beds, now that they are bereft of corn ears with loads of corn awaiting to be carried elsewhere. 221.1

But if the fields are barren, the orchards are a most pleasant sight, with the fruit about to ripen, changing colour from the green of the little hard ones to the soft yellowish, pinkish, waxy shiny shades of those that are more ripe. The figs open their very sweet caskets of flower-fruits, bursting their elastic skins to reveal, through whitish-green or violet cracks, a transparent jelly replete with tiny seeds, which are darker in colour than the pulp itself.

With each tiny wafting breeze the olive-trees shake, likewise, the oval-shaped fruits suspended on delicate stems amid the silver-green foliage. The dignified walnut trees sustain their firm stalked fruits, which swell within the plush of the husks, while the almond-trees are ripening their fruits as is proved by the velvety texture and changing colour of the individual nuts. Grapes in general are swelling while a few bunches, favourably placed, try to show the topaz or ruby of maturity. Day by day the cacti on the plain or lower hill sides are becoming a brighter sight with magnificent coloration on the seed clusters contained within and held skywards and ripened within the protection of the strong thorny leaves.

Isolated palm-trees and thick carob-trees remind one of nearby Africa and while the former click the castanets of their hard fan-shaped leaves, the latter have dressed themselves in dark enamel and are standing haughtily stiff on their lovely foliage.

Tall agile goats, both white and black, all with long curved horns and soft keen eyes, feed on cacti and attack fleshy agaves, those huge brushes with hard thick leaves which, like open artichokes, shoot up from the centre of their hearts their gigantic seven branched stalk, resembling a cathedral candelabrum, with its sweet-smelling yellow-red flower blazing on top.

Africa and Europe have come together to cover the ground
221.2 with most beautiful vegetation, [2]and as soon as the apostolic group leaves the plain to take a path that climbs up the hill literally covered with vineyards on this side facing the sea — a rocky calcareous slope where the grapes must be of immense value when their juice changes into julep — there appears the sea, my sea, the sea of John, the sea of God. It appears draped in its immense blue silk crêpe and it speaks of distances, of infinity, of power, while it sings with the sky and the sun the trio of the creating glories. And the plain stretches out in its full undulated beauty with simulations of hills, only a few feet high, adjoining flat areas, with golden dunes stretching as far as towns and villages on the sea, white spots on the blue sea.

«How beautiful! How beautiful!» whispers John ecstatically.

«My Lord! The sea is the life of that boy. You must destine him for the sea. He seems to be seeing his bride when he sees the sea!» says Peter who does not discriminate much between sea and lake. And he smiles kind-heartedly.

«He is already destined, Simon. You are all destined.»

«Oh! Good! And where are You sending me?»

«Oh! You!...»

«Tell me, be good!»

«To a place that is greater than your town and Mine and Magdala and Tiberias all put together.»

«I will get lost.»

«Do not be afraid. You will look like an ant on a large skeleton. But going to and fro untiringly you will bring the skeleton back to life.»

«I don't understand that at all... Tell me more clearly.»

«You will understand, you certainly will...» and Jesus smiles.

«And what about me?»

«And me?» They all want to know.

«This is what I will do.» And Jesus bends — they are on the gravelly bank of a torrent in the central part of which the water is still quite deep — and He picks up a handful of very fine gravel. He throws it into the air and it falls spreading in all directions. «There you are. Only this tiny stone is left in My hair. You will be scattered like that.»

«And You, brother, represent Palestine, don't You?» asks James of Alphaeus seriously.

«Yes, I do.»

«I would like to know who will be left in Palestine» asks James once again.

«Take this little stone. As a souvenir» and Jesus gives the little piece of gravel, which had remained entangled in His hair, to His cousin James and smiles.

«Could You not leave me in Palestine? I am the most suitable, because I am the coarsest, but I can still manage at home. Whereas abroad!...» says Peter.

«On the contrary, you are the *least* suitable to remain here.

[3] You are all prejudiced against the rest of the world and you 221.3
think it is easier to evangelize in a country of believers rather than in a country of idolaters or Gentiles. It is instead the very opposite. If you considered what *true* Palestine offers us in its higher classes and also, although to a lesser degree, in its people, and if you bore in mind that here, in a place where the name of Palestine is hated and the name of God, in its true meaning, is unknown, we have certainly not been received any worse than in Judaea, in Galilee and in the Decapolis, your prejudices would vanish and you would realise that I am right when I say that it is easier to convince ignorant people of the True God, than those of the People of God, who are subtle guilty idolaters, and proudly believe they are perfect and wish to remain as they are.

How many gems, how many pearls I see where you can see land and sea only! The land of the multitudes which *are not* Palestine. The sea of Mankind which *is not* Palestine and which, as sea, desires only to receive searchers to give them those pearls, and as land, to be searched to allow those gems to be taken. There are treasures everywhere. But they are to be looked for. Every clod of earth may conceal a treasure and nourish a seed, every depth may hide a pearl. What? Would you perhaps expect the sea to make havoc in its depths by means of furious storms to detach pearl-oysters from their beds and open them by the striking power of billows and thus offer them on the shore to lazy people who do not want to work, to cowards who do not want to run risks? Would you expect the earth to make trees out of grains of sand and give you fruit without any seed? No, My dear. Fatigue, work, courage are required. And above all, no prejudices.

221.4 [4] You, I know, disapprove, some more some less, of this journey among the Philistines. Not even the glories, which this land reminds us of, the glories of Israel that speak from these fields, fecundated by Hebrew blood, shed to make Israel great, and from those towns torn one by one from the hands of those who possessed them, to crown Judah and make it a powerful nation, are capable of making you love this pilgrimage. And I will not say to you: not even the idea of preparing the ground to receive the Gospel and the hope of saving souls can convince you. I will not say that to you, among the many reasons which I present to your minds so that you may consider the justice of this trip. That thought is still too high for you. You will arrive at it one day. And then you will say: "We thought it was a whim, a pretext, we thought that the Master lacked love towards us by making us go so far, on a long painful journey, risking unpleasant situations. Instead it was love, it was foreseeing, it was to smooth our way, now that we no longer have Him with us, and we feel more lost than ever. Because then we were like vine shoots which grow in all directions, but they know that the vine will nourish them and that nearby there is a strong pole to support them, now instead we are shoots which must form a pergola by themselves, being still nourished by the stump of the vine, but with no trunk on which to lean". That is what you will say and you will thank Me.

And after all!... Is it not lovely to go like this, dropping sparks of light, notes of heavenly music, celestial corollas, perfumes of truth, serving and praising God, on lands wrapped in darkness, in dumb hearts, on souls as sterile as deserts, to overcome the stench of Falsehood, and do that all together, thus, You and I, the Master and His apostles, with one only heart, one only desire, one only will? So that God may be known and loved. So that God may gather all peoples under His tent and *everybody* may be where He is. That is the hope, the desire, the hunger of God! And that is the hope, the desire, the hunger of souls, who are not of different races, but belong to *one race only: the one created by God.* And since they all are the sons of the One God, they have the same desires, the same hopes, the same hungers for Heaven, for Truth, for real Love...

[5] Centuries of errors seem to have changed the instinct of souls. 221.5
But it is not so. Errors wrap minds. Because minds are mingled with flesh and feel the effects of the poison with which Satan inoculated the animal man. And thus errors can wrap hearts because they are engrafted into the flesh as well, and feel the effect of the poison. The treble concupiscence bites senses, sentiments and thoughts. But the spirit is not engrafted into the flesh. It may be stunned by the blows which Satan and concupiscence deliver it. It may be almost blinded by the allurements of the flesh and by the sprays of boiling blood of the animal man, into whom it is infused. But it has not changed its longing for Heaven, for God. It cannot change. See the clear water of this torrent? It descended from the sky and it will go back to the sky through the evaporation of water caused by winds and sun. It descends and rises again. Elements are not consumed, they go back to their origin.

The spirit goes back to its origin. If this water here, among these stones, could speak, it would tell you that it longs to go back to the sky, to be blown by the winds along the fields of the firmament, a soft white cloud, or a pinkish one at dawn, or bright copper at sunset, or like a violet flower at twilight when stars begin to peep. It would tell you that it would like to act as a sieve for the stars peeping through the gaps of cirri to remind men of Heaven, or as a veil for the moon, so that she might not see the nocturnal ugly deeds on the earth, rather than be here, confined between banks, under the threat of becoming mud, compelled to see copulations of water snakes and toads, while it is so fond of the solitary freedom of the atmosphere. Also spirits, if they dared to speak, would say the same thing: "Give us God! Give us the Truth!". But they do not say that, because they know that man is not aware of, does not understand or mocks the entreaties of the *"great beggars"*, of the spirits who seek God to satisfy their terrible hunger: their hunger for the Truth.

221.6 [6] The idolaters, the Romans, the atheists, the unhappy we meet on our way, and you will always meet, those who are despised in their desire for God, either through politics or family selfishness, or through heresies born of filthy hearts and spread throughout nations: they are all hungry! *They are hungry!* And I have mercy on them. And should I not have mercy on them, being He Who I am? If out of pity I provide food for men and sparrows, why should I not have mercy on the spirits, who have been prevented from being of the True God, and who stretch out the arms of their spirits shouting: "We are hungry!"? Do you think that they are wicked, or savages, or unable to go as far as to love God's Religion and God Himself? You are wrong. They are spirits awaiting love and light.

This morning we were woken by the threatening bleating of the billygoat that wanted to drive away the big dog which had come to sniff Me. And you laughed seeing how the ram pointed its horns threateningly, after tearing the little rope by which it was tied to the tree, under which we slept, and with one leap it placed itself between Me and the dog, without considering that it might have been attacked and slaughtered by the Molossian hound in the uneven struggle to defend Me. Likewise, the peoples who seem wild rams to you, will go as far as to courageously defend the Faith of Christ, once they have learned that Christ is Love inviting them to follow Him. *He invites them. He does.* And you must help them to come.

221.7 [7] Listen to a parable.

A man got married and his wife bore him many sons. But one of them was born deformed in his body and seemed to be of a different race. The man considered him a dishonour and did not love him, although the child was innocent. The boy was brought up amongst the lowest servants and was thoroughly neglected and thus he was considered an inferior being by his brothers as well. His mother had died in giving birth to him and consequently she could not mitigate his father's harshness, or stop the mockery of his brothers, or correct the wrong ideas conceived in the primitive mind of the child, a little wild beast unwillingly tolerated in the house of the beloved sons.

And thus the boy became a man. His reason developed late but finally reached maturity and he understood that it was unfair for a son to be brought up in a stable, to be fed with a piece of bread and clothed with rags, without ever receiving a kiss, or being spoken to or being invited to his father's house. And he suffered bitterly and would lament in his den: "Father! Father!". He ate his bread, but there was still a great hunger in his heart. He covered himself with his clothes, but he felt bitter cold in his heart. Some animals and some pitiful people of the village were friendly to him. But his heart was full of solitude. "Father! Father!"... The servants, his brothers, his fellow citizens heard him moan thus all the time, as if he were mad. And he was called the "madman".

At last one of the servants dared to go to him, when he had become almost an animal, and said to him: "Why do you not throw yourself at the feet of your father?". "I would, but I dare not...". Why do you not come into the house?". "I am afraid". "But would you like to?". "Of course I would! Because that is what I hunger for, why I feel cold, and I feel as if I were in a desert. But I do not know how to live in my father's house". The good servant then began to teach him, to make him look more decent, to relieve him of his terror of being unpleasant to his father, saying: "Your father would like to have you, but he does not know whether you love him. You always avoid him... Relieve your father of the remorse of dealing too severely with you and of the grief of knowing that you are forlorn. Come. Your brothers also will no longer laugh at you because I told them of your grief".

And the poor son one evening was guided by the good servant to his father's house and he cried: "Father, I love you, let me come in!...". And his father, who was now old and was sadly pondering on his past and his eternal future, startled at that voice and said: "My sorrow is subsiding at last because in the voice of my deformed son I heard my own, and his love is the proof that he is blood of my blood and flesh of my flesh. Let him therefore come and take his place amongst his brothers and blessed be the good servant who made my family complete by bringing the rejected son among all the sons of his father".

[8] That is the parable. But in applying it, you must bear in mind 221.8

that the Father of the spiritually deformed sons, that is, God — because schismatics, heretics, those who are separated, spiritually deformed — was compelled to be severe by the voluntary deformities wanted by His sons. But His love never yielded . He is waiting for them. Take them to Him. It is your duty.

I taught you to say: "*Our* Father, give us this day *our* bread". But do you realise what "our" means? *It does not mean yours, of you twelve.* Not yours as disciples of the Christ. *But yours as men.* For *all* men. For the present and the future ones. For those who know God and for those who do not know Him. For those who love God and His Christ and for those who do not love Him or love Him badly.

I put on your lips a prayer for *everybody.* It is your ministry. You, who know God and His Christ and love Them, must pray for *everybody.* I told you that My prayer is a universal one, and will last as long as the world. And you must pray *universally,* joining your voices and your hearts of apostles and disciples of Jesus' Church to those of people belonging to other Churches, which may be christian but not apostolic. And you must insist, because you are brothers, you in the house of the Father, they outside the house of the common Father, with their hunger, their homesickness, until they also, like you, are given the *true "bread"* which is the Christ of the Lord, which is administered on apostolic tables, not on any other where it is mixed with impure aliments. You are to insist until the Father says to those deformed brothers: "My grief is subsiding, because I heard the voice and the words of My Only-Begotten First-Born in your voices. Blessed be those servants who have led you to the House of your Father in order to complete My Family". Servants of an Infinite God, you must put
221.9 infinity in every intention of yours. [9]Have you understood?

There is Jabneel. Once the Ark passed by here on its way to Ekron, which was not able to keep it and sent it back to Beth-Shemesh. The Ark is going to Ekron once again. John, come with Me. All the others will remain in Jabneel. Meditate and be careful how you speak. Peace be with you.»

And Jesus goes away with John and the ram which, bleating, follows Him like a dog.

222. The Apostle John Has a Secret. To Judaea by the Unsafe Modin Road.

18th July 1945.

1 The hills after Jabneel, running from west to east with regard to the pole-star, rise in height and behind them many more can be seen rising higher and higher. The green and violet summits of the Judaean mountains stand out in the distance, in the twilight. The day has rapidly come to its end, as is wont in southern regions. From the bright red sunset, in less than one hour it has passed to the first twinkling of stars and it seems impossible that the blazing sun has gone out so suddenly, deleting the blood-red sky with a thicker and thicker veil of red amethyst, which later becomes mallow and gradually changes colour becoming more and more transparent, showing an unreal sky, no longer blue, but pale green, which darkens into the greyish-blue shade of fresh oats, foreboding the indigo which will reign during the night, studded with diamonds like a royal mantle. And the first stars are already smiling in the east together with a little sickle of the moon at its first quarter. The earth takes on the appearance of paradise more and more in the light of the stars and in the silence of men. Now what does not sin is singing: nightingales, gurgling waters, rustling leaves, chirping crickets, and toads which with the accompaniment of oboes sing to the dew. Perhaps also the stars are singing up there... as they are closer to the angels than we are. The heat is abating in the air of the night, damp with dew so pleasing to herbs, men and animals! 222.1

2 Jesus Who had waited at the foot of a hill for the apostles coming from Jabneel where John had gone to fetch them, is now speaking to the Iscariot, to whom He hands some purses of money with instructions on how to distribute it. Behind Him there is John holding the billygoat. He is silent, between the Zealot and Bartholomew, who are talking of Jabneel where Andrew and Philip behaved so well. Farther back, there are all the others in a group, speaking loud and summarising their adventures in the Philistine region and openly expressing their joy for their return to Judaea for Pentecost in the very near future. 222.2

«Are we really going there soon?» asks Philip, who is very tired walking on the hot sand.

«That's what the Master said. You heard Him» replies James of Alphaeus.

«My brother certainly knows. But He seems lost in reverie. What they have done during these five days is a mystery» says James of Zebedee.

«Sure. I am dying to know. At least that as compensation for that... purgative at Jabneel. Five days during which we had to watch every word, every step and where we looked, to avoid getting into trouble» says Peter.

«However, we were successful. We are beginning to learn» says Matthew happily.

«To tell you the truth... I trembled with fear two or three times. That blessed boy of Judas of Simon!... Will he never learn to control himself?» says Philip.

«He will, when he is old. And yet, we may say that he does it for a good purpose. You heard Him? Also the Master said so. He does it out of zeal...» remarks Andrew to excuse him.

«Come off it! The Master said so because He is Goodness and Prudence. But I do not think He approves of him» replies Peter.

«He does not tell lies» retorts Thaddeus.

«It is not a question of telling lies. But He knows how to reply most prudently, and we do not know how to do that, and He speaks the truth without breaking anybody's heart, without arousing anybody's indignation and without reproaching. Of course, that is He!» says Peter with a sigh.

222.3 [3] They become silent while walking in the clearer and clearer moonlight. Then Peter says to James of Zebedee: «Try and call John. I do not know why he is avoiding us.»

«I can tell you at once: because he knows that we would torment him in order to find out» replies Thomas.

«Of course! And he is staying with the two most prudent and wise ones» confirms Philip.

«Well, try just the same, James, be good» insists Peter.

And James, condescendingly, calls John three times: the latter does not hear, or pretends not to hear. Bartholomew instead turns around and James says to him: «Tell my brother to come here» and then to Peter: «But I don't think he will tell us.»

John goes obediently at once and asks: «What do you want?»

«We want to know whether we are going straight to Judaea

from here» replies his brother.

«That is what the Master said. He was almost on the point of not coming back from Ekron and was going to send me to fetch you. Then He preferred to come as far as these last slopes... Because one can go to Judaea from here too.»

«By Modin?»

«By Modin.»

«It is not a safe road. Bandits wait for caravans along it and make sudden attacks on them» objects Thomas.

«Oh!... with Him!... Nothing can resist Him!...» replies John looking up to the sky enraptured in who knows what memories and smiling.

They all watch him and Peter says: «Tell me: are you perhaps reading a blissful story in the starry sky, with that look on your face?»

«Me? No...»

«Come off it! Also stones can see that you are miles away from the world. Tell me: what happened to you at Ekron?»

«Nothing, Simon. I can assure you. I would not be happy if anything unpleasant had happened.»

«Not unpleasant. On the contrary!... Come on! Speak up!»

«But I can tell you nothing more than what He has already told you. They were kind like people amazed at miracles. That's all. Exactly as He said.»

[4] «No» and Peter shakes his head. «No. You are not good at telling lies. You are as clear as spring water. No. You change colour. I have known you since you were a boy. You will never be able to tell lies. You are unable because of your heart, of your thoughts, of your tongue, of your very skin that changes colour. That is why I am so fond of you and I have always loved you. Listen, come here, to your old Simon of Jonah, your old friend. You remember when you were a boy and I was already a man? How I used to fondle you. You wanted stories and cork-boats "which never shipwreck", you used to say and which you needed to go far away... And also now you are going far away and you are leaving poor Simon ashore. And your little boat will never be wrecked. It is sailing full of flowers like the ones you used to launch, when a child, at Bethsaida, on the river, so that the river would carry them to the lake and they would sail and sail... Do 222.4

you remember? I love you, John. We all love you. You are our sail. You are our boat which does not wreck. We sail in your wake. Why don't you tell us of the miracle at Ekron?»

Peter has spoken clasping with one arm the waist of John, who endeavours to elude the question, saying: «Since you are our chief, why do you not speak to the crowds with the same persuasive strength as you are using with me? They need to be convinced, not I.»

«Because I feel more at ease with you. I love you, but I do not know them» says Peter excusing himself.

«And you do not love them. That's your mistake. Love them, even if you do not know them. Say to yourself: "They belong to our Father". You will then seem to know them and you will love them. You will see in them so many Johns...»

«That is easily said! As if asps and hedgehogs could be exchanged for you, my eternal boy.»

«Oh! no! I am like everybody else.»

«No, brother. Not like everybody. We, with the exception perhaps of Bartholomew, Andrew and the Zealot, would have told everybody what happened to us and made us happy. You are silent. But you must tell me, your elder brother. I am like a father to you» says James of Zebedee.

«God is my Father, Jesus my Brother, and Mary my Mother...»

«So blood counts for nothing with you?» shouts James anxiously.

«Do not be upset. I bless the blood and the womb that formed me: my father and mother; and I bless you, my brother of the same blood: the former because they begot me and brought me up enabling me to follow the Master, and you because you are following Him. Since my mother became a disciple, I love her in two ways: with my flesh and blood as a son; with my soul as her fellow-disciple. Oh! what a joy to be united in His love!...»

222.5 [5] Jesus has come back after hearing James' excited voice and the last words clarify the situation to Him. «Leave John alone. It is quite useless to torment him. He is very much like My Mother. And he will not speak.»

«Well, You tell us, then» they all implore.

«Well, here it is. I took John with Me because he is the most suitable for what I wanted to do. I have been helped and he has been perfected. That is all.»

Peter, John's brother James, Thomas, the Iscariot look at one another, making wry mouths, disappointed as they are. And Judas Iscariot, not satisfied with being disappointed, says so: «Why perfect him, who is already the best?»

Jesus replies to him: «You said: "Everybody has his way and makes use of it". I have Mine. John has his, which is very like Mine. Mine cannot be perfected. His can. And I want that to be, because it is right that it should be so. And that is why I took him. Because I needed one who had *that* way and *that* soul. So let there be no bad mood and no curiosity. Let us go to Modin. The night is serene, cool and clear. We shall walk as long as it is moonlight, then we shall sleep until dawn. I will take the two Ju-
* dases to venerate the tombs of the Maccabees, whose glorious name they bear.»

«Only the two of us with You!» exclaims the Iscariot happily.

«No. With *everybody*. But the visit to the tomb of the Maccabees is for you. That you may imitate them in a supernatural way, fighting and winning in a completely spiritual field.»

223. Jesus Speaks to the Highwaymen and Prevents an Attack on a Nuptial Caravan.

19th July 1945.

[1] «I will speak in the place where we are going» says the Lord 223.1
while the group goes more and more into valleys that assail the mountain with hard narrow stony roads, and go up and downhill, losing horizons and reconquering them. Finally, going down a very steep slope, where only the billygoat is at ease, as Peter remarks, they reach a deep valley, where they can rest and take some food near a spring, which is very rich in water.

There are other people spread in the meadows and thickets having their meal, like Jesus and His apostles. It must be a well known resting place preferred by travellers, since it is sheltered from winds and there are soft meadows and plenty of water. They are pilgrims who are going towards Jerusalem, travel-

* **tombs** in: *1 Maccabees 2:70; 9:19; 13:23-30.*

lers going perhaps to the Jordan, merchants of lambs destined to the Temple, shepherds with their flocks. Some are travelling on horseback, most of them on foot.

223.2 [2] There is also a nuptial caravan in festive array, which has just arrived. Gold jewels shine through the veil covering the bride, a little older than a girl, in the company of two matron-like women sparkling with bracelets and necklaces, and of a man, perhaps the matchmaker, besides two servants. They arrived on donkeys adorned with ribbons and harness bells and they withdraw to eat in a corner, as if afraid that the glances of the people present might violate the young bride. The matchmaker or relative, whatever he may be, mounts guard in a threatening attitude while the women eat. The curiosity of the other people is greatly aroused and in fact, with the excuse of asking for some salt, or a knife, or a drop of vinegar, there is always someone going here or there, to find out whether anyone knows who the bride is, where she is going, and many other nice things of the kind...

There is in fact one who knows where she comes from, where she is going and is more than happy to tell everything he knows, also because he is prompted by another man who makes him more talkative by pouring out some very good wine for him. In a few moments even the most secret details of two families are disclosed, with information on the trousseau, which the bride is taking in the cases which are there, and on the wealth that is awaiting her in her husband's house and so on. They thus learn that the bride is the daughter of a rich merchant in Joppa, and is getting married to the son of a rich merchant in Jerusalem, and that the bridegroom has preceded her to adorn the nuptial house for her impending arrival and that the man who is accompanying her is a friend of the groom and also the son of a merchant, of Abraham, who deals in diamonds and gems, whereas the bridegroom is a gold-beater, and the bride's father is a merchant dealing in woollen and cotton cloths, carpets, curtains...

223.3 [3] As the chatterbox is close to the apostolic group, Thomas hears him and asks: «Is the bridegroom perhaps Nathanael of Levi.»

«Yes, he is. Do you know him?»

«I know the father well, because I did business with him, I am a little less familiar with Nathanael. A wealthy marriage!»

«And a happy bride! She is covered with gold. Abraham, a relative of the bride's mother and father of the groom's friend, distinguished himself and so did the groom and his father. They say that the contents of those cases are worth many gold talents.»

«Good Lord!» exclaims Peter and he whistles a tune. He then says: «I am going to have a close look to see whether the main goods correspond to the rest» and he stands up, together with Thomas, and they both go for a short walk around the nuptial group. They watch the three women carefully, three heaps of cloth and veils, from which jewelled hands and wrists emerge and through which they can see ears and necks sparkling with jewels. They also watch the boastful matchmaker, who swaggers so much, as if he had to repel corsairs attacking the little virgin. He looks daggers also at the two apostles. But Thomas begs him to greet Nathanael of Levi on behalf of Thomas, called Didymus. And thus peace is made, so much so that while he is speaking, the bride manages to be admired, as she gets up in such a way that her mantle and veil fall off and she appears in all the gracefulness of her body and clothes showing her wealth worthy of an idol.

She must be fifteen years old, at the most, and her eyes are very alert! She moves about mincingly notwithstanding the two matrons' disapproval of her affected ways: she unpins her plaits and then fastens them again by means of precious hairpins: she tightens her belt which is studded with gems: she unlaces, takes off and puts on again her shoe-styled sandals, fastening them with gold buckles, and at the same time she displays her beautiful dark hair, her lovely hands and soft arms, a slender waist, well shaped breast and hips, her perfect feet and all her jewels which tinkle and glitter in the twilight or in the light of the flames of the first bonfires.

[4] Peter and Thomas go back. Thomas says: «She is a beautiful 223.4
girl.»

«She is a perfect coquette. It may be... but your friend Nathanael will soon find out that there is someone who keeps his bed warm for him, while he warms gold to beat it. And his friend is a perfect fool. He puts his bride in the right hands!» concludes Peter sitting down near his companions.

«I did not like that man who was encouraging that other fool over there to speak. When he had heard all he wanted to know, he went away up the mountain... This is a bad spot. And the weather is just right for highwaymen. Moonlight nights. Exhausting heat. Trees all covered with leaves. H'm! I don't like this place» grumbles Bartholomew. «It would have been better to go on.»

«And that imbecile who mentioned all the riches! And that other one who plays the hero and the watchman of shadows and cannot see real bodies!... Well, I will keep watch near the fire. Who is coming with me?» asks Peter.

«I am, Simon» replies the Zealot. «I can go without sleeping.»

Many of the people, particularly single travellers, have got up and gone away a few at a time. There are the shepherds with their flocks, the nuptial group, the apostolic one and three lamb merchants, who are already sleeping. The bride is also asleep with the matrons under a tent, which the servants have put up. The apostles look for a place where to rest, while Jesus withdraws to pray. The shepherds light a bonfire in the centre of the clearing where their flocks are. Peter and Simon light another one near the path of the cliff where the man disappeared, the one who had aroused Bartholomew's suspicion.

223.5 [5] Time passes and those who are not snoring, are nodding. Jesus is praying. There is dead silence. Also the spring shining in the moonlight seems to be silent. The moon is now high in the sky and the clearing is brightly lit up, whereas the edges are shadowed by thick foliage.

A big sheep dog snarls. A herdsman raises his head. The dog stands up raising the hair on its back and pointing in an alert position. It even trembles in its deep excitement while its hollow snarling becomes louder and louder. Simon, too, raises his head and shakes Peter who is dozing. A slight rustle can be heard in the wood.

«Let us go to the Master. We will bring Him with us» say the two apostles. In the meantime the herdsman wakes up his companions. They are all listening silently. Also Jesus has got up, before being called and is going towards the two apostles. They gather near their companions, that is, near the shepherds, whose dog is becoming more and more excited.

«Call those who are sleeping. Everybody. Tell them to come here, without making any noise, particularly the women and the servants with the coffers. Tell them that perhaps there are highwaymen about. But do not tell the women, only the men.» The apostles spread out obeying the Master Who says to the shepherds: «Put a lot of wood on the fire so that it will give a good light.» The shepherds obey, and as they look excited, Jesus says to them: «Do not be afraid. Not one flock of wool will be taken off you.»

The merchants arrive and whisper: «Oh! Our profits!» and they add a string of abuse against the Roman and Jewish governors who do not clear the world of robbers.

«Do not be afraid. You will not lose one single little coin» says Jesus comforting them.

The weeping women arrive and they are frightened, because the brave matchmaker, trembling with fear, is terrorising them moaning: «It will be our death! The robbers will kill us!»

«Do not be afraid. No one will touch you. They will not even look at you» says Jesus to comfort them and He takes the women to the centre of the little group of men and frightened animals.

The donkeys are braying, the dog is barking, the sheep are bleating, the women are sobbing and the men are cursing or swooning more than the women, a real cacophony caused by fear.

Jesus is calm, as if nothing had happened. The rustling in the wood can no longer be heard because of the uproar. But the presence of approaching robbers in the wood is evidenced by the
noise of breaking branches and rolling stones. [6]«Silence!» orders 223.6
Jesus. And He orders it in such a way that everything becomes quiet.

Jesus leaves His place and goes towards the wood, at the edge of the clearing. He turns His back to the wood and begins to speak.

«The wicked craving for gold drives men to base feelings. Man makes himself known because of his hunger for gold more than anything else. Consider how much evil is caused by this metal through its alluring but useless brightness. I think that the air in Hell is of the same shade, so hellish is its nature since man became a sinner. The Creator had left it in the bowels of that huge lapis-lazuli which is the earth, created by His will, that it might be useful to man with its salts and an ornament to temples. But Satan, kissing Eve's eyes, and biting man's ego, gave the savour of witchcraft to the innocent metal. And since then man kills and sins for the sake of gold. Woman for its sake becomes a coquette and inclined to carnal sin. Man for its sake becomes a thief, usurper, murderer, harsh against his neighbour and his own soul, which he deprives of its true inheritance, to follow transient things, and he deprives it also of the eternal treasure for the sake of a few shining scales, which he will have to leave at his death.

223.7 [7] You, who for the sake of gold, sin more or less lightly, or more or less seriously, and the more you sin, the more you laugh at what your mothers and teachers taught you, namely, that there is a reward or a punishment for actions done during life, will you not consider that because of such a sin you will lose God's protection, eternal life and joy, and you will have in your hearts remorse and malediction, while fear will be your companion, fear of human punishment, which is nothing when compared to the fear, which you should have, but you have not, of divine punishment? Will you not consider that you may have a dreadful end because of your misdeeds, if you have gone as far as being criminals; and an even more dreadful end, because it will be an everlasting one, if for the sake of gold, your misdeeds have not gone as far as shedding blood, but have despised the law of love and of respect for your neighbour, by denying assistance to those who are starving through your avarice, or stealing positions or money or defrauding by means of false weights, through your greed? No. You do not consider all that. You say: "It's all an idle story! And I have crushed such idle stories under the weight of my gold. And they no longer exist".

It is not an idle story. It is the truth. Do not say: "Well, when I am dead, that is the end of everything". No. That is the beginning. The next life is not an abyss without thought and without remembrance of the past you have lived or without longing for God, as you think the period of expectation of liberation by the Redeemer is. Next life is a happy expectation for the just, a patient expectation for the expiating, a dreadful expectation for the damned. For the first in Limbo, for the second in Purgatory, for the third in Hell. And while the expectation will end for the first when they enter Heaven after the Redeemer, it will be comforted for the second by a greater hope after that hour, whilst the dreadful certainty of eternal malediction will be confirmed for the third.

Think about it, you sinners. It is never too late to repent. Change the verdict which is being written in Heaven against you,
* by means of true repentance. Do not let Sheol be hell for you, but an expiating expectation, at least that, through your own will. Do not let it be darkness, but twilight, not torture, but nostalgia, not despair, but hope. [8]Go. Do not endeavour to fight against 223.8
God. He is the Strong and Good One. Do not insult the names of your relatives. Listen to the wail of that fountain, it is like the wail that breaks the hearts of your mothers knowing that you are murderers. Listen to the howling of the wind in that gorge. It seems to be threatening and cursing. As your fathers curse you for the life you lead. Listen to remorse crying in your hearts. Why do you want to suffer whilst you could be peacefully satisfied with little on the earth and everything in Heaven? Grant peace to your spirits! Give peace to men who are afraid, who must be afraid of you as if you were as many wild beasts! Grant peace to yourselves, poor wretches! Raise your eyes to Heaven, detach your mouths from the poisonous food, purify your hands dripping with the blood of your brothers, purify your hearts.

I have faith in you. That is why I am speaking to you. Because if the whole world hates and fears you, I do not hate you or fear you. But I stretch out My hand to say to you: “Rise. Come. Become meek amongst men, men amongst men”. I am so little afraid of you that now I say to everybody here: “Go back and rest. Bear your poor brothers no ill-will, but pray for them. I will remain here looking at them with loving eyes, and I swear that nothing will happen. *Because love disarms the violent and satisfies the greedy*. Blessed be Love, the true strength of the world, the unknown but powerful strength, the strength that is God”.»

And addressing everybody Jesus says: «You may go now. Be not afraid. There are no longer evil-doers over there, but dismayed men who are weeping. He who weeps does no harm. I wish to God they remained as they are now. It would be their redemption.»

---

* **Sheol**, a word that can be found in other points (for example in 357.11). It was the name given to the kingdom of the dead (also known as *Hades, Limbo, the bosom of Abraham*) in which the good and the bad remained, as they were all precluded, before the redemption, the vision of God. It was in any case a temporary “waiting” area.

224. The Secret of the Apostle John Revealed. The Arrival at Bether, in the Rose Gardens of Johanna.

20th July 1945.

224.1 [1] The train of animals following the apostolic college has undergone a change. The billygoat is no longer there and in its place there is a sheep and two lambs. A fat sheep with turgid udder, two little lambs as cheerful as urchins. A tiny flock that looks less magic than the very dark billygoat, and makes everybody happy.

«I told you that we would have a little goat to make Marjiam a little happy shepherd. Instead of the little goat, since you will not hear of goats, we got sheep. And white ones, exactly as Peter wanted them.»

«Of course! I thought I was pulling Beelzebub behind me» says Peter.

«In fact, since it was with us, how many unpleasant things have happened. It was a spell following us» confirms the Iscariot angrily.

«A good spell, then. Because what harm has really befallen us?» says John calmly.

They all shout at him reproaching him for his blindness. «Didn't you see how they were mocked at Modin?» «And do you think my brother's fall was just nothing? He might have been ruined. If he had broken his legs or his back, how could we have carried him away from there?» «And do you think that last night's incident was a pleasant one?»

«I saw everything, I considered everything and I blessed the Lord because nothing wrong happened to us. Evil came towards us, but then it ran away, as usual, and the incidents have certainly served to leave seeds of goodness both at Modin and with the vine-dressers, who came with the certainty that they would find at least one person wounded and with the remorse of having been without charity, and in fact they wanted to make amends; and the same happened last night with the robbers. They did no harm and we, that is Peter, got the sheep in exchange for the goat and as a present for their safety, and there is now a good deal of money for the poor because the merchants and the women gave us purses of money and offerings. And what is more important, they all received the word of Jesus.»

«John is right» say the Zealot and Judas Thaddeus. And the latter concludes: «Everything seems to be taking place through a clear foreknowledge of the future. It is odd that we should be there, and we were late, because of my fall, at the same time as the jewelled women, and the shepherds with large flocks, as well as the merchants lousy with money: all of whom were a wonderful prey for the robbers! [2]Brother, tell me the truth. Did You 224.2
know that all that was going to happen?» Thaddeus asks Jesus.

«I told you many a time that I can read the hearts of men, and when the Father does not dispose otherwise, I do not ignore what must happen.»

«Well, why do You at times make mistakes, such as going towards hostile Pharisees, or to towns that are completely hostile?» asks Judas Iscariot.

Jesus stares at him and then says calmly and slowly: «They are not mistakes. They are necessities of My mission. The sick need a doctor and the ignorant a master. Both the former and the latter at times reject doctor or master. But if they are good doctors and good masters, they continue to go to those who refuse them because it is their duty to go. And I go. You would like all resistance to *collapse* wherever I go. I could do that. But I do not use violence against anyone. I convince people. Coercion is to be used only in very exceptional cases and only when a spirit enlightened by God understands that it may serve to persuade that God exists, and is the strongest, or when many people are to be saved.»

«Like yesterday evening, eh?» asks Peter.

«Yesterday evening those robbers were afraid because they saw that we were wide awake and waiting for them» says the Iscariot with evident scorn.

«No. They were convinced by words» says Thomas.

«No. They would not dream of it! They are indeed tender souls that can be convinced by a couple of words, even if spoken by Jesus! I know what they are like when I was attacked with my family and many people of Bethsaida in the gorge of Adummim» replies Philip.

«Master, tell me. It's since yesterday that I wanted to ask You. Was it Your words or Your will to prevent anything from happening?» asks James of Zebedee.

Jesus smiles and is silent.

Matthew replies: «I think that it was His will to overcome the hardness of those hearts, which He almost paralysed in order to be able to speak and save them.»

«I say that, too. That is why He remained there by Himself, looking at the wood. He subdued them with His look, by means of His defenceless calm and by trusting them. He did not even have a stick in His hands!...» says Andrew.

«All right. That's what we say. That's what we think. But I want to hear it from the Master» says Peter.

There is a lively discussion, in which Jesus does not interfere. Some say that since Jesus has declared that He does not force anyone, He has not used coercion in the case of those robbers either. That is what Bartholomew states. The Iscariot instead, who is mildly supported by Thomas, declares that he cannot believe that the look of a man can do so much. Matthew retorts: «It can do that and much more. I was converted by His look even before He spoke to me.» The opposite opinions cause a lively discussion, as each stubbornly insists in his own. John, like Jesus, is silent and he smiles lowering his head to conceal his smile. Peter revives the discussion as none of the arguments of his companions convince him. He thinks and says that the look of Jesus is different from the look of an ordinary man, and he wants to know whether it is because He is Jesus, the Messiah, or because He is always God.

224.3 [3] Jesus speaks: «I solemnly tell you that not only I, but anyone who is united to God by means of faultless holiness, purity and faith will be able to do that and much more. The look of a child, if his spirit is united to God, can cause vain temples to collapse, without shaking them as Samson did, it can command wild beasts and men-beasts to be meek, it can repel death and defeat diseases of the spirit, and the word of a child, united to God and an instrument of God can also cure diseases, make the poison of snakes harmless, work all kinds of miracles. Because it is God Who works in Him.»

«Ah! I understand!» says Peter. And He stares at John. And after a long internal conversation with himself, he concludes in a loud voice: «Yes! You, Master, can do that, because You are God, and because You are Man united to God. And the same happens to those who go so far, or have gone so far as to be united to God. I understand! I really understand!»

«But are you not inquiring about the key to that union, or about the secret of that power? Not all men are successful in going so far, although they all have the same means to succeed.»

«Quite right! Where is the key to that strength which unites man to God and dominates matter? A prayer or secret words...»

«A short while ago Judas of Simon was blaming the billygoat for all the unpleasant incidents that happened to us. There are no spells connected with animals. Reject superstitions, which are also a form of idolatry and can cause misfortunes. And as there are no formulas to work witchcraft, so there are no secret words to work miracles. There is only love. As I said yesterday evening, love calms the violent and satisfies the greedy. Love: God. With God within you, fully possessed through perfect love, your eye will become a fire capable of burning every idol and knocking down their simulacra, and your word will become power. And your eye will become an arm that disarms. You cannot resist God, you cannot resist Love. Only the demon can resist it, because he is perfect Hatred, and his children can resist with him. The others, the weak people seized with passions, but who have not sold themselves voluntarily to the demon, cannot resist. Whatever their religion may be, or their indifference to any faith, whatever the level of their spiritual base, they are struck by Love, the great Winner. Endeavour to arrive there soon, and you will do what the children of God and the bearers of God do.»

[4] Peter does not take his eyes off John; also the sons of Al- 224.4
phaeus, James and Andrew are lively and watchful.

«Well, then, my Lord» says James of Zebedee, «what has happened to my brother? You are speaking of him. He is the boy who works miracles! Is that it? Is it so?»

«What has he done? He turned a page of the book of Life, and he read and learned new mysteries. Nothing else. He preceded you, because he does not stop to consider every obstacle, to weigh every difficulty, to work out every profit. He no longer sees the earth. He sees the Light, and goes towards it. Without stopping. But leave him alone. The souls burning with greater flames are not to be disturbed in their ardour which gladdens and burns.

You must let them burn. It is utmost joy and utmost toil. God grants them moments of darkness because He knows that fierce heat kills delicate souls, when they are exposed to continuous sunshine. God grants silence and mystic dew to such delicate souls, as He grants it to wild flowers. Let the athlete of love rest, when God allows him to rest. Imitate gymnasiarchs who grant their pupils due rest... When you arrive where he has already arrived, and beyond, because both you and he will go beyond that point, you will realise the need for respect, silence and dim light that souls feel when they become the prey of Love and its instrument. Do not think: "I will be glad to be known, and John is a fool, because the souls of our neighbours, like the souls of children, want to be attracted by wonders". No, when you are there, you will have the same desire for silence and dim light as John has now. And when I shall no longer be amongst you, remember that when you have to pronounce sentence on a conversion or on possible holiness, you must *always* use humility as your measure. If a man is still proud, do not believe that he is converted. And if pride reigns in a man, who may even be said to be a "saint", you may be sure that he is not a saint. He may quackishly and hypocritically play the saint and pretend he works wonders. But he is no saint. His appearance is hypocrisy, his wonders are satanism. Have you understood?»

«Yes, Master.»... They are all quiet and pensive. But if their lips are closed, it is possible to guess their thoughts by their countenance. A deep desire to know quivers like ether around them, emanating from them...

224.5 [5] The Zealot endeavours to divert their attention and thus gain time to speak to them separately and advise them to be quiet. I think that the Zealot has taken that task upon himself in the apostolic group. He is the moderator, the adviser, the peacemaker of his companions, besides being one who understands the Master so well. He says: «We are already in Johanna's estate. That village in that little valley is Bether. The large building on that top is the castle where she was born. Can you smell this perfume in the air? It comes from the roseries which begin to give off scent in the moring sun. In the evening it is a powerful fragrance. But it is so beautiful to see them in the cool morning, covered with dew drops, like millions of diamonds thrown on to millions of opening corollas. When the sun sets they pick all the roses that are completely open. Come. I want to show you from a knoll the view of roseries that overflow from the top, like a waterfall, down the crags on the other side. A cascade of flowers, which climbs back up again, like a wave, on two other hills. It is an amphitheatre, a lake of flowers. It is really wonderful. The road is steeper. But it is worth while climbing up, because from that spot one overlooks all this paradise. And we shall soon be at the castle. Johanna lives there in perfect freedom, amongst her peasants, who are the only guards of so much wealth. But they are so fond of their mistress, who has turned these valleys into a paradise of beauty and of peace, that they are worth much more than all Herod's guards. Here, look, Master. Look, my friends» and he points at a semicircle of hills invaded with roses.

Wherever one's eyes rest, one can see roseries, under very tall trees, to shield them from winds, from excessive heat of the sun and hailstorms. There is sunshine and air also under this light roof, which is like a veil but is not oppressive, and is duly controlled by the gardeners, and the most beautiful roseries in the world grow there. There are thousands and thousands of all kinds of rose-bushes. There are miniature, low, tall, very tall plants. They grow in tufts, like cushions studded with flowers, at the foot of trees, on very green meadows, as hedges along paths, on the banks of streams, in circles around irrigation vats, spread over the whole park which comprises hills, or twined round tree trunks, or from tree to tree forming flowery festoons and garlands. It is really a dream. All sizes and shades are present blending beautifully, with the ivory hue of tea-roses close to the blood red of other corollas. The true roses, which like the cheek of a child, shade on the contours into white tinged with pink, reign as queens, also because of their number.

They are all struck by so much beauty.

«But what does she do with all this?» asks Philip.

«She enjoys it» replies Thomas.

«No. She extracts the essence and thus employs hundreds of servants and gardeners who work at the presses. The Romans make great use of it. Jonathan was telling me when he showed me the figures of the last crop. [6]But there is Mary of Alphaeus with 224.6
the boy. They have seen us and they are calling the others...»

In fact there are Johanna and the two Maries, who are preceded by Marjiam, who runs down towards Jesus and Peter, with his arms stretched out ready for an embrace. The women arrive as well and they prostrate themselves before Jesus.

«Peace to you all. Where is My Mother?»

«Among the roseries, Master, with Eliza. Oh! She is definitely cured! She can now face the world and follow You. Thanks for making use of me for that purpose.»

«Thanks to you, Johanna. You can see that it was useful to come to Judaea. Marjiam: here are your presents. This lovely puppet and these beautiful sheep. Do you like them?»

The boy is breathless with joy. He leans towards Jesus Who has bent to give him the puppet and has remained thus to look at him in the face, and he clasps His neck, kissing Him with utmost ardour.

«And thus you will become as meek as the little sheep and then you will become a good shepherd for those who believe in Jesus. Is that right?»

Marjiam replies «Yes» in a choked voice, while his eyes shine with joy.

«Now go and see Peter, because I am going to My Mother. I can see a strip of Her veil moving along a hedge of roses.»

And He runs to Mary embracing Her to His heart at a corner of a path. After a first kiss, Mary, still panting, explains: «Eliza is coming behind Me... I ran to kiss You, because it was not possible for Me not to kiss You... but I did not want to kiss You in front of her... She has changed a great deal... But her heart still aches in the presence of other people's joy, now denied to her forever. Here she is coming.»

Eliza walks the last few yards with a rapid step and kneels down to kiss Jesus' tunic. She is no longer the tragic woman of Bethzur. She is an old austere lady, marked by sorrow that has left a deep trace on her countenance.

«May You be blessed, my Master, now and ever, for giving back to me what I had lost.»

«May a greater peace be with you, Eliza. I am happy to see you here. Stand up.»

«I am happy, too. I have so many things to tell You and to ask You, Lord.»

«We shall have plenty of time because I am staying here for a few days. Come, that I may introduce My disciples to you.»

«Oh!!! You have already understood what I wanted to tell You?! That I want to start a new life: Yours; and have a new family: Yours; and sons: Yours; as You told me speaking of Naomi, in my house, at Bethzur. I am the new Naomi through Your grace, my Lord. May You be blessed for it. I am no longer depressed and barren. I will still be a mother. And if Mary allows me, I will also be a mother to You, besides being a mother to the sons of Your doctrine.»

«Yes. You will be. Mary will not be jealous and I will love you so much that you will not regret coming with us. Let us go now to those who wish to tell you that they love you as brothers.» And Jesus takes her by the hand and leads her towards her new family.

The journey made while waiting for Pentecost is over.

225. The Paralytic at the Pool of Bethzatha (Bethesda) Cured on Sabbath: "My Father Is at Work Until Now, so I Am at Work, Too".

21st July 1945.

1 Jesus is in Jerusalem, in fact quite near the Antonia. All the apostles are with Him, with the exception of the Iscariot. Many people are hurrying towards the Temple. They are all wearing their best clothes, both the apostles and the pilgrims, and I think therefore that it is Pentecost time. Among the people are many beggars, pitifully lamenting over their miseries and directing their steps towards the best places for seeking alms, near the gates of the Temple, or at the crossroads from which people come towards the Temple. Jesus, while passing, gives alms to the poor wretches, who meticulously give every detail of their misery. 225.1

I am under the impression that Jesus has already been to the Temple, for I can hear the apostles talking of Gamaliel, who pretended not to see them, although Stephen, one of his pupils, had pointed out Jesus to him.

I can also hear Bartholomew asking his companions: «What

did that scribe mean by saying: "A herd of rams for the slaughter-house"?»

«He might have been talking of some business of his own» replies Thomas.

«No. He was pointing at us. I saw him clearly. In any case his next sentence confirmed the earlier remark. He said sarcastically: "Before long also the Lamb will be ready to be shorn and slaughtered".»

«Yes, I heard him, too» confirms Andrew.

«Of course! I am yearning to go back and ask the scribe's companion what he knows about Judas of Simon» says Peter.

«He knows nothing! This time Judas is not here because he is really ill. We know that for certain. Perhaps he really suffered too much during the trip we made. We are sturdier. He always lived here, in comfort, and he tires easily» replies James of Alphaeus.

«Yes, we know. But that scribe said: "The chameleon is missing from the group". Does the chameleon not change colour any time it wants to?» asks Peter.

«Yes, Simon. But they were certainly referring to his clothes, which are always new. He is proud of them. He is young and we must bear with him...» remarks the Zealot to reconcile them.

«That is true, too. But!... What a strange expression!» concludes Peter.

«They are eternally threatening» says James of Zebedee.

«The trouble is that we know we are threatened and yet possibly imagine threats even where there are none...» points out Judas Thaddeus.

«And we see faults where they do not exist» ends Thomas.

«And of course! Suspicion is unpleasant... I wonder how Judas is today? In the meantime he is enjoying that paradise and those angels... I would not mind being ill myself, to enjoy those delights!» says Peter, to which Bartholomew adds: «Let us hope that he recovers soon. We must finish our trip, for the warm weather is at our heels.»

«Oh! He is well looked after, in any case... the Master will see to it, if necessary» assures Andrew.

«He had a very high temperature when we left him. I don't know how he got it, so...» says James of Zebedee. Matthew replies to him: «Sure everybody gets it! Troubles just come. But it is nothing serious. The Master is not worried about it. If He had envisaged anything serious, He would not have left Johanna's castle.»

[2]Jesus in fact is not at all anxious. He is speaking to Marjiam and John, walking ahead of the others and giving alms. He is obviously showing and explaining many things to the boy because I see Him pointing here and there. He is going towards the end of the Temple walls, towards the north-east corner. There are many people making for a place where there is a number of porches in the vicinity of a gate, which I hear being called «the Sheep Gate». 225.2

«This is the Probatica, the Bethzatha pond. Now look at the water carefully. See how still it is? In a short while you will see that it stirs, swells, reaching up to that damp mark. Can you see it? It is the angel of the Lord who descends, the water perceives him and venerates him as best it can. He brings to the water the order to cure the man who is ready to jump into it. See the crowd? But the minds of many wander easily and thus they do not see the first motion of the water; or the stronger ones uncharitably push aside the weaker ones. One must never divert one's attention in the presence of the signs of God. We must ensure that our souls are always vigilant, because we never know when God may show Himself or send His Angel. And we must never be selfish, not even for health reasons. Very often these unhappy people lose the benefit of the Angel's visit, because they waste time quarrelling over whose turn it is or who is in greater need» Jesus patiently explains to Marjiam, who looks at Him with an attentive gaze, keeping an eye at the same time on the water.

«Can one see the Angel? I would like to.»

«Levi, a shepherd, when he was about your age, saw him. You should look carefully as well, and be ready to praise him.»

The boy's mind is no longer diverted. He looks alternately at the water and above it, he hears nothing else, and sees nothing else. Jesus in the meantime looks at the small group of invalids, blind people, cripples, paralytics, who are waiting. The apostles are also watching carefully. The sunshine causes a play of light on the water and invades like a king the five porches encircling the pond.

«There, there!» trills Marjiam. «The water is rising, it is moving, it shines! How bright! The Angel!» and the boy kneels down.

In fact the water, in its motion in the pond, seems to be raised by a sudden huge wave swelling up to the edge of the pond, and it shines like a mirror in the sun. A dazzling flash for a moment.

A lame man is ready to dive into the water and he comes out, shortly afterwards, with his leg, previously contracted and marred by a large scar, completely cured. The others complain and quarrel with him, stating that after all he was not unable to work, whereas they are. And they continue arguing.

225.3 [3] Jesus turns around and sees a paralytic lying in his little bed and weeping. He approaches him, bends over and caresses him asking: «Why are you weeping?»

«Master, nobody ever thinks of me. I stay here all the time, everybody is cured, except me. I have been lying on my back for thirty-eight years, I spent all I had, my relatives are dead, I am now a burden to a distant relation who carries me here in the morning and takes me back in the evening... But what a burden I am to him! Oh! I wish to die!»

«Do not grieve. You have had so much patience and faith. God will hear you.»

«I hope so... but one has fits of depression. You are good. But the others... Those who are cured, in order to thank God, could remain here to assist their poor brothers...»

«They should do that, in fact... Have no ill-feeling. They do not think of it. They are not malevolent. It is the joy of being cured that makes them selfish. Forgive them...»

«You are kind. You would not do that. When the water moves, I try to drag myself over there with my hands. But there is always someone who precedes me, and I cannot stay near the edge, because they would trample on me. And even if I stayed there, who would lower me into the water? If I had seen You before, I would have asked You...»

«Do you really want to be cured? Then, stand up! Take your bed and walk!» Jesus has stood up to give the order, and while rising He seems to have raised the paralytic also, who stands up on his feet, takes one, two, three steps, almost incredulously, behind Jesus Who is going away, and when he realises that he is really walking, he utters a cry that makes everybody turn around.

«But who are You? In the name of God, tell me! Are You perhaps the Angel of the Lord?»

«I am more than an angel. My name is Piety. Go in peace.»

People gather around them. They want to see, to speak, to be cured. But the guards of the Temple, who I think were also watching the pond, arrive and they disperse the noisy gathering, threatening punishment.

The paralytic picks up his stretcher: two bars fitted with two pairs of small wheels and a piece of torn cloth nailed on them, and he happily goes away shouting to Jesus: «I will find You. I will not forget Your name or Your face.»

[4] Jesus, mingling with the crowd, goes away in the opposite di- 225.4
rection, towards the walls. But He has not yet gone through the last porch when He is caught up by an excited group of Jews, of the worst castes, who seem to be blown by a furious wind, and are all urged by the same desire to insult Jesus. They look, they search, they scan people's faces. But they are not successful in finding out who it really is, and Jesus goes away, while they, disappointed as they are, following the information of the guards, rush at the poor but happy man who has just been cured and they reproach him saying: «Why are you taking this bed away? It is the Sabbath. You are not allowed.»

The man looks at them and says: «I know nothing. I know that He Who cured me said to me: "Take your bed and walk". That's all I know.»

«He must certainly be a demon because he ordered you to violate the Sabbath. What was he like? Who was he? A Judaean? A Galilean? A Proselyte?»

«I don't know. He was here. He saw me weeping and He approached me. He spoke to me and He cured me. He went away holding a boy by the hand. I think it was His son, because He is old enough to have a son of that age.»

«A boy? Well it is not He!... What did He say His name is? Did you not ask Him? Don't tell lies!»

«He told me that His name is Piety.»

«You are a fool! That's not a name!»

The man shrugs his shoulders and goes away.

The others say: «It was certainly He. Hania and Zaccheus, the scribes, saw Him.»

«But He has no children!»

«And yet it is He. He was with His disciples.»

«Judas was not there. He is the one we know well. The others... might be anybody.»

«No. It was them.»

And they continue arguing while the porches become crowded once again with sick people...

[...].

225.5 [5] Jesus enters the Temple again on another side, the western side, which faces the town. The apostles follow Him. Jesus looks around and at last sees him whom He is looking for: Jonathan, who, in turn, was looking for Jesus.

«He is better, Master. His temperature is going down. Your Mother says that She hopes to come by next Sabbath.»

«Thank you, Jonathan. You were punctual.»

«Not very, as Maximinus of Lazarus kept me. He is looking for You. He has gone to Solomon's porch.»

«I will go and meet him. Peace be with you, and take My peace to My Mother and the women disciples, and also to Judas.»

And Jesus walks fast towards Solomon's porch, where in fact He finds Maximinus.

«Lazarus heard that You are here. He wishes to see You to tell You something important. Will You come?»

«Of course, I will. And soon. You can tell him to wait for Me during the week.»

Maximinus also goes away after a few more words.

«Let us go and pray again, since we came back so far» says Jesus and He moves towards the hall of the Hebrews.

But when He is near it, He meets the cured paralytic, who has gone to thank the Lord. The happy man sees Jesus among the crowd, greets Him joyfully and tells Him what happened at the pond after He left. And he concludes: «Then a man, who was surprised to see me here and completely cured, told me who You are. You are the Messiah. Are You not?»

«I am. But also if you had been cured by the water or by any other power, you would still have the same duty towards God. That is, to make use of your health for good work. You are cured. Go, therefore, and resume your activity in life with good intentions. And do not sin anymore, so that God may not have to punish you more severely. Goodbye. Go in peace.»

«I am old... I know nothing... But I would like to follow You and serve You. Do You want me?»

«I reject no one. Think about it before coming. And if you make up your mind, come.»

«Where? I do not know where You are going...»

«I move about the world. You will find My disciples everywhere and they will send you to Me. May the Lord enlighten you for the best...»

Jesus now goes to His place and prays...

[6] I do not know whether the cured man has gone spontaneously 225.6
to the Judaeans or the latter, being on the look out, have stopped him to find out whether the man, who was speaking to him, was the one who had cured him. I know that the man speaks to the Judaeans and then goes away, while they come towards the steps that Jesus must come down, to go through the other yards and go out of the Temple. When Jesus arrives they say to Him abruptly, without greeting Him: «So You continue to violate the Sabbath, notwithstanding You have been reprimanded so many times? And You expect to be respected as a messenger of God?»

«Messenger? Much more: as Son. Because God is My Father. If you do not wish to respect Me, you may refrain from doing so. But I will not cease accomplishing My mission because of that. God does not cease operating for one moment. Even now My Father is operating, and I operate as well, because a good son does what his father does, and because I have come into the world to operate.»

People have approached them to listen to the debate. Among them, there are some who know Jesus, some who have been helped by Him, some who see Him for the first time. Some love Him, some hate Him, many are uncertain. The apostles form a group with the Master. Marjiam is almost frightened and looks as if he is going to weep.

The Judaeans, a mixture of scribes, Pharisees and Sadducees, shout at the top of their voices that they are scandalised: «How dare You! Oh! He says He is the Son of God! What sacrilege! God is He Who is, and has no children! Call Gamaliel! Send for Sadoc! Gather the rabbis that they may hear and confute Him.»

«Do not become excited. Call them, and they will tell you, if

it is true they know, that God is One and Triune: Father, Son and Holy Spirit and that the Word, that is the Son of Thought, has come, as prophesied, to save Israel and the world from Sin. I am the Word. I am the foretold Messiah. There is no sacrilege, there-
225.7 fore, if I say that the Father is My Father. [7]You are upset because I work miracles and through them I attract crowds and convince them. You accuse Me of being a demon, because I work prodigies. Beelzebub has been in the world for many centuries, and he truly does not lack devout worshippers... Why, then, does he not do what I do?»

The people whisper: «It is true! Very true! Nobody does what He does.»

Jesus continues: «I will tell you: it is because I know what he does not know and I can do what he cannot. If I accomplish deeds of God, it is because I am His Son. One can do by oneself only what one has seen being done by others. I, the Son, can only do what I have seen done by the Father, as I have been One with Him forever, and I am like Him in nature and power. Everything the Father does, I do as well, as I am His Son. Neither Beelzebub nor anybody else can do what I do, because Beelzebub and the others do not know what I know. The Father loves Me, His Son, and He loves Me immensely as I love Him. He has therefore shown Me and still shows Me everything He does, so that I may do what He does, I on the earth, in this time of Grace, He in Heaven, even before Time existed on the earth. And He will show Me greater and greater deeds so that I may accomplish them and you may be amazed. His Thought is inexhaustible in depth. I imitate Him as I am inexhaustible in accomplishing what the Father thinks and, by thinking, wants.

225.8 [8]You do not yet know what Love creates inexhaustibly. We are Love. And there is no limit for Us, and there is nothing that cannot be applied to the three grades of man: the inferior, the superior, the spiritual grades. In fact as the Father raises the dead and gives them life, I, the Son, can likewise give life to whoever I wish, and more than that, because of the infinite love the Father has for His Son, I can not only give life to the inferior part but also to the superior one, by freeing the minds and hearts of men from mental errors and evil passions, and I can give life to the spiritual part by giving back to the spirit its freedom from sin, because the Father does not judge anybody, having left all judgement to the Son, as the Son is He Who, through His own sacrifice, acquired Mankind to redeem it: and the Father does that according to justice, because it is just that He, Who has purchased with His own money, should be given what He purchased, so that everybody may honour the Son as they already honour the Father. You must know that if you separate the Father from the Son, or the Son from the Father, and you do not remember the Love, you do not love God as He is to be loved, that is, in truth and wisdom, and you commit a sin of heresy, because you worship One only, whilst They are three in an admirable Trinity. Thus, he who does not honour the Son, does not honour the Father either, because the Father, God, does not want only One of the Three Divine Persons to be worshipped, but He wants Them all, as a Whole, to be worshipped. He who does not honour the Son, does not honour the Father either, Who sent Him out of a perfect thought of love. He therefore denies that God can accomplish just deeds. I solemnly tell you that he who listens to My word and believes in Him Who sent Me, will have eternal life and will not be condemned, but will pass from death to life, because to believe in God and to accept My word means to infuse into oneself the Life that does not die.

The hour is about to come, or rather, it has already come for many, when the dead will hear the voice of the Son of God, and whoever hears its vivifying sound in the depth of his heart, shall
live. [9]Scribe, what are you saying?» 225.9

«I am saying that the dead can no longer hear anything, and that You are mad.»

«Heaven will persuade you that it is not so, and that your knowledge is nothing as compared to God's. You have humanised supernatural things to such an extent, that you give words only an immediate and earthly meaning. You have taught the Haggadah according to fixed formulae, *your* formulae, without any effort to understand the allegories in their true meaning, and now, since your souls are tired of being urged by a human mentality, which crushes your spirits, you do not even believe what you teach. And that is the reason why you can no longer fight against occult powers. The death of which I am speaking is not the death of the flesh, but of the soul. People will come who will listen to

My word with their ears, will accept it in their hearts, and will practise it. Even if their spirits are dead, they will receive life again, because My Word is Life that will be infused into them. And I can give it to whomsoever I wish, because in Me there is perfect Life. As the Father has in Himself perfect Life, so also the Son had from the Father, in Himself, perfect, complete, eternal, inexhaustible, transfusable Life. And with Life, the Father gave Me power to judge, because the Son of the Father is the Son of Man, and He can and must judge man. And do not be amazed at this first resurrection, the spiritual one, which I work by My Word. You will see stronger ones, which will appear stronger to your dull senses, because I solemnly tell you that there is nothing greater than the invisible but real resurrection of a spirit. The hour will soon come when the voice of the Son of God will penetrate tombs and those who are in them will hear it. And those who did good actions come out of them to go to the resurrection of eternal Life, and those who did evil deeds will go to the resurrection of eternal damnation. I do not say that I will do that by Myself, by My own will, but by the will of the Father joined to Mine. I speak and judge according to what I hear and My judgement is correct, because I do not seek My own will, but the will of Him Who sent Me.

I am not separated from the Father. I am in Him and He is in Me and I know His Thought and I express it in words and action.
225.10 [10] What I testify on My own behalf cannot be accepted by your incredulous spirits, which refuse to see in Me anything but a man like yourselves. But there is another one who testifies on My behalf, whom you say you venerate as a great prophet. I know that his testimony is true. But although you say that you venerate him, you will not accept his testimony, because it differs from your thought, which is hostile to Me. You do not accept the testimony of the just man, of the last Prophet in Israel, because, with regards to what you do not like, you say that he is only a man and can be mistaken. You sent messengers to interrogate John, hoping he would say of Me what you wanted, what you think of Me, what *you want to think* of Me. But John gave his testimony to the truth and you could not accept it. Because the Prophet says that Jesus of Nazareth is the Son of God, you are saying in the secret of your hearts, as you are afraid of the crowds, that the Prophet

is insane, as Christ is. I, however, do not depend on the testimony of man, not even of the most holy one in Israel. I tell you: John was a lamp alight and shining, but only for a short time you wanted to enjoy the light that he gave. When his light was cast on Me, to make the Christ known for what He is, you allowed the lamp to be hidden under a bushel, and before that, you had built up a wall between the lamp and yourselves, in order not to see the Christ of the Lord in its light. I am grateful to John for his testimony, and the Father is grateful as well. And John will receive a great reward for his testimony, shining in Heaven also because of it, the *first* of all men up there to shine like a sun, and he will shine like all those, who have been faithful to the Truth and hungry for God. But I have a greater testimony than John's. The testimony of My works. Because the works the Father has given Me to carry out, those works I accomplish and they testify that the Father has sent Me giving Me all power. And thus, the Father Who sent Me, bears witness to Me Himself.

You have never heard His Voice or seen His Face. But I have seen it and I see it, I have heard it and I hear it. His Word finds no home in you, because you do not believe in the One He sent. You study the Scriptures, believing that in their knowledge you have eternal Life. And do you not realise that the very Scriptures testify about Me? Why then do you continue to refuse to come to Me for life? I will tell you: it is because you refuse what is opposed to your inveterate ideas. You lack humility. You are uncapable of saying: "I made a mistake. He, or this book is right, and I am wrong". That is what you have done with John, with the Scriptures, and that is what you are doing with the Word Who is speaking to you. You cannot see or understand, because you are enveloped with pride and deafened by *your own* voices.

[11] Do you think that I am speaking to you because I want to be 225.11
glorified by you? No, you must bear in mind that I neither seek nor accept glory from men. What I seek and want is your eternal salvation. That is the glory I seek. My glory as a Saviour cannot exist unless I have souls that have been saved, and the greater their number, the greater My glory, which is to be given to Me by the souls saved and by the Father, the Most Pure Spirit. But you will not be saved. I know you for what you are. You have no love for God. You are without love. And that is the reason why you do

not come to the Love speaking to you, and thus you will not enter the Kingdom of Love. You are not known there. The Father does not Know you, because you do not know Me, Who am in the Father. You do not want to know Me. I have come in the name of My Father and you refuse to accept Me, whereas you are willing to accept anyone who comes in his own name, providing he says what is agreeable to you. You say that you are faithful souls. No, you are not. How can you believe, when you beg glory of one another, and you do not seek the glory of Heaven, which proceeds only from God? The glory of Heaven is Truth and not a matter of worldly interests which end here on the earth and attract only the vicious humanity of Adam's degraded children. I will not accuse you before the Father. You can be sure of that. There is already one who will accuse you: Moses in whom you hope. He will reproach you for not believing in him because you do not believe in Me, as he wrote about Me, but you do not acknowledge Me by what he wrote. You do not believe in the words of Moses, the great Prophet in whose name you swear. Thus, how can you believe in My words, in the words of the Son of Man, in whom you have no faith? From a human point of view that is logical. But here we are in a spiritual sphere and your souls are at stake. God scrutinises them in the light of My works and He compares your actions with what I have come to teach you. And God judges you.

I am going away. You will not see Me for a long time. But do not consider that as a triumph of yours. On the contrary it is a punishment. Let us go.»

Jesus pushes His way through the crowd. Some of the people remain silent, some express their approval, but only in a whisper for fear of the Pharisees, and they go away.